at Doncaster, on the first Wednesday in August ... ...ered :—

CLASS 26.—For the best Mare and Foal for Hunting	£5	
Second ditto	2	
CLASS 27.—For the best Mare and Foal for Coaching	5	
Second ditto	2	
CLASS 28.—For the best Roadster Mare and Foal	5	
Second ditto	2	
CLASS 29.—For the best Mare and Foal for Draught	5	
Second ditto	2	
CLASS 30,—For the best three-year old Hunting Gelding or Filly	5	
Second ditto	2	
CLASS 31.—For the best three-year old Coaching Gelding or Filly	5	
Second ditto	2	
CLASS 32.—For the best two-year old Coaching Gelding or Filly	5	
Second ditto	2	
CLASS 33.—For the best three-year old Hackney Gelding or Filly	5	
Second ditto	2	
CLASS 34.—For the best three-year old Gelding or Filly for Agricultural purposes	5	
Second ditto	2	

No animal which has gained a first prize in any class, at the previous Meetings of this Society, will be allowed to compete in the same class at any future Meeting. No animal can be entered in more than one class.

SHEPHERD.

To the Shepherd, being an annual servant, who shall have lost the smallest proportionate number of Ewes and Lambs previous to the 12th of May, from those that produced lambs in 1843, the number of his flock not being less than fifty 5
the second approved Candidate 3
the third ditto 2

Competitors for this Prize must send in their certificates, including locality and intelligence, to the Secretary, on or before the 19th July.

Persons wishing to exhibit Implements, must communicate with the Secretary, and lodge with him a memorandum descriptive of the articles to be shewn, on or before the 19th of July; and all Implements must be in the Show-Yard on the day before the Show.

The Judges will make a selection of such Ploughs, and other Implements, as appear to them to possess peculiar merit, and reserve their final decision, where necessary, until they shall have tested them in a subsequent trial, to be hereafter arranged, and to take place at a suitable season of the year. All Implements admitted into the Show-Yard, at Doncaster, will be liable, on the recommendation of the Judges, to be reserved for such subsequent trials.

REPORT FOR 1843.

Keep of Farm Horses.

For the best account of the mode in which a team of not less than four horses has been kept from Lady-Day, 1842, to Lady-Day, 1843; stating the quantity and quality of their food, and the manner in which it has been supplied to them £10

All Reports must be delivered to the Secretary, on or before the 1st of June.

Competitors in Reports shall not communicate their names, but shall transmit, along with the Report, a sealed note containing their names and addresses, and inscribed on the back with some distinguishing motto or device, which shall also be inscribed on the Report. No prize will be awarded to Reports that have been previously published.

In addition to the above prizes, the Society has placed £25 at the disposal of the Publication Committee, to procure Essays for the Society's Transactions.

BEST CULTIVATED FARM.

The Society proposes to add £10 to a Sweepstakes of £5 each, from occupiers, being members of the Society, for the best cultivated Farm, not less in extent than 100 acres, situate in Yorkshire, and within 25 miles of Doncaster. The second best cultivator to have his stake returned. The entries to be made by letter, addressed to the Secretary, prior to the 1st of March, 1843, on which day they will close; when, if there should not be five competitors, no inspection nor award, will be made. Persons becoming members of the Society before the 1st of March next, will be qualified to compete for the prize.

CERTIFICATE.

For Classes 17, 18, 19, 20.

I, of near do hereby request you to enter my (if sow, state whether she is in pig or milk,) of the breed, aged bred by for the prizes in class
The contents of this certificate are true, to the best of my belief and knowledge.

Dated_____(Signed)_____

For Class 21.

I, of near do hereby request you to enter my three store pigs of the same litter, bred by weeks old, for the prizes in class 21.
The contents of this certificate are true, to the best of my belief and knowledge.

Dated_____(Signed)_____

A HISTORY OF
THE YORKSHIRE
AGRICULTURAL
SOCIETY
1837–1987

A HISTORY OF
THE YORKSHIRE AGRICULTURAL SOCIETY
1837–1987

In celebration of the 150th anniversary
of the Society

Vance Hall

B.T. Batsford Ltd, London

Typeset by Servis Filmsetting Ltd, Manchester
and printed in Great Britain by
Anchor Brendon Ltd
Tiptree, Essex

Published by B.T. Batsford Ltd
4 Fitzhardinge Street, London W1H 0AH

British Library Cataloguing in Publication Data
Hall, Vance
    A history of the Yorkshire Agricultural Society 1837–1987:
    in celebration of the 150th anniversary of the Society.
    1. Yorkshire Agricultural Society ————
        History
    I. Title
    630'. 6' 04281   S218.2.Y6
    ISBN 0-7134-5783-X

'History is not like some individual person, which uses men to achieve its ends. History is nothing but the actions of men in pursuit of their ends.'

Karl Marx, *Die Heilige Familie*, 1845

CONTENTS

ACKNOWLEDGEMENTS

I am deeply grateful to the fine and generous people within the Yorkshire Agricultural Society whose own enthusiasm and devotion to the Society will, I hope, bear fruit in this book. It has been a great pleasure to work with them and I can only hope that other historians, working the rich mine of British agricultural history, might occasionally enjoy such civilized and generous company.

It is customary for an author to appear reluctant to name persons to whom he is indebted in an undertaking of this sort. I have no such qualms. Foremost, to Lt Col Martin Young, the present Secretary General of the Society, I am indebted for his total support and trust. To Mr Alan Martindale, the long-serving Deputy Secretary, I am indebted for his time and knowledge, given so freely. To Mr Lance Gilling, the Chairman of the Society's Executive Committee, I am indebted for his encouragement and belief in this venture. And to Major General G. de E. Collin, the Honorary Show Director, I am grateful for whatever insights I might have into the actual character of The Great Yorkshire, as the annual show is proudly called.

To other members of the secretariat of the Society, particularly to Mrs Anne Donovan and Mrs Katie Boyle, I am also grateful for their warm concern for myself as the task got heavier.

And to various members of the Society I wish to record my thanks for a variety of favours: for attic-trunks thrown open and cellars plumbed, for reminiscences over cream tea, for conversations which have led me into nuances of the Society's life that I would otherwise have missed, and for detailed correspondence. Mr Frank Abbey, Miss Jacob Smith, Mr Mark Messey Thompson and Mr 'Mac' Baldwin, I would like to thank in particular.

I wish also to thank Mr Don Quarrie, of Henry Bushell and Sons Ltd, for providing a number of the photographs for this book.

I also wish to acknowledge the smooth professionalism of the staff of the Yorkshire Record Office at the North Yorkshire County Library in York, and the interest shown by Mr Brian Horner at the Yorkshire Museum of Farming at Murton Park, near York. The library staffs of the British Library, University College, London, and Senate House, London, have also facilitated my research.

To Surender Bhart, Kuljinder Kaur and Toh Bee Hoon I am very grateful for converting my manuscript into typescript and for being so cheerful and reliable in that task.

To Margaret Hall I wish to record my deep-felt thanks for her interest.

And I must express my gratitude to Anthony Seward and Simon Prosser for seeing this book through the press.

Vance Hall

Universiti Malaya,
Kuala Lumpur, 1987

LIST OF ILLUSTRATIONS

LIST OF TABLES, FIGURES AND APPENDICES

FOREWORD

by
President of the Yorkshire Agricultural Society
The Marquis of Normanby
KG CBE
Her Majesty's Lord Lieutenant in the county of North Yorkshire

Throughout the last one hundred and fifty years the Yorkshire Agricultural Society has been a major influence on agricultural development and progress in Yorkshire and northern England.

In the early years the society encouraged innovation and improvements in the husbandry of crops and livestock. Competitions and field days were organised to demonstrate new techniques. Every aspect of rural craftsmanship received attention and encouragement.

The pace of change in farming increased as the influence of the industrial revolution made itself felt in rural areas. Increasing numbers of people left the land for the towns and horsepower gave way to machines.

In this century two world wars emphasised the need for food production at home and the society played a major part in making the achievement of this greater production possible. Now in the postwar period the society has again demonstrated the spirit of innovation and adventure by, amongst other things, being the first agricultural society in the country to establish a permanent site for the annual show.

The success of this initiative has enabled the society to aid directly agricultural development and research by awarding travel scholarships annually, underwriting technical demonstrations similar to the recently established arable trials centre and supporting activities such as the Farming and Wildlife Advisory Groups aimed at bringing about a better understanding and appreciation of the countryside.

The 150th year of the society's existence is a very appropriate time to record how the society has developed over these years and how it has been closely involved in both initiating and responding to change, the speed of which in recent years has become swift and compelling.

I commend this history of the society's first 150 years as an important record of what has been achieved and in the knowledge that the society is well placed to face the future with confidence and enthusiasm.

Mulgrave Castle
April 1987

MAPS

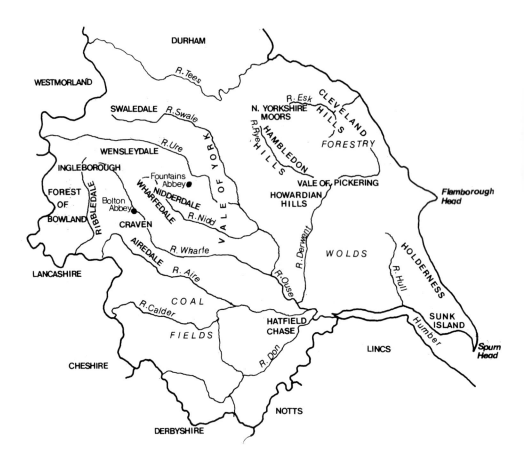

The rivers and other natural features of Yorkshire

Yorkshire, with main towns and some other places mentioned in the text

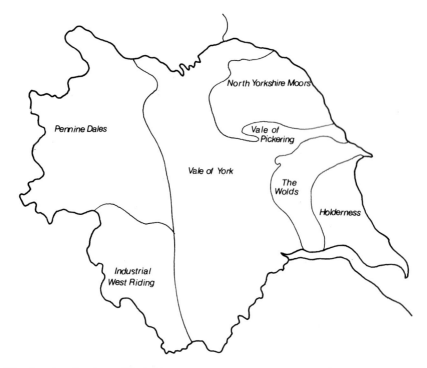

The farming districts of Yorkshire

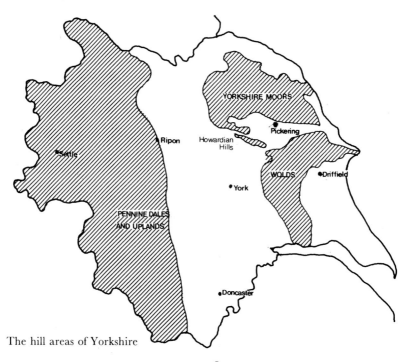

The hill areas of Yorkshire

INTRODUCTION

This *History* is written for the 150th anniversary of the Yorkshire Agricultural Society (hereafter abbreviated YAS). Being commissioned by the Society in the first place, it naturally has in mind the Society's members as its main readers. It has therefore been written to be of interest to them.

But the agricultural community of Yorkshire is not likely to be its sole readership. In fact, scholars (in particular, general historians and specialist agricultural historians) will share some of its concerns and hopefully will benefit from its labour. It has therefore been written with their academic interests in view too.

There is another type of historian whom this *History* addresses: the historian of nineteenth-century *science*. In part, this arises from the author's own professional training as a historian and philosopher of science. But it also arises from one of the principal personal concerns of a nucleus of zealous and influential landowner-agriculturists; during the period c. 1835–50 (and beyond), these men strove both to make English agriculture more scientific and to determine whose science should be promulgated among the English agricultural community, and to what ends.

This nucleus consisted of a dozen or so men, of whom just a handful seem to have occupied crucial, pivotal positions in the scientific reform movement within English agriculture during the few years spanning the mid-century. These figures were the third Earl Spencer (1782–1845), Philip Pusey (1799–1855), Harry Stephen Meysey Thompson (1809–74) and Thomas Dyke Acland (1809–98).

It shall be argued that these men set out to engineer the improvement of English agriculture in a number of key directions: in reforming (but not revolutionizing) the landlord-tenant relationship, in education, in the dissemination of information on better farming practice and economic conditions, and in the applications of science. They were conspicuously successful in these efforts for at least three reasons. First, they were all members of what had become by the mid-1840s the most influential agricultural society in the whole of England, namely the Royal Agricultural Society (hereafter abbreviated RASE). Second, they all occupied key positions in the RASE, which enabled them to determine its policy and enact its strategy, so ensuring a large measure of correspondence between their membership. Third, they each had hold of the reins of an important agricultural publication. Pusey was chairman of the RASE's *Journal*

Committee, and *de facto* editor. Acland was long-standing chairman of the Journal Committee of the Bath and West of England Society (hereafter abbreviated BWES, despite the fact that its precise name has altered several times), and was also the official editor of its journal for a few years. Thompson was chairman of the Journal Committee of the YAS, becoming its official editor too. He succeeded Pusey as chairman of the RASE's Journal Committee upon the latter's death in 1855, thus becoming chairman of two Journal Committees, clearly playing an active editorial role in both.

These four men exerted an enormous and deliberative influence through at least three of the agricultural societies and their journals. (Spencer was also influential within a number of other societies, most notably the Smithfield Club.) Through these societies and journals the four sought to propagate, amongst other things, the latest and most practicable findings in agricultural science. In developing this theme, this *History of the Yorkshire Agricultural Society* breaks new ground for the growing number of science- and agriculture-historians whose focus is the nineteenth century, that period when science emerged both as a profession and as a social force.

In writing the type of history attempted here, a number of technical issues in the craft of history have had to be tackled. In particular, the author has tried to identify as felicitously as his research-material permits the actual agents (personal or otherwise) of the YAS's functioning and progress, and occasional regress. Who and what really determined its policies, shaped the management of its affairs, and sustained what we with hindsight perceive as its substantive directions? When were these agents the Society's own members? And when were they creatures of an institutional type, or the representatives of wider concerns?

That such questions are asked at the outset of this *History* indicates that it is not greatly concerned with certain things that histories often deal with. For instance, it is not primarily interested in the big names, the 'landocrats' who lent their prestige to the Society. Rather, it seeks to identify those who formulated policy and actually managed the Society's affairs, often, perhaps, behind the scenes. In doing this, conventional forms of evidence and interpretation have had to be queried.

For example, this author's own research into the *Journal of the Bath and West of England Society* (*JBWES*) during the nineteenth century suggested that the official historian of that society was seriously misled by the *public* evidence he had available on Acland's role. He asserted that Acland's active participation in the BWES, and his control over its journal, declined after 1859, when the official editorship was handed over to someone else.[1] Indeed, the historian is led to this conclusion if he focusses on the official positions that are published in the *JBWES*. But in this case one actually finds that, despite there being another figure in the editor's chair, Acland continued to control the journal by simple virtue of his consolidation of the chairmanship of the Journal Committee. Indeed, Acland held that office, even when it no longer appeared to exist in a formal sense, from 1850 until 1898!

We are especially fortunate in our attempt to reconstruct an 'actual agents' picture of the YAS to have a complete run of original minute books for its Council meetings from the very moment of its founding on 10 October 1837 right up to the present day. When this author became interested in the Society some seven years ago, it was believed that all the primary management sources pertaining to the first hundred years and more had been lost during the Second World War. Likely as that seemed, one nonetheless knew from time-consuming experience that historical material has an entropic character. It tends to get out of order, escape, disappear from view and from memory – yet still exist.

This gave the author hope, and a hectic few days in 1982 led to our discovering the nine volumes of the Council's minute books (mostly in manuscript, often in bold and beautiful hand) for the period 1837 to 1943, in the forgotten archives of the Society's former solicitors, Munby and Scott, in Blake Street, York. We thus have one of the most extensive and complete original management-records of any extant agricultural society in Britain, out-running even that of the RASE (which was founded some months after the YAS, in May 1839).

We are therefore in a strong position to examine the actual management of a still-eminent and vital agricultural society, from its founding at the very start of Victoria's reign up to the present. We are able to ask fundamental questions about the ideology of its founders, about the achievement of their aims, about their perception of how the Society could, and did, serve not only the three Ridings but also the nation. We are able to ask questions about finance, about influence and power. And we are able to answer these questions, if not decisively (for the historical record is never perfect, and all history is but interpretation), yet plausibly.

This *History*, therefore, should not be read simply as a narrative. Of course, it does narrate a story, a success-story at that, but it pretends to more. It tries to open out a number of issues of historical enquiry, and so enlarge our understanding of how England has changed during the past century and a half. In particular, it supports the belief that our understanding of what was happening within English agriculture during an apparently paradigmatic few years, c.1835–60, needs heavy revision. For example, evidence presented in Chapter 2 should oblige a radical revision of our ideas on the founding and early years of the Royal Agricultural Society of England, and of our conception of the promotion of agricultural science at that time. It should also help to cast the history of agricultural shows in a different light.

For instance, Sir E. John Russell's generally excellent *History of Agricultural Science in Great Britain* (1966), an authoritative reference in its field, is entirely mute on a central argument of this *History*: that the YAS made a seminal contribution to the new scientific orientation within the English agricultural community of the late 1830s, 1840s and 1850s. Indeed, Russell's *History* does not even mention the Society's existence!

On the question of the agricultural show, the history of the YAS's annual show will oblige a reinterpretation of the balance between the national show of the RASE and the local ones of the many provincial societies, such as can be found in Kenneth Hudson's *Patriotism with Profit: British Agricultural Societies in the Eighteenth and Nineteenth Centuries* (1972).

This *History of the Yorkshire Agricultural Society* is as much reinterpretation as interpretation, as much exploration as narration. If thereby it should prove polemical that would but be in the Society's character. The Yorkshire has often not played safe, especially in its founding years.

I THE GENERAL CONTEXT, 1830–50

The founding of the Yorkshire Agricultural Society, on 10 October 1837, took place within a period when there appears to have been widespread enthusiasm for setting up agricultural associations. A number of these were clearly established with sufficient capital, and sufficient commitment to their avowed aims, to become quickly and widely recognized. To mention only the most conspicuous and national ones, the English Agricultural Society was founded in 1838, and as the Royal Agricultural Society (after obtaining its Royal Charter in March 1840) it rapidly built up a national membership and reputation; the Royal Irish Improvement Society was set up in 1841, and the Farmers' Club, in 1844. The period from the late 1820s to the 1840s also witnessed a proliferation of local agricultural societies throughout Britain.[1] What was the cause of this enthusiasm?

Some of the promoters of agriculture during that period have left us their explanations. A founder of the YAS, Harry Stephen Meysey Thompson, suggested (somewhat quaintly to the ears of a critical historian) that the period was 'one of those recurring fits of associative activity to which Englishmen are periodically prone', and (less quaintly) that this was simply 'the application to agriculture of the same tendency to organize companies which was so strongly developed about that time and culminated in the railway mania of 1845–6.[2]

A more intricate explanation was offered by Earl Cathcart, Thompson's obituarist for the *JRASE* and, like Thompson, a central figure in both the YAS and the RASE. Cathcart argued that the many troubles attending English agriculture in the twenty years after the Napoleonic Wars (which ended in 1815) created a deep need for systematic rural reform. This need, he felt, was met in part by legislation passed during the 1820s and '30s. New currency laws led to the setting up of joint-stock banks nationwide; the Reform Act of 1832, which widened the franchise, was followed by the Tithe Commutation Act of 1836. The Railway Bills facilitated an explosion in nationwide communication, and

> thus [suggested Cathcart] in a period of extreme depression, an absolutely essential clearing was made for the foundation of high farming and for the advent of the great English agricultural associations.[3]

There is some validity in these comments. Without doubt, the period 1814–35 had been one of prolonged and extraordinary distress for English farmers. In large measure it had arisen as a consequence of the artificial buoyancy of English farming during the French Revolutionary and Napoleonic Wars, when poor harvests coupled with low imports of wheat and inflationary government corn-purchases had sustained high grain-prices; when farming costs had risen but receipts had risen faster; when there had been a spate of enclosure and a large extension of land under cultivation; when farmers had borrowed heavily and country banks had lent readily, and when rents had risen consistently. In fact, during these wars the perimeter of English farming was pushed even beyond the limits attained in the Land Reclamation Programme of the Second World War![4]

And so, during the war years of the early nineteenth century, the *potential* supply of grain in Britain – the traditional mainstay of its agriculture – grew enormously, whilst *actually* being held back. A run of wet seasons added to this check, but the inflationary bubble burst towards the end of the wars. The 1813 harvest was a bumper one. Wheat, barley and oat prices began to tumble; the price of wheat (the perennial yardstick of agricultural prosperity) more than halved between January 1813 and December 1815, and was not to recover for twenty years or more. Acute agricultural deflation and depression set in, most acutely in heavy arable regions (for grain prices fell more than those of meat, wool and other products) and on the heavy clays, which had always been more expensive to work than lighter soils. Compounding this widespread agricultural depression was, of course, the general deflationary trend in the British economy, which persisted until the mid-century.[5]

This brief overview of the economic conditions of the postwar period is of particular relevance to the institutional developments we are interested in, of which the YAS's founding was a part. Towards the end of the 1830s, English agriculture began to emerge from its depression, although a number of its features, such as fluctuations in prices and the often painful structural changes, persisted until the 1850s.[6] One aspect of this emergence was a shift in farming values and practice, most conspicuously a trend towards greater livestock production at the expense of wheat acreage. In contemporary opinion this marked a dramatic turn in the very fabric of farming – a turn that the YAS was created, in part, to serve.

The setting up of agricultural associations in the 1830s and '40s was part of a general effort to revitalize and redirect farming. In the case of the more substantial associations, it was an effort by 'landocrats' and gentry to provide a lead to the whole agricultural community, small and large farmers alike.

This can be clearly seen in the founding documents of a number of these associations. For example, the first General Address of the Management Committee of the YAS, on 19 December 1837, announced as one of its aims:

> The promoting of good farming generally, and that not merely to the large farmer, but more especially to the small farmer, who has not always been equally considered, though in greater need of encouragement.[7]

In a like vein went several of the objects of the RASE, as announced in its Royal Charter, March 1840:

. . . to embody such information contained in agricultural publications and in other scientific works as has been proved by practical experience to be useful to the cultivators of the soil; . . . to take measures for the improvement of the education of those who depend upon the cultivation of the soil for their support; . . . to promote the comfort and welfare of labourers, and to encourage the improved management of their cottages and gardens.[8]

Similarly, one of the pamphlets most influential in this whole movement in the late 1830s, an open letter to the Earl Spencer urging the formation of a national agricultural association, argued that the fundamental task should be

to unite, in active co-operation, all, be they landlords, tenants or others, who feel an interest in advancing the prosperity of British agriculture.[9]

The promotion of such interests would affect a large proportion of England's population, and enter into the economic and political fibres of the country. Precise figures are hard to come by for England's population and pattern of employment c.1840, but we can estimate the population of the whole of Britain at that time at 18–19 million (or of England and Wales at 16 million), of whom some 1.75–2.25 million (or 1.5–1.75 million in England and Wales) were probably engaged in crop-cultivation, livestock or managing woodlands. In other words, those employed on the land represented slightly over one-quarter of all gainfully occupied persons.

Substantial as this proportion was, it was of course shrinking. In 1801 for instance, it has been estimated that not less than two-thirds of the population were directly dependent on the produce of the soil for their livelihood.[10] By 1871, the proportion had shrunk to about one-fifth.[11] But still, even by the mid-century, and despite the Reform Act, the economic and socio-political significance of the land and of agriculture remained massive and far transcended the confines of mere employment figures. With the exception of tropical products such as sugar and tea, the soil of Britain (together with its seas) provided virtually all the food consumed by the British people.

Moreover, the abundance of the harvest could have a profound effect on the state of the nation. Low yields of grain and potatoes would force up the cost of the basic diet, as it continued to do for some while, even after the repeal of the Corn Laws became fully implemented in 1849. This in turn would lower the volume of purchase in other commodities, such as textiles. Compensatory imports of grain (from Russia for example) could add strain to the balance of payments and to the cost of credit. Expensive credit, costlier food and under-employment made a potent recipe for unrest. On the other hand, large harvests and low food prices created higher employment among agricultural workers and their families, as well as among those who supplied other domestic needs on which the rapidly growing urban and industrial population spent their surplus wages.[12]

In addition to food, the land supplied materials for industrial and commercial ventures, sustaining a variety of trades and manufactures and modes of business.

These included agents of all sorts (for land, livestock, manure, etc.); bakers; brewers and beer retailers; bone crushers and merchants; butchers; butter factors; cheese factors and cheese mongers; chemical manure manufacturers (few in 1840, but a rapidly accelerating number by 1850); chicory makers; corn and flour dealers, factors and merchants; curriers; dairymen; flax dealers; glue manufacturers (often on the same premises as the bone crushers and dealers); grindery dealers; leather cutters, dressers, dyers and sellers; lime burners and merchants; maltsters; (ordinary) manure manufacturers and merchants; market gardeners; seedsmen; oil-cake makers and dealers (a rapidly increasing number from the 1820s onwards); oil manufacturers and dealers; smiths and farriers; starch manufacturers; tallow chandlers and refiners; timber dealers; vinegar makers; and many more. Indeed, as one works through that monumental nineteenth-century institution, the *Trades Directory* (from which the above are taken), one sees how intimate were the avenues of interest and profit between town and country.[13]

As well as feeding Britain's population and supporting a multitude of trades, the land supplied the wherewithall for the high administration of the state. Agricultural rents supported both Houses of Parliament, financed numerous entrepreneurial ventures, and generally provided security to landowners who found their talents or their foibles drawn in other directions.[14] In short, the *landed* interest could be identified, as it often was, with the *national* interest, so that the promotion of agriculture was perceived not only as a pursuit of profit but also as a patriotic endeavor.[15] The more closely agriculture was connected with other pursuits, the more obvious this was – at least in the eyes of its practitioners and promoters.

The mutual dependence between agriculture and the railways is one example. Recall Thompson's assertion that the promoting of agricultural associations in the late 1830s and early 1840s was 'the application to agriculture of the same tendency to organize companies which was so strongly developed about that time and culminated in the railway mania of 1845–6'. The railways had a three-fold effect on agricultural development, an effect that has not been fully explored by historians.

First and foremost, the railways brought hitherto undreamt of mobility to the agricultural community, making it easier, quicker and eventually cheaper than ever before to distribute livestock, deadstock, machinery and men. By c.1850, the railways could already boast some 6000 miles of track throughout England and Wales.

Secondly, the railways facilitated (but did not themselves initiate) something that all mid-century contemporaries regarded as a necessary agent for agriculture's development and for the expansion of agricultural societies: the migratory agricultural show. It is probably no coincidence that Thompson was apparently the prime mover in the development of a *moveable* YAS Show (see Chapter 2) at the very time that he was putting his own money into the North Eastern Railway Company, of which he became Chairman.[16] The Highland and Agricultural Society of Scotland was probably the first to utilize the moveable show system, in the late 1820s, and it appears subsequently to have been adopted as a matter of course by those associations that were sufficiently capitalized by means of membership donations and subscriptions to afford the risk – associations such as the YAS, the RASE and the Royal Irish, the North Lincolnshire Agricultural Society (founded 1836) and the British Association for the Advancement of Science (founded 1831).[17]

Thirdly, for a large number of landowners the economic connection between their land and the railways was intimate. Many landowners received substantial compensation from companies building lines across their estates, and a significant proportion of that money must have been ploughed into estate-development.[18] Some would be re-invested in railways stocks and shares, another form of capital-security favoured by those agricultural societies with capital to spare. Again, the YAS illustrates this rather well: by 1839, it was investing its surplus in debentures with the York and North Midland Railway, and this remained the YAS's sole form of investment until it developed a new financial strategy in the twentieth century.[19]

This account of factors in the interplay between agriculture and railways is probably uncontroversial (although the topic is inadequately explored as yet). A factor which is more difficult to substantiate, but which deserves consideration since it ties up with Thompson's comments, is the 'tendency to organize companies', which Thompson mentions would have entailed an availability of capital. We do know that a tremendous amount of capital was made available for the development of railways, which, from the 1830s to the 1870s, were part of the actual dynamics of England's economic expansion. But that capital was not acquired evenly. The first wave of railway promotions peaked in 1833–7, the second and greater wave in 1843–7, and there were later ones too. At the end of the first wave, many fingers were badly burned in hasty speculation, and undoubtedly the public and the entrepreneurs drew back from fresh railway investment for the next five years or so. Indeed, new railway ventures were virtually non-existent between 1837 and 1842.[20]

This was precisely the period when certain agricultural associations were being set up with substantial capital, an ample testimony to the availability of finance. The YAS and the RASE are perhaps the two most successful examples. It therefore seems plausible that the hiatus in railway promotion and speculation made money available from which the new agricultural associations benefitted. There are grounds for suspecting that there was a more close and complex relationship between the capitalization of railways and the capitalization of agriculture and its institutions than has hitherto been appreciated. Further research, on the membership of the YAS's early General Management Committee, for example, might uncover much of interest to the economic historian, for Thompson was not the only founder of the YAS to have substantial interests in railways too.

In 1840 by far the largest proportion of the farming community in England, and Britain as a whole, was made up of small farmers working less than 50 acres. The returns of the 1851 census may be taken as a reasonable indication of this, even though the two smallest categories were probably underestimated. From the 1885 census it is clear that there was a trend towards small farming as the century went on.

Table 1.1: Agricultural holdings in Britain, 1851 and 1885

Size of holding	1851 Number of holdings	1885 (in thousands)
1–5 acres	19.0	135.7
6–50 acres	118.3	233.0
51–100 acres	53.3	64.7
101–300 acres	73.5	79.6
Over 300 acres	19.3	19.4
Not stated	2.6	–
Total	285.9	532.4

(From the Census of Population, 1851; Agricultural Statistics, 1885)

We may say that just before mid-century approximately 50 percent of all holdings were less than 50 acres in size, with perhaps a further 20 percent occupying between 50 and 100 acres. A large majority of farmers were therefore small-holders, with limited working capital and often scant experience of farming practices different from their own. Strongly resistant to innovation, they were usually tied to some convention in crop-rotation laid down by local custom, an informal tenancy agreement, the localized nature of the market or sheer economic prudence.[21]

Throughout England, much of the farming was a variant on the 'Norfolk System', basically a four-course pattern in which grain crops alternated with green or fodder crops. Perhaps 'variant' is too mild a description, for there was already considerable departure away from the classic Norfolk pattern in many areas. It might be more accurate, then, to describe much of English farming as a 'considered departure' from the Norfolk standard; such departures were usually made in the light of local farming exigencies, almost entirely empirical and with little theoretical rationale beyond classical conceptions of the soil as 'sick' or 'tired' of some crop or other, or 'deaf' or 'friable'.[22]

The basic four-course system could be schematized as follows, showing the primary role of turnips and other roots:

1 Turnips or swedes (and later, mangolds; and later still, kale).
2 Barley.
3 Clover (generally the hardier, indigenous red rather than the white).
4 Wheat, or rye.

Presented in the form of a working sequence this would be a spring corn, under-sown with clover or rye-grass, cut for hay or seed and then grazed; wheat, or a crop of rye after the corn harvest (roughly in August), to be fed off green by livestock in early spring (when fresh food would be most needed for the livestock); then turnips or another root-crop, to be fed off the land or carted to the cattle.[23]

At a time when artificial manures were virtually non-existent, this four-course system generally maintained the soil's fertility at a reasonable level, insuring the landlord against depreciation of his capital, the land. It also assured the tenant of a succession of reliable crops, weather permitting, and gave continuous employment throughout the year. Autumn was occupied with pulling some of the root crop, preparing wheat, ditching and hedging; winter went with threshing corn, feeding livestock in yards and folding the sheep, ploughing for more roots and barley. Spring would see the completion of ploughing, drilling for spring corn and clover, cleaning land for a root crop, and spring-tillage of corn; summer would be busy with drilling and hoeing roots, harvesting hay and corn, and attending one or more of the many local shows, auctions or itinerant fairs.

With one quarter of the land given over to root crops, the four-course pattern was fairly labour-intensive. But in principle this was offset by its two cash-crops, wheat and barley, and its abundance of food for livestock, namely roots and hay, as well as cereal-straw for litter. The livestock side was itself a third 'source of income', which also provided a valuable input into the crop side by way of farmyard manure. This had become the basic pattern upon which many farmers elaborated their own practices, for the excellent reason that it did secure a basis for both *self-sufficient* farming (almost everything was recycled on the farm, except for some of the seeds which had to be bought, perhaps some lime or chalk,[24] and the corn-crop for sale) and *mixed* farming (i.e. corn and livestock). Properly managed, and combined with good drainage, this undoubtedly supplied the springboard for 'high farming' at the mid-century.

Yet, as indicated, there were many considered departures, not only in the choice of seed to sow and crop to reap, but also in the number and periodicity of courses decided upon. It is worth noting some of the factors responsible for these departures. To begin with, it has to be realized that the classic four-course system is most suitable for light, dry soils, where the trampling of livestock on the field will not adversely affect the soil's tilth or texture, and where animal manure will improve the physical as well as the chemical condition of the land (provided the folding is controlled). However, it was frequently found that other types of soil could not be so treated, or needed other components. These other soils might be heavy clays (as in the Leeds valley), needing heavier ploughing and drainage to sustain productivity. Sheep folding in winter and early spring was found to injure the soil's texture, and stunt the growth of barley in particular. On the heaviest clays, the root crop was often eliminated and replaced by bare fallow. Other soils were deficient in certain minerals, which, as early as the first decade of the nineteenth century, could be identified with some accuracy, and suggestions for improvement made.[25]

Sometimes these defects could be circumvented by making the rotation six- or eight-course, or even more, by spacing out the crops, growing red clover every fourth year (as did a Mr Kelly, at Went-Bridge), or every twelfth (as did a Mr Scissons, at Womersley), or every twentieth (as did a Mr Reynolds, again at Womersley). Problems could also be tackled by spreading one of the traditional fertilizers on the land: gypsum was considered a specific manure or stimulant for red clover, common salt for wheat, chalk for a variety of crops (in Lincolnshire it had been found beneficial for turnips as well as corn) and for a number of soil conditions.

Yet soil tilth and composition, however well or poorly understood, were not the only factors causing departures from the four-course pattern. Indeed, from the 1830s onwards these were probably not the major determinants, for a new factor began to regulate farming in England – market orientation. With the rapid growth of an urban, industrial proletariat and better transport networks, agriculture was gearing itself more and more to *distant* as well as *local* market demands.[26] By the mid-century, for instance, on the loams around Wakefield, well-managed and highly profitable market gardens and small farms followed a six-course scheme that was geared both to consumption by the local urban market and to the plentiful supply of town manure (human as well as animal). Turnips, then wheat, were followed by two seed crops, wheat again, and barley. Around Bawtry, Tadcaster, Whixley Green, Hamerton and Boroughbridge a six-course was also common, including a crop of tares for soiling horses and an extra turnip crop.[27] One of the most striking illustrations of Yorkshire agriculture being stimulated by distant markets and abetted by ever-improving transport facilities was the growth of wheat and barley farming in the region of the East Riding around the market-town of Driffield. Between 1819 and 1838, the wheat exported from this district to Hull and other places by the Driffield Navigation Company rose from 8000 quarters plus 8000 sacks per annum, whilst barley jumped from 5000 quarters to 20,000.[28] It would seem, in fact, that throughout England as a whole, the best farming was to be found at a modest distance from its growing markets.[29] Evidence of Yorkshire farming in 1840 might support this generalization, but there were also exceptions.

The West Riding seems to have become the most entrepreneurial of the three Ridings by 1840. At mid-century, Caird noted that

> . . . the capitalist manufacturer is in many parts of the West Riding purchasing the estates and taking the position of the gentry. Some who do not purchase the land occupy large farms as tenants, and into the management of these they carry the same business habits and the same command of capital which gained them success in trade.[30]

John Charnock, an eminent agricultural authority resident in the West Riding, wrote to the same effect:

> The broadcloths of Leeds, the cutlery of Sheffield, the worsteds and stuffs of Bradford and Huddersfield, the linens of Barnsley, the blankets of Dewsbury, the pig- and bar-iron of Rotherham, Low Moor, etc., with their innumerable adjuncts and appliances, have each and all their lives' sinews from the apparently inexhaustible supply of this greatest of national treasures. Unlike some of the more northern coal districts . . . the more grateful sons of this locality have bestowed upon mother earth a culture which, if not of the highest order, is at least perhaps

commensurate with the time that could be spared from more immediately profitable occupations.[31]

One example of manufacturing manner and money being ploughed into the land in this riding is the enterprise of a Mr Horsfall, at Burley in Wharfedale. He was a wealthy manufacturer who, by extensive drainage, raised the productivity of his pastures by some 50 percent, and by overseeing the farming himself as a *business* venture reckoned to make a net profit of £7 per acre per annum (whereas he could let it at only £3–4).

The symbiotic nature of this relationship between town and farm in the manufacturing areas of the West Riding was also manifest in the development of prosperous market gardening businesses, and in the burgeoning of grass-husbandry. The former supplied the towns with vegetables and fruit, and the latter supplied dairy products.[32] The town, as already mentioned, in turn provided a plentiful supply of night-soil and other manures, thus allowing heavy yields to be obtained, not only on the market gardens and pasturages, but also on more traditional farms. For example, the tract of dry soil rising up from Leeds to Rothwell Haigh produced very heavy crops of wheat, barley, clover and swedes thanks to the night-soil of the city.[33] This symbiosis was further cultivated by a considerable overlap in certain business interests: Caird tells us that a sizeable proportion of dairy farmers were also in business as clothiers in the towns.

Away from urban and manufacturing areas in the West Riding (as elsewhere) the farms became larger. In the immediate vicinity of large urban areas most holdings were between 10 and 50 acres (often letting at £3–5 per acre), whilst in the rural regions most were between 80 and 100 acres (letting at 25–30s for good land, and 15–20s for wet low land).[34] Rural farming was largely traditional, with little departure from a basic four-course rotation of turnips, barley, seeds and wheat, sometimes substituting red clover for seeds, and sometimes adding peas. The rearing of livestock was not especially enterprising, compared with the other two ridings, although there were areas with specialist interests and expertise. Doncaster, Wetherby and Ripon were already established centres for breeding hunters, whilst the central region of the riding had some reputation for Shorthorns, and the easterly region for Craven Longhorns. Among the notable breeders of Shorthorns by the 1840s were several figures who were also active founding members of the YAS: the Earl Fitzwilliam, and Messrs Fawkes, Stansfield and Wentworth (see Chapter 2). Around 1840 more careful attention was also being given to sheep-breeding, with the introduction of the Leicester, the improved Lincolnshire and the South Devon.

Accompanying the apparently steady development of this riding's agriculture from the mid-1830s was a considerable extension of its arable acreage. During the first half of the century, some 100,000 acres of arable had been added. Although much of this must have been opened up under the artificial buoyancy of wartime, it seems to have either remained profitable or become profitable again, for by the mid- to late 1840s the wheat yield of the whole riding was some 30 bushels per acre, above the national average for the time.[35]

It appears that considerable capital was being invested in the region as a whole, as indeed it had to be for farming the rather sparsely populated non-urban areas with profit. In the 1840s this became especially notable, with the willingness of landowners to undertake extensive, and expensive, drainage. Another form of entrepreneurial capital-investment that was well under way in the West Riding before mid-century was warping – the alternate flooding and reclaiming of land – which was being practised all along the Humber. The top-soil of such warp land, if managed methodically, consisted of a rich alluvial deposit several feet thick, permitting lusher crops than normal. By 1850, Caird reported,

> ... the art is now so well understood that the expert warp-farmer, by careful attention to the currents, can temper his soil as he pleases.[36]

Preparation of warp-land cost around £10 per acre, taking up to two years to complete – a major commitment of both money and time. Yet it was worth the expense, for not only were huge crops attainable, but the warp-farmer could easily adopt a crop-rotation best suited to his market. Thus, in the late 1840s the Wells family at Pastures Farm were using a very unusual six-course, consisting of:

1 Potatoes, with 20 tons of farmyard manure per acre.
2 Wheat, sown out with mixed seeds.
3 Seeds, part-mown for green fodder, and part for hay.
4 More seeds, top-dressed with 3cwt. of guano per acre.
5 Potatoes, manured with 7cwt. of Peruvian guano per acre.
6 Wheat again.

Even more remarkable was the warp-land around Airmyn, 3600 acres belonging to the Earl of Beverley, who was renowned as a 'liberal landowner' (in the sense of being a progressive and generous landlord, rather than in any political sense), whose capital-investment in his estate fired his tenants with their own enterprise.

There was at least one significant difference between warp-farming in the late 1840s and that practised in the late 1830s, when the YAS was founded. This was the extensive use of guano fertilizer, watchfully promoted by the YAS, and first imported and tried in English farming in 1839–40.[37] The 1840s saw a great increase in either previously token or new 'artificial' manures. These included various brands of natural and manufactured guanos; nitrate of soda; bones and bone-dust treated in varying degrees with sulphuric acid to form a range of 'superphosphates'; and other mineral manures. Developments in the *chemistry* of agriculture became a multi-million pound phenomenon by the mid-1840s, and it is worth mentioning here (although it will be dealt with in the next chapter) that the YAS was perhaps the earliest major county-based agricultural society in England to take upon itself the task of monitoring and promoting that scientific development, as a part of its central policy. Significantly for historians of nineteenth-century science, this interest within the YAS pre-dated the advent of the German chemist, Justus Leibig, and his programme for the scientific reorientation of English farming.[38]

Returning to Yorkshire agriculture at about the time of the YAS's founding, the East Riding was the most traditional and unprogressive of the ridings. Of the three topographical regions into which it was usually divided – namely the Wold district, the division of Holderness, and the Vale of York – the Vale of York had developed the least since the late eighteenth century, when Arthur Young (in 1770) and William Marshall (in 1788) had visited Yorkshire and found the East Riding so wretched. With the exception of the warp-land along the river Ouse, and some limited areas of oolite and gravel beds, the Vale consisted of 'tenacious clay and blowing sands'. On the clay-soils, 'the old three-course, viz., fallow, wheat, beans, is the adopted practice, with such infringements of it as the farmer thinks he can with safety or profit introduce'. The main obstacle to improving this farming was, of course, inadequate drainage. Good drainage was also needed on the sandy soils where, however, a four-course of turnips, barley, seeds and wheat was common by 1840.[39]

The soils of the Holderness region were so varied, compared with the Vale, that there was no general pattern of farming. Nonetheless, by the late 1830s this district possesed a variety of examples of quite successful husbandry: prodigious crops of rape on the peaty area between Brigham and Tickton (known as The Carrs); good four- or five-course husbandry in South Holderness, which also contained some 20–30,000 acres of loose alluvial soil and warp-land between Hull and Patrington along the Humber; and less productive farming on the gravels and reddish clays of North and Middle Holderness.

The Wolds had been the most progressive region since the wars. In the late eighteenth century they had had a rather miserable agricultural reputation, seen as fit only for sheep. The gradual introduction of the Norfolk pattern, however, and particularly the turnip, which when fed to the sheep produced manure, dramatically raising the soil's fertility, worked wonders. By 1840 the region was a net exporter of grain, whilst it also boasted a stronger-than-ever reputation for its sheep. Cattle rearing had increased too, and the newly improved Shorthorn had almost wholly replaced the older 'Holderness Short-horn' although it was still rare to find a herd of more than fifty beasts.

A number of the most active founding members of the YAS farmed in this East Riding, and it appears that their capital and enterprise had played a significant role in what progress had occurred in the area. The most conspicuous of these figures was Sir Tatton Sykes (1772–1863) of Sledmere, whose annual sheep-auction drew buyers from all over Britain. His father had been principally responsible for reclaiming the Wolds and showing others that it was profitable to keep cattle, and cultivate corn, there. Another YAS founder, Robert Denison, at Kilnwick Percy in the Vale of York, busily set an example in draining, marling and subsoiling – exercises which he was prepared to finance on his tenants' behalf since he knew how much more valuable his land would be in consequence.[40] It was reported that he had converted some 300 acres 'from a mere rabbit warren into very good farming land, and which may now be worth nearly twenty shillings per acre'. Yet another YAS founder, Robert Maxwell of Everingham Park, also in the Vale of York, had set a similar example.[41] Denison and Maxwell were members of the inner circle of the YAS, and in Chapter 2 their own clear commitment to the YAS's basic agricultural aims will be discussed.

The question was asked at the time – what were the causes of the East Riding's general backwardness? The nature of the soils was one factor. Some argued that the absence of long leases was another (and this will be touched on later). Caird attributed the general low level of entrepreneurship to the absence of manufacturing industry in the area, finding his view supported by the fact that the most conspicuous farming enterprise in the whole region was on the estate of a Leeds industrialist, at Patrington, where uniquely for the East Riding 'the influence of capital and the energy of the manufacturer have converted the quiet of a retired village into a scene of bustling industry'. Here could be found 'every imaginable machine for converting the corn and vegetable produce of the farm into food for the sustenance of man and beast'.[42]

The agriculture of the North Riding was radically different from that of the West and East, for its tradition was essentially in the breeding of cattle, most notably the Shorthorn (the name was spelled as two separate words, or hyphenated, until the twentieth century), conspicuously along the south bank of the river Tees, in the neighbourhoods of Northallerton and Catterick, and on the estates of large landowners such as the third Earl Spencer and the Earl of Ducie. The breed had emerged in the 1770s as a product of selective breeding in Durham and the North Riding, and was central to the development of English agriculture nationwide at precisely the time when the YAS was established. As one historian succinctly puts it,

> . . . the Shorthorn became not only the fashionable speculation of the richest landowners and farmers, but the commonplace and essential improved beast of the age of high farming. In fact, it was so successful that it almost eliminated its rivals, its reputation as a converter of grass, roots, straw, or cake into meat and milk together with muck (and thus money) in almost any environment or locality belying its seemingly localized origins on Teesside.[43]

Concentrated first along the Tees and in the grazing valleys of the upland limestone districts of Wensleydale, Swalesdale and Bishopdale, it initially supplied the markets of the industrial West Riding and Lancashire. By about 1840, the Shorthorn had become crucial to much of the North Riding's agriculture and dairying, determining crop-rotations and raising crop-yields. By the late 1840s, this was so much the case that one commentator declared that 'to enumerate the breeders of the North Riding were therefore to name the greater part of the landed gentry and aristocracy'.[44] Many of the farms, which tended to be larger here than elsewhere in the county, also seem to have bred their own type of man alongside their distinctive type of stock. Caird reported that

Men are still to be found who have been bred from their childhood to study the peculiarities of form and symmetry which, combined with early maturity and great weight, have given the improved Short-horn its celebrity.[45]

One might suspect Caird of being too sober here, for the Yorkshire newspapers and other periodicals of the nineteenth century are eloquent on the 'love-affair' of Yorkshiremen (at least in the North Riding) with the Shorthorn cow. Here, writing in all seriousness, is a visitor to Mr Booth at Warlaby:

Into a grass field . . . and in the hollow before us . . . lay a dozen or so cows, prominent among which is old Margaret, by Commander-in-Chief 21451, out of Maggie, by Lord of the Hills. With her white face, her fine flat waxy horn, and her rough lightish-red coat, this old dame, the mother of seven calves, is a grand one. Though thin in condition, the old cow is undoubtedly worthy of her position, and as we handle that well-formed frame, her daughter, Marchioness, by Royal Benedict 27348, safe in calf to King James 28971, raises herself up as if proud of her level back, her great loin, round rib, and wealth of hair. As she walks gracefully away, we cannot help thinking that she is a lovely maiden, and that her three years have not been lived in vain. The next is a white, Marcia, by King James 28971, which has seen four summers, and is the dam of two calves. 'Come now, show yourself, and you know so well how to do it.' And in obedience to the command, the lovely cow draws herself up with her face to the brae, and then we have before us a model. Her outline is perfection; her head, 'Roman nose', and horn all that we could wish, and stepping backwards we can see the broad shoulders, the lovely front and light offal, which are the well-known characteristics of the Warlaby cattle.[46]

Clearly, even if Britain had succumbed to the spirit of republicanism at the end of the eighteenth century, the North Riding would have retained its own form of monarchy! Indeed, from the breeding-farms of that Riding purebred Shorthorns were being sold at royal prices in the period from the late 1820s to the 1840s. £400 for a bull was not an unrealistic price, while a heifer fetched £300. (These sums would be equivalent to tens of thousands of pounds today.)

The remainder of the North Riding was taken up with quite prosperous four- and five-course husbandry in the sandy and gravel districts of the south-west and the east (encompassing much of the land east of Northallerton), with less progressive two-crop and fallow in the western margin of the Vale of York, and 'a medley of cultivation adopted in districts where, from varieties of soil, aspect, or the prevalence of stagnant water, scarcely any definite system can be said to apply'.[47] To discuss just one of these, the south-western and eastern light soils were among the best cultivated of the whole county by the 1840s, characterized by extensive mixed farming where large herds of livestock were well-integrated with a successful four- or five-course, usually of turnips, barley, seeds and wheat. As elsewhere in the county, a number of the landowner-agriculturists who were experimenting in this region (with different methods of dibbling and sowing, with departures from the basic Norfolk pattern, with livestock management and, in the 1840s, with the new fertilizers) were also key founder-members of the YAS. Pre-eminent among them was H.S. Thompson, then farming at Moat Hall.[48]

And so, with the expansion and profitability of specialized breeding, the development of urban markets and the gradual introduction of four-course husbandry, accompanied by considerable capital-investment in the land, it may be said that on the whole Yorkshire had emerged reasonably strong from the post-Napoleonic agricultural malaise. Several specific economic indicators also support this conclusion. For instance, the quantity and value of imports servicing Yorkshire agriculture (feed-seeds, feed-cakes, bones and other fertilizers) at the principal port of Hull rose steadily in the 1830s, and in 1841 their total value stood at a staggering £1 million.[49] The county's agricultural-economic health, however, has to be seen in a nationwide context, for we know that throughout England the rearing counties had generally fared best, their agricultural incomes dropping severely only in the worst troughs of cereal prices, when demand for their leanstock to fatten on southern and eastern arable land fell.

This survey of Yorkshire agriculture would be inadequate to its task – establishing a context for the YAS's founding – if it did not mention the issue of leases and tenants' rights, for that was a major point of debate at the time, and struck many agricultural analysts as fundamental to farming progress. On the one hand, there were those who argued that a tenant-farmer needed the security of tenure that only a formal tenancy-agreement with the landlord could provide, in order to feel confident that his expenditure and his enterprise would not be jeopardized by the chance of eviction. In this view, tenancy-agreements and tenant-rights were fundamental requisites for sound farming. In the late eighteenth century, Arthur Young had felt this mutual contract and security to be almost solely responsible for improvements in English agriculture, while in the mid-nineteenth century Caird felt that its (by then) frequent absence was one of the greatest causes of wastage.

On the other hand, there were those who objected that formal agreements were restrictive of enterprise: tenants might be tied down to rigid rotations or stuck with a level of rent which could not be adjusted in keeping with fluctuations in prices or weather. Moreover, many leases surviving from the eighteenth century abounded in 'restrictions and repetitions only calculated to puzzle the poor man anxious at once to fulfill his contract and obtain a return from his capital', and some of the later nineteenth-century leases were no less obfuscating. Added to which, the landowner could also be liable to a raw deal, for, as well as footing the legal fees for a new lease, he too could be tied down beyond his own legitimate convenience.[50]

At times, this debate was conducted along a priori and political, rather than agricultural, lines. Yet in the long run, this politicization of the issue enabled the agricultural societies to make their own distinctive contribution to the debate. In resolving to eschew politics (as the RASE formally declared to do, following the example of the YAS), they had perforce to tackle it analytically and empirically. Both societies did just that, publishing their findings in their journals.

In Yorkshire there was probably a general custom of tenancy-agreement in the West Riding, but nothing equivalent in the East and North. Even in the West, the agreements were usually unwritten, and therefore not proper leases as such; nonetheless, they were felt to be binding. It is debatable whether tenant-farming was more enterprising as a consequence of the presence or absence of a form of lease. Surveys of the county sponsored by the YAS in the 1840s indicate that there was no general correlation. For instance, the considerable success of the Wold farmers had developed without anything more than an unwritten yearly tenancy entailing covenants of benefit to both parties.[51] Caird was in agreement, strongly doubting whether the West Riding had benefitted directly from its custom. Indeed, he had abundant evidence of its conducing to all sorts of fraud: toll-men taking bribes to sign for false loads of manure passing through their gates; officials bribed to give extra-high valuations on out-going tenants' land; and some tenants notoriously so adept at taking on a farm at falsely-low valuation, and quitting at falsely-high, that they could make a living simply from this manoeuvre – at the landlord's expense.[52] Such malpractices were to be special concerns of the larger agricultural societies, and the YAS and the RASE were to see in agricultural chemistry a means of checking them.

From the late 1830s, a certain re-orientation and restructuring in English agriculture occurred, justifying its own epithet, 'High Farming'. Like most labels, this meant different things to different men, as their own priorities and paths differed. In a narrow sense, the term was equated with the high feeding of livestock, on roots and oil-cakes, coupled with the production of grain within the framework of the four-course rotation and its derivatives. In a broader sense, the term could be applied to any system which was both capital- and labour-intensive, and which placed a premium on innovation and technical expertise. Modern historians, too, hold differing views of the essence of high farming: some regard it as an essentially economic phenomenon, the product of increased availability of capital and of loans for land improvement, whilst others see it as the extension and continuation of the classical agricultural revolution.[53] Certainly, high farming did entail an increase in capital outlay by landlords and the amount of working capital needed by tenants. Money was made available for permanent or semi-permanent improvements such as drainage, for redistributions of crops and livestock, and (after the mid-century) for extensive permanent pasturage. There was conspicuous expenditure too on new build-ings, such as covered fold-yards (where livestock could be housed in winter, thus reducing the danger of fatal heat-loss, and allowing their manure to be collected and utilized, and on fertilizers and feeds (oilseed cake in particular).

One historian considers the whole gamut of capital-intensive developments so significant that he has labelled it 'The Second Agricultural Revolution' (locating its beginning at around 1815), for which he suggests the following scenario:

. . . [it] involved the technical changes of crop rotations and livestock improvement; it generally involved the physical changes of enclosure, and it embodied the economic changes of increased intensity of cultivation; that is, production functions were altered by an increase in the amounts of both capital and labour that could be profitably employed in relation to land. Farmers clearly became more market-orientated than before, in deciding what crops to grow, when, and in what proportions. But the supply of the major part of the extra capital required came from landlords. . . .

From the tenant's point of view, this agricultural revolution was mainly a managerial revolution, in the sense that the new husbandry required him to manage the resources of his farm in an orderly, competent, rational, and efficient manner in order to reap the rewards of larger yields, better stock, and greater income per acre farmed, which mixed farming offered. On the whole, these things did not cost him very much money, but they did cost him a great deal of intelligence in comparison with that displayed by his ancestors.[54]

These were the broad features of that movement in English farming which, over some 20–25 years, took agriculture out of the slough of the late 1810s to early 1830s into the buoyancy of the 1850–70 period. At the heart of this movement was an entrepreneurship encouraged by the agricultural societies and associations, and by certain central figures operating both as private landowners and as public promoters. Men like Spencer, H.S. Thompson and Pusey, were directly responsible for the fact that 'farming moved from being an extractive industry . . . into being a manufacturing industry'. The technical agents of this transformation were improved farming implements and machinery, together with the products of chemical science – first fertilizers, and then, somewhat later, more nutritious and purposeful feed-stuffs, whose consumption rose enormously from about 1850.[55] One further facet of this transformation was the idea of *farming as investment* – the tenant's capital being in the form of livestock, crops, implements, seeds, fertilizers and ready cash, and the landowner's capital in the form of the land itself and the buildings of the farm.[56]

If high farming had at least three fundamental dimensions – economic, educational and technical – it also had a deep political aspect. For instance, Caird, who was one of its most ardent exponents, represented many in envisaging it as the only politically appropriate response to free trade (which was a growing consequence of the repeal of the Corn Laws) and the only proper re-orientation of the landed interest, given the changing nature of English society and power.[57]

Moreover, the eventual success and nationwide extension of high farming was seen by many of its advocates and 'managers' to depend critically upon social and legislative changes, in, for example, a loosening of the often strangling conditions of inheritance and entailment that were encumbent on landowners, and in the area of the landlord-tenant relationship. Caird himself believed that an appropriate form of security for the tenant, coupled with a much greater availability of capital, was the *sine qua non* of its success. Politically radical though he was, Caird's prognosis received wide support from many landowner-agriculturists, such as Thompson and Pusey, who undoubtedly set out to make the spread of judicious high farming the special task of their agricultural societies, the Yorkshire and the Royal. There can be little doubt that they, together with a small group of 'landocrats' like the ultra-Tory Duke of Richmond and the ultra-Whig third Earl Spencer, the Earl of Zetland and Earl Fitzwilliam (to mention some of those who were early Presidents of the Yorkshire and the Royal), were determined to pilot the new course for English agriculture and to hold the helm in their own most English and most patriotic hands.

2 THE EARLY YEARS, 1837–50

The Yorkshire Agricultural Society officially came into the world on 10 October 1837, at the Black Swan Hotel in York. Among the gentry in attendance were a good number of figures known within and without the county for their active concern with agricultural development. Those whom the *Yorkshire Gazette* felt worthy of mention included: Earl Spencer, Earl de Grey, Lord Huntingfield; the Hon. Sir H.E. Vavasour, Bart., of Hazlewood Hall; the Hon. C. Langdale, of Holme; Sir F.L. Wood, Bart., of Hemsworth; Sir J.V.B. Johnstone, Bart., of Hackness; G.L. Fox, MP, of Bramham Park; J.W. Childers, MP, of Cantley; W.R.C. Stansfield, MP, of Esholt; S. Crompton, MP, of Woodend; P.B. Thompson, of Escrick Park; W.B. Wrightson, MP, of Cudworth; J. Walker, of Sand Hutton; W. Busfield, MP, of Bradford; Mark Foulis, of Heslerton; T. Duncombe, of Copgrove; A. Empson, of Blacktoft; F. Cholmeley, of Brandsby; Henry Preston, of Moreby; Captain Dowker, of Huntington; H.S. Thompson, then at Fairfield, York; W.M. Hatfield of Newton Kyme; Rev. T. Harrison, of Firby; William Allen, of Malton; T. Donkin, of Westow Hall; Godfrey Wentworth, of Woolley Park; R.F. Shawe of Brantingham Thorpe; Robert Denison, of Kilnwick Percy; Charles Tempest, of Broughton, Skipton; Alderman George Hudson, of York; H. Smithson, of Malton; T. Barstow of Garrow Hill; James Barber of Tang Hall; T. Price, of Clementhorpe; and R. Hey, of York. The crowd must have numbered at least fifty, and probably more.

Earl Spencer, one of the most respected Englishmen of his day and an active livestock breeder, statesman, and cousin to the newly-annointed Queen, was proposed (by Robert Denison) for the chair, whereupon he moved the Society's founding, with its general object:

> . . . to hold an Annual Meeting for the exhibition of Farming Stock, Implements, etc., and for the general promotion of agriculture.[1]

It is clear that Spencer was not co-opted as a mere figurehead, for among the services he had rendered already to agriculture were his reforming presidency of the Smithfield Club (since 1821), his presidency of the Bedfordshire Agricultural Society (in 1827), his long support of the Northamptonshire Farming and Grazing Society (whose presidency he had refused, insisting that he had joined this society as a tenant of his father's and not as the heir to Althorp Park), and the building up of his estate at Wiseton, which he ran essentially as an experimental research-station, where he maintained the largest and one of the most famous of the nineteenth-century Shorthorn strains – the Wiseton Herd.[2]

In addition to his many real services to agriculture, Spencer possessed the type of character that the farming community could warm to. He was never more relaxed than when in the company of farmers and breeders like John Booth, Thomas Bates, Thomas Coke of Holkham, and John Grey of Dilston, all of whom were his friends. Spencer struck observers as a 'farmer-looking man' in 'farmer-like dress', and he loved to live the part whenever his political duties allowed (see footnote below). It is recorded that he gleefully told a Duke whom he had invited to a meeting of the Smithfield Club that 'we dine at the Crown and Anchor, like farmers in boots'. Moreover, his own personal passion for farming and breeding and his ease among farmers were forged into a formidable capacity to act tangibly and decisively in the agricultural interest by a third factor in his character: his powerful sense of duty, combined with a genuine sense of humility and a natural gift for leadership. As all his contemporaries noted, he lacked personal ambition but packed a powerful punch in public enterprise and patriotism. As a recent biographer says:

> Althorp* felt profoundly inadequate in the presence of God and Lord Grey. Otherwise, he was a man of strong, even stubborn, opinions, endowed with a compelling talent for leadership made additionally powerful by a rigid adherence to his conception of aristocratic duty.[3]

All of this must have been evident to those who invited him to the 10 October meeting to become their President. Indeed, their confidence in him might be gauged from the fact that he was initially elected for a Presidential term of six years.

As this *History* unfolds, it will be seen that Spencer was not only an eminent, but also a key, active founder-member of the YAS, as he was also to be of the RASE (whose formation, unlike that of the YAS, he actually mooted and canvassed for, at a Smithfield Club dinner in London, 14 months later). The actual idea of forming a Yorkshire agricultural society was not his but probably that of H.S. Thompson, a young man of 28, well travelled, with a keen concern for agriculture and a taste for chemistry (shared by Spencer). He was heir to a 15,000-acre estate in the East Riding, at Kirby Hall, and had boundless energy, a gift for entrepreneurship, and the valuable ability to channel these judiciously. We are told by his orbituarist in the *JRASE* that 'Mr Thompson had an

---

* Spencer was better known to his contemporaries as Viscount Althorp, for as such he was a key statesman and politician in the 1820s and '30s. When Earl Grey's administration was formed in 1830, Althorp was appointed Chancellor of the Exchequer and Leader of the House of Commons, where his crowning achievement was the 1832 Reform Bill, whose responsibility it was to steer through the House. An opponent of the Bill declared: 'Althorp carried the Bill; his fine temper did it.' He retired from active politics in November 1834, when he succeeded to the Earldom, thereafter keeping company with the creatures he most respected – his Shorthorns, his sheep and the farming community.

agreeable theory that all truly British institutions commence with a dinner.'[4] The YAS was no exception, for at a country-house party at the home of Robert Denison, at Kilnwick Percy near Pocklington, on 28 August 1837, Thompson and friends were engaged in post-prandial conversation on the subject of cattle and local cattle shows, when Thompson asked, 'Don't you think we could form a Yorkshire Agricultural Society movable from place to place throughout the country?' The next morning, a small meeting was held, apparently at Pocklington possibly not at Denison's home again, but perhaps in that of Thomas Duncombe, who was one of the Denison-Thompson coterie. At this meeting Thompson developed his scheme, obtaining the firm support of his friends. We have no further details of this meeting, except that Thompson appears to have argued, against some opposition, that this should be a society consisting equally of tenant farmers and landowners – a point that he won, and which was to determine much of the YAS's character and success.[5]

In declaring that the Society should be for the exhibition of livestock and implements, and that it should be open to tenant-farmers, Thompson and friends were certainly drawing upon the practice and experience of earlier, local agricultural societies. By 1837, a rather large number of agricultural, horticultural, market gardening and other societies and associations had been established in Yorkshire, most of which were very largely composed of tenants, and some of which sponsored a show, a market or a fair. As far as we know, however, none of these shows were peripatetic. Even the larger of these societies, such as the Wharfedale Agricultural Society (founded 1806), the Doncaster Agricultural Association, the East Riding Agricultural Society (founded c.1834), the Whitby District Agricultural Society (founded c.1833/4) and the Cleveland Agricultural Society (founded c.1833), were able to manage only local shows.

Some of the shows may have been very sizeable indeed, like the East Riding Agricultural Association's 4th Show (1837) at which 'The number of farmers and agriculturists present was immense, many of them having come from the remotest portions of this county, and others from a still greater distance'.[6] As yet, very little historical research has been done on the subject of agricultural societies in Yorkshire in the late eighteenth and early nineteenth centuries.[7] We do know, however, that a number of the YAS's founders were also members of these local societies, and that it is likely that their experience of these very local organizations entered into their planning of the YAS on the large, county-wide scale hitherto unattempted. Certain founders of the YAS were already active in the Wharfedale (Sir Tatton Sykes and Lord Harewood in particular), the East Riding Agricultural Association (especially Robert Denison) and the Cleveland Agricultural Society (by the late 1850s, H.S. Thompson in particular, but he may have been an active member even earlier). But the actual model for the scale of the YAS was the Highland and Agricultural Society of Scotland (HASS), as Spencer indicated in his founding speech:-

> The object, gentlemen, of this meeting is to establish a large agricultural society, so
> as to embrace the whole of the County of York, for the general improvement of

43

agriculture by every means in our power, and more particularly by the exhibition of breeding stock and agricultural implements. It is a remarkable fact that in England there is no society which embraces a large district of country. In Scotland, they have one, called the Highland Society, which has proved of the greatest possible use in promoting an improvement in the breed of stock. The Highland Society has proved itself of the greatest consequence and value. I really cannot see why the County of York should not unite and have a society to confer the same benefits, as are enjoyed by our northern neighbours; however, I think it worth while trying the experiment.[8]

Spencer went on to say that to service such a large area as the whole county of Yorkshire (which occupied about one-eighth of the entire area of England and Wales), the HASS's expedient of a *moveable* show would need to be followed and the YAS's founders would have to think big. As he put it:

The object of the society we are about to form must be large and comprehensive – if it is not, it will be useless.[9]

Robert Denison then rose and proposed five resolutions, which were carried, and thus set the YAS in motion:

1. That a Society be formed called the 'Yorkshire Agricultural Society', the object of which shall be to hold an annual Meeting for the Exhibition of Farming Stock, Implements, etc., and for the General Promotion of Agriculture.
2. That such Meeting shall be held successively, in different places in the County, on the last Wednesday in August, in each year, and that the First Meeting be held at York, in August 1838.
3. That every subscriber of One Pound annually be a Member of this Society.
4. That Donations for forming a Fund to carry into effect the views of the Society be received by the Treasurer.
5. That the Society shall consist of a President, six Vice Presidents, three Stewards, Secretary, Treasurer and Members.[10]

W.B. Wrightson brough forward the sixth resolution:

That the President be elected for three years, and that Earl Spencer be requested to accept the office of President.

This was seconded by Robert Fleetwood Shawe, who also made a little speech which was to have far-reaching consequences for the Society; he reported that he had just attended the HASS's show, which had been excellent in every way save one, 'and that was an allusion to politics after dinner, which he hoped would never be the case with the Yorkshire Society'. Wrightson's resolution and, it seems, Shawe's addendum on politics were carried 'with acclamation'.[11] Thus was enshrined the principle (formally stated as Rule 8 in the 'Rules of the Society') that the YAS should not engage in any form of political debate. This principle was to be adopted by the RASE, of which Shawe was also a founder-member.

The next two resolutions, proposed by George Lane Fox and seconded by Charles Tempest, established the Vice-Presidencies:

7. That the two senior of the six Vice Presidents shall go out annually, and that there shall always be at least one Vice President belonging to each Riding.
8. That the following gentlemen be requested to accept the office of the Vice Presidents for the coming year:

    For the East Riding   : Earl of Carlisle
                            : Sir Tatton Sykes
    For the North Riding : Duke of Leeds
                            : Lord Feversham
    For the West Riding : Earl of Harewood
                            : Earl Fitzwilliam.

And the remaining six resolutions went as follows:

9. That the senior of the three Stewards shall go out annually.
10. That Charles Howard Esq., be appointed Secretary. That Messrs Swann and Co. be appointed Treasurer.
11. That a Committee be formed, not exceeding twenty one members, in addition to the President, Vice Presidents and Stewards, for the purpose of setting the prizes to be given at the Annual Meeting, fixing the places of such Meeting, supplying vacancies in the officers of the Society, defining their duties, and for setting all other matters required for the arrangement of the Society: and that such Committee be elected annually.

    That the Committee do consist of [See Table 2.1] with power to fill up their numbers, and that there be a quorum.
12. That no subject with any legislative enactment be ever introduced at any meeting of this Society.

    [Proposed by Godfrey Wentworth, who was also to be a founder of the RASE]
13. That all Prizes shall be open to competition to the United Kingdom.

    [Proposed by Sir Edward Vavasour who had also just attended the HASS Show and had been impressed by the distances that its exhibitors had travelled. Seconded by Thomas Duncombe.]
14. That the thanks of this Meeting be given to Lord Spencer, for his kindness in taking the chair.[12]

Finally, the Society's funds were opened with a £100 donation by P.B. Thompson.

All these appointments are shown in Column A of Table 2.1. Column B shows the *actual* list of officials and committee, after one or two had declined and others had been co-opted, as printed in the first issue of the Society's *Transactions*. The differences between the two lists did not have significant consequences for the Society, although it should be noted that Sir Tatton Sykes declined his Vice-Presidency (although he did become a member) and the size of the General Committee was actually 22 (in violation of Resolution 11).

Table 2.1: Officers and members of the General Committee elected at the founding meeting of the Yorkshire Agricultural Society

A	B
(As recorded in minute book)	(As printed in the *Transactions*)

A	B
President: Earl Spencer* #	*President*: Earl Spencer* #
Vice Presidents	*Vice-Presidents*
Earl of Carlisle	Earl of Carlisle
Sir Tatton Sykes	W.C. Maxwell Esq.
Duke of Leeds	Duke of Leeds
Lord Feversham	Lord Feversham
Earl Fitzwilliam* #	Earl Fitzwilliam* #
Earl of Harewood	Earl of Harewood
Hon. Sec.: Charles Howard	*Hon. Sec.*: Charles Howard
General Committee:	*General Committee*:
J.W. Childers Esq., MP* #	J.W. Childers Esq., MP* #
Cooke, Sir W.B. Bart.	Cooke, Sir W.B. Bart.
Denison, Robert Esq.	Denison, Robert Esq.
Duncombe, Thos. L. Esq.	Charge, Thos Esq.* #
Fawkes, F.H. Esq.	Duncombe, Thos. S. Esq.
Harrison, Rev. Thos.	Edwards, Henry Esq.*
Legard, George Esq.	Harrison, Rev. Thomas
Maxwell, W.C. Esq.*	Legard, George Esq.
Shawe, R.F. Esq.*	Maxwell, W.C. Esq*
Stansfield, W.R.C. Esq. MP	Newman, W. Esq.
Swann, G. Esq.	Paley, W.F. Esq.
Thompson, H.S. Esq.* #	Rhodes, Rev. A.
Thompson, P.B. Esq.	Shawe, R.F. Esq.*
Vavasour, Hon. Sir Edward*	Stansfield, W.R.C. Esq., MP
Wentworth, Godfrey Esq.*	Swann, George Esq.
Wrightson, W.B. Esq., MP	Thompson, P.B. Esq.
	Thompson, H.S. Esq.* #
	Vavasour, Hon. Sir Edward*
	Wentworth, Godfrey Esq.*
	Whitaker, J. Esq.
	Wrightson, W.B. Esq
	Wiley, Samuel. Esq.

* These persons also on the first printed membership list of the Royal Agricultural Society, in *JRASE*, 1840, *1*.

Also office-holders in the Royal (then still called the English Agricultural Society), 1839–40.

NB The two Thompsons in column B appear not to have been related. P.B. Thompson resided at Escrick Park; H.S. Thompson at Kirby Hall, with a town address at Fairfield, York.

The commitment of this first General Committee, not only to Yorkshire farming but also to the national promotion of agriculture, can be seen from the fact that six of its members were soon to become founders of the RASE. Two of them were also to be members of the RASE's own first General Committee, namely H.S. Thompson, and Childers (of Cantley Hall, Doncaster). Additionally, the President and one Vice-President (Fitzwilliam) were to be founder-officers in the RASE. By the time that this list was published in the *Transactions*, two more members had become founder-members of the RASE. This overlap of interests between the managements of the YAS and the RASE is suggestive of a theme that shall be developed in this and the next chapter: that there was a marked convergence of ideology and effort between the two societies, with the YAS providing much of the early direction and expertise for the national association.

The commitment to local agriculture among the YAS's first General Committee can be gauged from the presence of members who were already active experimenters and improvers on their own estates, and from those who went on to devote time and effort to formulating and implementing the Society's policy. As one works through the minutes, a number of these members' names recur again and again: Childers, Denison, Fawkes, Legard, Maxwell, Swann, H.S. Thompson and Earl Spencer. Indeed, the nuclear role that they would play in the Society during its formative years was foreshadowed in the attendance at the General Committee's first meeting, immediately after the founding General Meeting on 10 October. This was the first getting-down-to-brass-tacks session, and its attendance was: Spencer in the chair, Childers, Denison, Harrison, Legard, Stansfield and H.S. Thompon.

Several resolutions were passed at this General Committee meeting (held at Etridges Hotel, York) with regard to the offices and functions of the Society, and five nominations were made for additional members of the committee. The resolutions show that there already had been some determined planning for the launching of the Society on 'a large and comprehensive scale', and for its show. It was moved

1. That the resoslutions [of the founding General Meeting] be printed and published in three Yorkshire Saturday papers, two Leeds papers – *Mercury* and *Intelligencer*, two Hull papers – *Rockingham* and *Packett*, and in the *Doncaster Gazette*.

2. That the Secretary do write to the Vice Presidents to request them to accept office.

3. That the Secretary do write to Mr Whitaker, Mr S. Wiley, Mr H. Edwards, Mr T. Charge and Mr Paley, requesting them to become members of the Committee.

4. That Mr Paley, Mr H. Edwards and Mr T. Charge be requested to accept the office of Stewards, whose business it will be to appoint Judges for the Stock.

5. That R. Denison Esq., and G. Swann Esq., be a sub-committee to appoint Judges for Horses.

6. That a copy of these resolutions [of the founding General Meeting] be sent to every member and to every influential Gentleman in, or connected with, the County.[13]

Noteworthy here is the setting up of a specialized sub-committee, to appoint Judges for Horses, reflecting a substantial interest in both agricultural and non-agricultural horses shown then and ever since by the Society's members.

The next meeting of the General Committee (actually recorded as a 'sub-meeting') was held on 26 October, again at The Black Swan. Only three members were present: Fawkes, Legard and Thompson. The business included the decision to invite two further members onto the General Committee, violating Resolution 11 of the founding meeting on two counts (that the size of the General Committee should not exceed 21, and that there be a quorum).

On 13 November there was another 'sub-meeting' with five members present: Denison, Harrison, Legard, Swann and P.B. Thompson (the minutes might be erroneous here, for it was more likely to have been H.S. Thompson). Several organizational matters were dealt with, and the Secretary was instructed to place announcements in three more newspapers in addition to those already chosen at the 10 October meeting – the *Isis* (a Sheffield paper), the *London Times* and the *Morning Chronicle* – in order to announce the aims of the Society, and explicitly to enlist the 'Nobility, Gentry and Agriculturists of the County of York'. These announcements were also to say that 'This Society was formed on the 11th [*sic!*] October last, upon the model of the Highland Society of Scotland'.[14]

At this point, we ought to look in more detail at the HASS, to see what precisely the YAS hoped to emulate. Founded in 1784 as the Highland Society, and re-oriented and re-named as the Highland and Agricultural Society in 1800, it had become influential throughout Scotland and down into the northernmost counties of England. A central feature of its ideology and effort was the encouragement of farmers and tenants to analyse and experiment upon the character of Scottish agriculture. The first actual experimental scheme was carried out in 1818–21, to ascertain the value of common salt as a fertilizer. The HASS's journal was first published in 1799, and the Society held its first annual show in 1822 at Edinburgh. This became peripatetic in 1826, when its location moved to Glasgow (although it was only in 1829 that the show broke with the Edinburgh-Glasgow tradition, with its visit to Perth).

In fact, the Highland was not the only institutional inspiration that one finds in the YAS's early deliberations. At least one of the local societies mentioned above, the Doncaster Agricultural Association, had already been conducting investigations into local practices, and publishing reports thereon.[15] The YAS's General Committee was soon drawing attention to these reports, in the first issue of its *Transactions*, adding that it 'is a mode of inquiry which the Committee strongly recommend and purpose hereafter to pursue.'[16] That method of investigation and education did indeed become a major endeavour of the YAS (and the RASE). Coupled with the centralized planning of farming experiments, it became a key feature of the YAS's promotion of science.

The frequent meetings and 'sub-meetings' in October–December 1837 laid the constitutional basis and established the controlling core of management of the Society. The General Committee meeting on 19 December (at The Black Swan, which had clearly been settled upon as a regular meeting place, and continued to be used until the 1860s) was the first to deal with the details of the forthcoming show. Present were: Charge, Childers, Cooke, Denison (in the chair), Edwards, Fawkes, Harrison, Legard, Maxwell, Paley, Rhodes, Shawe, H.S. Thompson, Vavasour, Wentworth, Whitaker and Wiley.

A great deal of decision-making took place. The date of the first Annual Meeting or show 'for the Exhibition of Farming Stock, Implements, etc.' was confirmed as the last Wednesday of August 1838, and the 'premiums', or prizes, were fixed at a remarkably generous level: £130 for Shorthorns, £108 for horses, £82 for Leicester sheep, £16 for pigs, £45 for tenants' farm-management, and £10 for tenants' efforts in drainage. For the Shorthorns, the premiums were allocated as follows:

	£
For the best bull of any age	25
For the second best bull of any age	10
For the best two-year old bull	15
For the second best two-year old bull	5
For the best yearling bull	10
For the second best yearling bull	5
For the best cow of any age in calf or milk	10
For the second best cow of any age in calf or milk	5

It was also resolved that 'The Bull which gains the first prize [is] to be retained in the County for nine months after the Show, and to serve, if required, sixty cows belonging to members, at a sum not exceeding one sovereign each; and if removed within that period, the premium should be returned'.[17] This stipulation was to be retained into the 1840s and it certainly provided a substantial source of income to the prize-winner, as well as a useful service to the YAS's members.

This meeting was adjourned to the following day when, as had happened at the meeting immediately after the General Meeting on 10 October, only five members stayed on, with Denison chairing. Despite this low attendance, some important decisions were taken, such as that of writing to 42 eminent gentry in the county, asking them each to form a District Committee of five persons to recruit new members. This stratagem was to be repeated several times in the Society's history, in an effort to increase the membership. On this first occasion it succeeded rather well, raising the number of annual subscribers from 229 (19 December 1837) to some 800 (by late 1838), although much of this increase was also due to the success of the first show. Throughout its first hundred years or so, the Society was never as large as its General Committees or Councils wanted. There was always a feeling that it should and could have a large membership, and initially a thousand members was its aim. As the General Committee stated in their Annual Report, drawn up on 19 December 1837,

> They feel that, in order to be of the use which the Committee propose to themselves, the Members should amount, at least, to from 500 to 1000: and that they ought to have Correspondents in, and receive great assistance from, every town in the County.

If they could achieve such a membership, the General Committee felt that they would be able 'to enlarge the sphere of their labours, and to turn their attention by the distribution of Premiums, to other subjects besides the breed of Stock which, though a very valuable, they do not consider by any means as the most important branch of the many objects of their Society.'[18]

Two points in the latter declaration are worth commenting upon here. First, it never seems to have been questioned whether the premium- or prize-system was the best method of promoting and spreading good farming and useful innovation. Apparently, this was always taken for granted. Perhaps the YAS's view on this issue was the same as that expressed nearly twenty years before by the Management Committee of the Lincolnshire Agricultural Society – that there was hardly any object of 'rational improvement' which premiums could not promote.[19] Even when, in 1846–7, there was controversy within the YAS Council (as the General Committee renamed itself in September 1840) between H.S. Thompson and Fawkes, concerning the excessively fat animals that the Show prizes tended to encourage, the principle of premiums as agents of progress-in-farming was not itself doubted.[20] Moreover, the General Committee was now intimating that livestock breeding was *not* the most important of the Society's aims and pursuits. This, of course, scarcely squares with what we know of the earliest, informal overtures at the time of the YAS's founding, nor with the personal passion for livestock breeding shared by several of the Society's most influential members. What had happened? It appears, indeed, that the General Committee were doing precisely what Spencer had urged: it had become large and comprehensive in its objects. Within the next few months, the Committee would be exploring a range of ways to promote not only farming but also rural reform, and at the start of the 1840s it launched on an 'enlarged sphere of labours' very much wider than a simple concern with livestock breeding. This enlarged sphere of interest was, perhaps, also promoted by the very composition of the General Committee, whose members, coming as they did from the very different farming regions of the three Ridings, inevitably brought a catholicity of interests and needs into the Society.

The General Committee met again on 7 March 1838, with Denison in the chair and 11 others present, including Legard, Maxwell and Thompson, and on 2 May, in a meeting which confirms the consolidation of the role that the half-dozen or so nuclear members (Childers, Denison, Fawkes, Legard, Maxwell, Spencer and Thompson) were determined to play. Spencer chaired, for the first time since 10 October 1837. A number of resolutions were passed, detailing how policy was to be implemented. Resolution No. 3 moved

> That George Legard Esq., R. Fleetwood Shawe Esq., and H.S. Thompson Esq.,
> be requested to appoint three judges to inspect the farms for which the above
> claims are made for superior cultivation or for improved drainage.

And Resolution No. 5 moved

> That Earl Spencer, Sir W.B. Cooke, Bart, J.W. Childers Esq. MP, be requested to
> decide upon the several detailed Reports which may be offered for the Society's
> Premiums. . . .[21]

The significance of these two resolutions should not be lost: Spencer, Childers, Shawe, Legard and Thompson were being entrusted with determining the Society's standards. It will become apparent that their criteria were to be decisive in determining the direction that the YAS would follow, particularly as one of them – Thompson – would be at the heart of the Society throughout the next thirty years.

In the next few months, leading up to and beyond the first show on 30 August 1838, the General Committee met often. Spencer was usually in the chair (occupied by Denison when he was absent), and Childers, Legard and Thompson were the steadiest attenders. They had a lot to get done: recruiting subscribers, preparing the first volume of the Society's *Transactions*, and planning the intended showpiece of the year, the show and the AGM.

It appears that from the outset there had been the idea of publishing a journal, presumably along the lines of the HASS's. Item 19 of the original 'Rules of the Society', drawn up in 1837, actually specified that 'The Secretary shall edit the Journal of the Society'.[22] The first secretary, Charles Howard, appears to have done so. However, certain questions may be asked concerning the role and the policy of the journal. Who determined its contents, the official editor or someone else? Who had the task of matching its contents with the founding aims and ideology of the Society? What was the journal supposed to achieve?

At first glance, Howard seems to have been the answer to the first two of these questions. What little evidence survives indicates that he handled the technical task of getting the *Transactions* to the press and distributed. The fulsome praise which he received on his resignation in December 1842 suggests that he had indeed carried out all the tasks expected of him. Yet there are reasons to suspect that, perhaps even as early as 1837, the nucleus of the General Committee was itself closely involved in producing the journal. Reading the minutes of 1837–8 convinces one that Thompson, in particular, and his mostly young friends were determined to handle every aspect of the fledgling Society's life with meticulous attention to detail (one of Thompson's personal characteristics, viewed by Earl Cathcart as strong almost to a fault). Then, in August 1839, the General Committee gave Childers and Thompson the task of handling the reports on farming practices which were coming in from the farming community as a consequence of the policy of emulating the report-system of the Doncaster.

They had 'to revise the essays before they go to the press'.[23]

By mid-1840 the overall task of organizing the journal was evidently hard work, for the General Committee appointed an official sub-committee 'to arrange and edite [sic] the Journal and appoint Judges of the Prize Essays – three to be a quorum and the following names to constitute the Committee for the year: Earl Spencer, J.W. Childers, George Legard, Robert Denison and H.S. Thompson Esquires'.[24] This Publication Committee (renamed the Journal Committee in August 1844) was most probably steered by Thompson. This is suggested by a resolution of August 1842 'that £10 be placed at the disposal of H.S. Thompson Esq. to remunerate any literary assistance he may procure for the Society'.[25] Moreover, by then the Publication Committee was playing an overt editorial role – despite the fact that Howard remained the official editor – actively procuring reports for the *Transactions*.

Both of these points, that the *Transactions* was under the policy-control of a watchful core of the Society's managers, and not of the official editor, and that Thompson was agent-in-chief, came into the open in December 1842 when, on Howard's resignation from the secretaryship, Thompson offered his services formally as editor. The Council accepted unhesitatingly.[26] By then, it should be noted, Thompson was also sitting on the Journal Committee of the RASE, alongside his friend Philip Pusey who was the chairman. Thompson was, it seems, acquiring an absolutely central role in the communication of agricultural advances in England.

Returning to business for 1838, the most important single task was preparing for the holding of the show. After all, this had apparently been the most conspicuous single function originally mooted for the Society (both at Denison's house-party in August 1837 and in Spencer's founding speech). Given the intention that it should be peripatetic, it was also the Society's boldest experiment in its early days. The show, held in the Barrack Yard (the home of the 5th Dragoons at the time) on the outskirts of the city of York, on the last Wednesday in August, turned out to be a portentous succes. Spencer arrived in the city on Monday and spent the rest of that day and the next feverishly making last-minute plans and overseeing the construction-work; the riding school had to be decked out for the Great Dinner (an incomparable, early Victorian institution), for which an elegant marquee accomodating 400 persons had to be erected; three Union Jacks had to be hoisted on top of the marquee; the grounds had to be apportioned, by means of railings, into main sections for the livestock – one for mares and foals, another for bulls, cows and calves, and a further section for 'extra stock'; smaller pens had to be erected for boars, sows, young pigs, sheep, stallions and other animals; a section had to be marked off for agricultural implements and machinery; stewards had to be readied with bands and white rosettes; and so on.

On the Tuesday, too, most of the show-animals arrived, some with majestic pomp and ceremony. Earl Carlisle's 'large caravan' of two fine oxen drawn by four grey horses, from Castle Howard, greatly excited the townspeople, as did Lord Dundas's great bull standing 'securely fixed on a wooden wagon.'

Early on Wednesday morning the streets began to throng with visitors from outside the city, alongside the eager citizens themselves, the whole area taking on the festivity of a fair. More livestock arrived (all had to be in by ten o'clock), the press were admitted, and finally, at twelve o'clock sharp, the two gates were opened. The ordinary public poured in unabatingly until two o'clock, and then at a more civilized rate. The members themselves were not, apparently, so civilized, for by two o'clock the pressure against the member's gate was so great that it burst apart and several hundred people streamed in either without paying or without showing their members' metallic tickets. A scuffle broke out between the crowd outside and the soldiers and police, who 'after almost exemplary patience . . . were obliged to use their sticks, the blows of which were returned'. The Lord Mayor hurried up, directing the police, exhorting the crowd and generally 'tendering most efficient service', until the officials were able to repair the breach in the gate and admit the remainder of the throng properly. Amazingly, no serious injury was sustained, despite 'the wild and prancing horses' out on the road.

The Show lasted only one day (in fact, less than a whole day) but it made a huge impression upon all who attended, apparently accomplishing its ends and justifying the generosity of the premiums. On the livestock side, it was reported in the *Yorkshire Gazette* that 'the show of stallions was the finest which we have ever witnessed', and that 'with such a breed of horses as we now possess we need not fear the loss of our reputation as Yorkshiremen'. The cattle exhibited were 'admirable in point and symmetry'. The display of sheep was 'equal to anything ever seen before', and 'the monster pigs were viewed with admiration and astonishment'. The reporter added, 'We have heard of pigs being blind with fat, but never saw any which were so situated until this day'. The list of those who won reads like a roll-call of the eminent in early Victorian breeding circles. For Shorthorns, the premium of £25 for the best bull of any age went to Spencer's animal, and the second prize of £10 to Samuel Wiley's (of Brandsby). The premium for the best 2-year-old bull went to Thomas Bates (of Kirkleavington). That for the best yearling bull, £10, went to Samuel Wiley again, and the second prize to Childers. For the best cow of any age, the first premium of £10 went to John Collins (who was competing in this class against Henry Edwards, John Colling, Richard Booth and Thomas Bates, amongst other nationally-famed breeders). Thomas Bates also swept up two more Shorthorn premiums.[27]

For Leicester sheep, the premiums were only slightly less generous and they too were won by top breeders, including Spencer and Denison. Among the pig breeders who walked away with premiums were Earl Fitzwilliam, Sir Edward Vavasour and Samuel Wiley. The largest group of premiums went to horses, which took up 12 classes of awards; Shorthorns took up 7 classes, Leicester sheep 5, and pigs 4 – which indicates fairly accurately the contemporary economic significance of the different livestock. The horse-classes included, of course, hunters, coaching-horses, roadsters, and farm- and draught-animals.

Premiums were also awarded to tenant-farmers and labourers for a variety of achievements: one James Hall (of Scarborough) received £20 as the tenant of the best cultivated farm in Yorkshire of 100 acres or more; Robert Wiley (of Warren House Farm, near Brandsby) received £10 as the tenant of the best turnip-soil farm in Yorkshire of 50–100 acres; George Legard won £10 for his report 'of the best mode of cultivation upon which a Farm of stony land, in the County of York, has been actually managed'; Matthew Milburn (of Thorp Field, near Thirsk) got £5 for his 'Report on the Natural History of the Black Caterpillar and also of the best means to be adopted in order to effectually avoid its ravages'; the Secretary, Charles Howard, received a medal for his 'Report containing the best practical information on the subject of forming, improving and repairing Public High Roads, not being Turnpike Roads'; Mr Alexander Kiddy (a labourer of Robert Denison's) received a £5 premium as the 'labourer in Husbandry (who has not occupied more than half an acre of land) who has brought up and placed out to service the greatest number of children without receiving parochial relief' – at the age of 82, and having 14 children to his credit; and to Ellen Linton went a £3 premium for having been a servant for 47 years.

Finally to round off the disbursements at the show were the sweepstakes for livestock, the maximum set out at £2 and several of which went to Spencer for his bulls.

Such was the pattern of premiums or prizes formulated for the show, and adopted for all subsequent occasions. This pattern remained essentially unchanged throughout the rest of the nineteenth century, although there were to be additions and deletions when the need arose. As the show moved from place to place, it was found to be occasionally expedient to add a class or two of awards to cater for some specific agricultural interest in a certain locality – such as poultry or bee-keeping or cheese-making. During periods of epidemic, whole groups of classes (for cattle when there was foot-and-mouth disease, or for pigs when there was swine-fever) might be deleted. Moreover, as the finances of the show system developed, more classes were introduced, so that Shorthorns were no longer the only breed of cattle entitled to enter the competition, and Leicesters no longer the only breed of sheep. Even so, it was the evident success of the first show which set the precedent for the future.

One further feature of the show merits mention: the display of agricultural implements and machinery. Implement and machinery manufacturers and inventors were present, from throughout the county and beyond. On display were turnip drills, a patent drag harrow, a new type of land roller, Scotch ploughs, at least one type of subsoil plough, reaping scythes (including a Scotch scythe from the Walker Foundry in York), wheat drills, straw-cutters, a portable thrashing machine, a patent machine 'for crushing clods on a rough road', made by what was probably the largest machinery manufacturer in the county at that time – Crosskill of Beverley, other cutting machines, a new device for spreading seeds, made by Buxton of Malton, a new type of churn, a curd-breaking machine, and so on. No premiums were awarded for these exhibits, although they did attract much attention.

Rounding off the first show was the Great Dinner, which must have been attended by almost a thousand people, the tickets costing a hefty 7s 6d. This was punctuated by several speeches. Spencer was followed by about fifteen others in a lengthy, but apparently entertaining, proceeding. (One must bear in mind the nineteenth-century love of speechifying).

Spencer's speech was noteworthy on several counts. He reminded everyone that stock-breeding was not the only object of the Society, but that the aim was also 'the collecting together of a body of the farmers of England, in order that there may be communication with each other, and that from the variety of information they receive they may improve themselves in the profession in which they are engaged' (at which there was applause). Spencer emphasized that a fundamental concern of the YAS was the *small* farmer, with limited capital, who was anxious to have a reasonably speedy return on his expenditures – and in this matter Spencer felt that the question of manures was the most germane. He also declared his genuine optimism about the Society's prospects, for he admitted 'that at the first commencement of this society I was not so sanguine as I am now of its success'. And, finally, Spencer revealed the reforming political context within which the Society had been created, stating that YAS should surely deserve the support of not only landowners and farmers, but also manufacturers, traders and labourers. There can be little doubt that Spencer, or 'Honest Jack', as he was popularly known even by his political opponents, was totally sincere in his outline of what the YAS should aspire to, as well as sanguine in his aspirations. Certainly, everyone at the Great Dinner approved his words.

One further speaker at that dinner deserves mention: Robert Denison, in whose home the YAS had been mooted. It is recorded that when he rose to speak there was a rapturous applause – which indicates that he (and perhaps other members of the management-core that we have identified) was a popular figure amongst the farmers of Yorkshire, a factor which would help to account for the spirit of confident enthusiasm in the Society's formative years. The minutes of the General Committee (or Council) reveal a remarkable certainty of purpose within the management of the Society, founded upon men like Spencer, Denison and Thompson, who knew that in effect they had a mandate from their community as a result of their tremendous popularity as well as the respect which they had earned as practical men. Sureness-of-purpose, popularity and respect – these have remained ingredients in the Society's development from that day to this.

The first annual show was a success in almost every way. The actual receipts from the show (£243 17s 6d) together with the huge increase in membership-subscriptions that it generated, after the subtraction of the total disbursements of the year, left the Society with an impressive balance of £994 2s 9d.[28] (See Table 2.2 for the first year's budget.) The General Committee was thus convinced both that the show should become an annual event, and that the Society had sufficient reserves to try the experiment of making it peripatetic. Leeds was now chosen for the next venue, presumably in accordance with Spencer's insistence that the YAS should look for support from the non-agricultural community. The Committee raised the total monies for premiums to £600 which, although a large sum (amounting to 60 percent of the Society's annual profit), was now amply covered by membership subscriptions (by late 1838, membership had reached about eight hundred).

Table 2.2: Receipts and disbursements for the YAS during its first year.

Receipts	£	s	d	Disbursements	£	s	d
From donations	748	0	0	Printing bills	52	10	0
				Stationery bills	8	7	4
From subscriptions	799	16	0	Advertising bills	69	0	11
				Lithographics	1	11	0
From non-members showing stock	14	10	0	Engraving	34	13	0
				Expenses of the show	104	16	0
From entrance receipts at show	231	7	6	Premiums	423	18	6
				Judges expenses	40	18	6
				For Committee Rooms	3	15	0
Total	1773	13	6	For the Marquee	35	19	0
				Total	779	10	9
				Balance for year	£994	2	9

(From *TYAS*, 1838, *1*:79.)

The second year of the YAS's life, 1838–9, was one of consolidation. The premiums for Leeds followed exactly the classification employed at York. Again, there were to be topics for reports or prize-essays, but the list was now lengthened, testifying beyond doubt to the concern for the small farmer and the Society's will to communicate with him. The topics were: the agriculture of Skyrack and the Barkston Ash area, the turnip crop, the turnip crop on stony land, the subsoil plough, quickwood fences, and strong land farming. In March 1839 the judges for two of these topics were appointed – Spencer, Legard, Fawkes, 'and if necessary H.S. Thompson Esq.' for the first, and Thompson, Maxwell and Henderson for subsoil ploughing. By August, a good number of reports had been received, indicating that tenant-farmers were responding to the Society's policy. A number of these reports were judged to be useful enough to be published in the second issue of the *Transactions*, which was henceforth to be sold as a commercial venture, in addition to being distributed to all the subscribers via booksellers in the market towns of the county.[29]

At the end of the second year, however, the orientation of the General Committee (and thus of the YAS itself and of the *Transactions*) apparently took a new turn. Although there had been some recognition of scientific developments, and their importance, the Society had not embraced any explicitly scientific orientation. However, in August 1839 a definite and specific concern for science became explicit in the setting up of an Agricultural Geology Committee. The General Committee now resolved

That a sum not exceeding £50 be placed at the disposal of a Committee for the purpose of having a District surveyed with reference to its Agricultural and Geological Character – the system of Agriculture and Arboriculture at present practised upon it – the Report to state how far these are dependent upon or modified by the Geological Character of the District and whether any improvement could be effected by a more minute knowledge of the Stratification of the District under survey:– and that Sir John Johnstone Bart, George Legard and H.S. Thompson Esq. do form a Committee for carrying this resolution into effect.[30]

The establishment of this committee is noteworthy on several counts. First, the date coincides with a more conspicuous concern for science in the *Journal* of the Highland, for in its 1839 issue there appeared for the first time in its premiums-list a section on agricultural science, with essays invited on the subject of problems in soil fertility and plant growth. It is quite probable that the General Committee of the YAS was aware of the Highland's expanding interest in science.

Second, the founding of the committee testified to the considerable concern with geological science that had been growing in England, and particularly in Yorkshire. The work of men like William Smith (1769–1839), Adam Sedgwick (1785–1873) and Charles Lyell (1797–1875) was widely known, and the general public's awareness of geology had been cultivated through the British Association for the Advancement of Science, which had been founded in 1831 and held its annual meetings peripatetically. In fact, the BAAS had not only visited Yorkshire (for its very first meeting, at York, in 1831) but it had also become a forum for the considerable talent of the county's remarkable young geologist, John Phillips (1800–74). It is possible that Phillips work on the geology of Yorkshire prompted the idea of setting up an Agricultural Geology Committee within the Society.

Phillips was a self-made man in the classic Smilesian mould. His formal education ended at the age of fifteen and he spent the next nine years apprenticed to his engineer-geologist uncle, William Smith, who had been his guardian since the age of eight, when Phillips had been orphaned. Phillips happened to make contact with the Yorkshire Philosophical Society in 1824, and in 1825 he secured for himself the post of Keeper of the York Museum (at a salary of £60 per annum). From his York base he quickly established himself as a geological lecturer throughout the north of England, and as the foremost authority on the geology of Yorkshire. In 1829 he published what was to become a classic work on the geology of the Yorkshire coastline,[31] and in 1836 this was followed by an important study of 'The Mountain Limestone District' of Yorkshire.[32] He was quickly wooed by metropolitan men of science, becoming an Assistant Secretary of the BAAS in 1832 (remaining so until 1862), Professor of Geology at King's College, London in 1834, and an FRS in the same year.[33]

A third factor behind the setting up of the Society's new committee was the increasing publication of literature on the likely relevance of geological and chemical science in farming practice. In fact, the potential role of science in the progress of English agriculture was no new idea. During the first few years of the century, the work of the chemist and natural philosopher, Humphry Davy (1779–1829), for the Board of Agriculture, and his appointment at the Royal Institution in London, had emphasised the potential of natural science as an aid to agriculture.[34]

Moreover, the depression of the post-Napoleonic period had made it more important than ever to explore any likely means of stimulating farming productivity. By the early 1830s a detailed realization of the benefits of scientific agriculture seems to have emerged. For instance, a Parliamentary Select Committee set up in 1833 'to enquire into the present State of Agriculture & of Persons employed in Agriculture in the United Kingdom' came to the conclusion that a more extensive application of the principles of science to farming would benefit the whole national agricultural effort. The Select Committee were particularly impressed by the discovery that the comparatively few farmers who had weathered the most recent crisis were precisely those who had adopted better rotations, made more liberal use of fertilizers and been more systematic in the breeding and feeding of their livestock.[35]

Geology was particularly amenable to English gentlemen-amateurs, and by the 1830s a good number of landowners were well-versed in the agricultural, chemical and geological writings that had been trickling through the printing press. These included the writings of the eccentric Earl of Dundonald at the close of the eighteenth century, the extensive work of Davy, the more recent investigations and writings of the Norfolk apothecary, William Grisenthwaite (who advocated mineral fertilizers in particular), and the Scottish agricultural chemistry of David Low.[36] The ideas of Grisenthwaite seem to have been especially acknowledge among the *agricultural* (if not the *scientific*) community, partly because his patron was none other than Thomas Coke of Holkham, through whom he had become personally acquainted with many of the progressive landowners of the day.[37]

A number of these agriculturists and landowners were indulging in chemical experimentation. One such was H.S. Thompson. In the 1830s he was consulting two chemists on the question of soil composition; the first was a London analyst, J.T. Cooper, and the second a Quaker chemist and druggist in York, Joseph Spence, of whom the Thompsons of Kirby Hall were apparently old customers.[38] It cannot be a mere coincidence that Spence was appointed the Yorkshire's official 'Analysing Chemist' in 1844, nor that his services were at the Society's disposal as early as 1839–40. This last point we know, for in the *Transactions* of that year Thompson published a paper, 'On subsoil ploughing', to which he appended a list of soil-analyses that Spence had offered to conduct for the members of the Society.[39] (See opposite page.)

ON SUBSOIL-PLOUGHING.

The following scale of charges has been drawn up, in order to facilitate the obtaining of information on any particular point, without incurring needless expense.

For finding in any Specimen of Soil, the quantity,

	s.	d.
1st. Of Vegetable and Animal Matter	5	0
2nd. Of Calcareous Earth	5	0
3rd. Of Matter Soluble in Water	5	0
4th. Of Carbonate of Lime and Carbonate of Magnesia	10	0
5th. Of Alumina	10	0
6th. Of Gypsum, (Sulphate of Lime)	10	0
7th. Of Gypsum and Phosphate of Lime	12	6
8th. Of Alumina and Oxide of Iron...	12	6
9th. Of Silica, Alumina, Oxide of Iron, and Vegetable Matter	15	0

A statement of the quantity of Water of Absorption, and of Soluble Matter, as also of the Specific Gravity, will be supplied in addition to any of the above, at a further charge of Two Shillings and Sixpence each.

| 10th. Of Silica, Alumina, Oxide of Iron, Carbonate of Lime, Carbonate of Magnesia, Vegetable, Animal, and Soluble Matter, and of Water of Absorption, and the Specific Gravity ... | 21 | 0 |

Accuracy may be equally relied upon whether one or more particulars are required. No. 9 would frequently exhibit all the essential constituents of the soil. No. 10 would supply (except in some unusual cases) abundant information for any practical purpose. In any analysis of a more complicated kind, as where separate statements of the composition of the sand, of the minutely divided matter, and of the soluble contents are required, the cost will be increased in proportion.

Original list of charges for chemical analysis by Mr Spence, of York, from the 1840 *Transactions*

This chemical and geological interest within the Society is significant because it pushes back by several years the historians' view of the promotion of 'mineral chemistry' within English agricultural institutions at the mid-century. The phrases 'mineral chemistry' and, even more broadly, 'agricultural chemistry', have tended to be associated exclusively with the eminent German chemist, Justus Liebig (1803–73). Liebig set out to provide a scientific basis for the reform of agriculture, and in Britain he had a large and devoted following of *chemists*. He, along with his many disciples, has been regarded as the initiator of the study of chemistry as an aid to agriculture.[40] For instance, Sir John Russell's very substantial *History of agricultural science in Great Britain* (1966) dwells at great length on Liebig and implies that it was one of his disciples, Lyon Playfair (1818–98) later Lord Playfair, who had the distinction of being the first consulting chemist to be appointed by an agricultural society in high-farming England. Scott-Watson, in his *History of the Royal Agricultural Society, 1839–1939* (1939), is also emphatic on this point.[41]

Playfair was indeed a conspicuous figure in English agricultural science in the early 1840s. He was appointed Consulting Chemist to the Royal in May 1844, and retained that post for two years. But we now see that the Yorkshire preceded the Royal by several years (and the Highland by about ten years) in placing the services of a professional chemist at its members' disposal. Clearly, this was not mere window-dressing, for even before the Yorkshire's founding that chemist, Spence, was being consulted by the man who was to emerge as the Society's central policy-maker – H.S. Thompson.

One strongly suspects that further research into the other local agricultural societies founded in this period will persuade agricultural historians to radically revise their views.[42] Analysis of the Yorkshire's scientific orientation from 1838–9 onwards leads one to feel that the following account given by Orwin and Whetham in their otherwise excellent *History of British Agriculture* is really inadequate:

> By 1850, therefore, the chemist had done little more than confirm the practices of the best farmers. . . . The two national societies had already appointed consulting chemists to advise their members on the composition of these purchased requisites (fertilizers and oilcakes): Dr Thomas Anderson in Edinburgh for the Highland and Agricultural Society from 1849 to his death in 1874; and first Lyon Playfair and then J. Thomas Way performed similar functions for the Royal Agricultural Society. Anderson at Edinburgh, Way in London, Voelcker newly appointed to succeed Way at the Royal Agricultural College at Cirencester, Lawes and Gilbert at Rothamsted, were almost the only professional workers at this time in the field of agricultural chemistry. . . .[43]

The YAS and Spence, who was soon joined by his business-partner in the York Glass Works, William Holden, in 1851–2, must now be seen as a part of this picture.[44]

With the setting up of its Agricultural Geology Committee in August 1839, the YAS was placing the natural sciences within its ambit. Not only was this just the second of the many specialized committees to be set up in its history, but the membership of this committee included two of the Society's most zealous founders, Legard and Thompson. It quickly secured the confidence of the General Committee, who, in March 1840, raised its grant to £75 per annum. The General Committee also suggested that the English Agricultural Society (as the RASE was still called) might wish to enter into its survey on Yorkshire agriculture and geology, and agreed that a newly-completed report by the committee should be printed forthwith (without waiting for the next issue of the *Transactions*) and circulated to all the Society's members.[45]

This report was eventually printed, probably in abbreviated form, in the 1839–40 issue of the *Transactions* where, most tellingly, one reads that

> The Council has uniformly been of opinion, that one of the peculiar duties of the leading Agricultural Societies is to extract from the discoveries of Science all that can be made useful to Agriculture.[46]

In that issue of the *Transactions* one does indeed find substantial interest in science, particularly in questions of mineral chemistry. In a paper on farming experiments using nitrate of soda as fertilizer, Legard discussed his own field-trials with Peruvian nitrate as well as similar trials by Thompson at Kirby Hall (the family seat). Thompson found the nitrate to be especially productive for barley if one used twice the customary quantity.[47]

Also in this issue of the *Transactions* is a very thorough report by Thompson himself 'On subsoil ploughing'. This had been one of the prize-essay topics chosen in 1838, and apparently in the absence of any other contribution Thompson had submitted his own. His essay is noteworthy, for in addition to drawing upon his own farming experience and offering his own scientific hypothesis (that alumina is a crucial soil ingredient for successful subsoil ploughing), Thompson indicated that he was already coordinating the collection of scientific and practical data on the question from around the county. He had received submissions from a Mr Black, land agent to the Earl of Zetland; from Robert Denison of Kilnwick Percy; from a 'Mr Stevenson, of Rainton, near Borough-Bridge, a very enterprising and judicious tenant-farmer'[48]; and from the Rev. Croft, at Hutton-Bushel.

So, it is clear that it was Thompson who resolved to emulate the Doncaster Association's practice of asking its members for reports on important farming matters. It was also in this essay that Thompson announced Spence's services to the Society:

> I am aware that chemical analysis has hitherto been unobtainable, without so much trouble and expense as to put it out of the reach of most practical farmers; but I am happy to be able to state, that Mr Spence, Chemist and Druggist, Pavement, York, whose chemical attainments are beyond dispute, has kindly offered to furnish an analysis of any soil sent to him on very moderate terms.[49]

Thompson's essay was highly regarded not only in the farming community of the county, but also nationwide. Indeed, Pusey republished it, along with

Spence's list of analyses, in the *JRASE*, adding that Spence's services were being extended to the Royal's members too.[50] It may thus be said that, courtesy of the Yorkshire, the Royal did indeed have a professional chemical consultant two years before it appointed its own chemist, Playfair; and that it was the Yorkshire, through the good offices of Thompson, which thus aided the Royal's earliest efforts to fulfill the intentions proclaimed in its own charter, namely

. . . to embody such information contained in agricultural publications, and in other scientific works, as has been proved by practical experience to be useful to the cultivators of the soil

and

. . . to encourage men of science in their attention to the application of chemistry to the general purposes of agriculture.[51]

Of course, it should not be supposed that science was the only concern of the Society in its second and third years. The second annual show at Leeds had to be planned, under the aegis of a special 'Leeds Committee' within the General Committee. This Show was a fine success, despite the low numbers of livestock; what was lacking in quantity seems to have been made up in quality (see Table 2.3 for numbers of entries). As the Council Address put it:

The Meeting was fully attended, and though the distance from the great breeding districts rendered the quantity of stock somewhat smaller than might have been expected, yet the animals were on the whole of a quality never exceeded, and perhaps not even equalled. . . . It was gratifying to observe, that the Meeting had the tendency to promote that feeling of unity, which evidently exists between the enlightened body of Manufacturers and Agriculturists. . . .[52]

One development at the Leeds Show was the award of premiums for agricultural implements (but not yet for 'machinery'). Manufacturers from around the county (from Easingwold, Malton, Thirsk and York) as well as outside it (from Lincolnshire and Nottingham) sent implements, which included improved corn- and turnip-drills, corn- and turnip-cutters, patent harrows and subsoil ploughs (again entered by John Walker of York), rollers and scythes – mostly basic and inexpensive equipment of the type most urgently needed by the farming community.[53] But there was one notable absence – Crosskill of Beverley – suggesting that the YAS still had to work at building up a truly county-wide field of entry. Of the £30 allocated 'for the invention and improvement of such Agricultural Implements', three premiums totalling five guineas went to the large manufacturer from Malton, Thomas Buxton; one to the Easingwold manufacturer, George Barker, for his 'ten countered drill, used for sowing turnips and grain with all sorts of manure', value 3 guineas; one 5-guinea premium to the Nottingham manufacturers, Messrs Winrow and Carey, for a patent exterminator of weeds and insects; one 5-guinea premium to the Lincolnshire manufacturer, Thomas Hunter, for his improved corn- and turnip-drill; and two other awards to Yorkshire manufacturers.[54]

Other developments in this show were the increase in Shorthorn classes (eleven, compared with seven at York) and the abolition of awards to labourers and servants, although there were now several shepherds who meritted premiums for the rearing of lambs. The receipts of the Leeds Show easily justified the additional outlay in premiums, and at the end of this calendar year the Society had a balance of £1271 2s 7d, sufficient for the General Committee to invest £900 in railway debentures.[55] Moreover, the show itself began to tap a useful source of income, by way of a donation from the place where it was to be held. The Mayor and Town Council of Leeds donated £63 towards expenses, scarcely a princely sum, but the setting of a precedent for which the Society would be grateful and upon which it would actually depend on certain occasions in the future. From 1842 onwards, with the show at Doncaster, this borough or corporation donation rarely dropped below £150; and after the fourth show at York (1853) the level rose to £250. By the 1870s this donation would hover around £1000 (the precedent for this level being set by Beverley in 1868) – testifying not only to the Society's county-wide popularity but also to the close correlation of interests between town and country (discussed in Chapter 1) which, we have seen, was one of Spencer's own concerns too.

To return to late 1839, with the success of the show confirming the belief that there was a diverse set of needs to be met, the General Committee entertained further extensions to its programme. Howard was instructed to see whether the Society might establish an agricultural school and model farm, a plan which appears not to have lasted long, however, presumably because of cost.[56] A less costly, and soon to be more significant, decision was the General Committee's resolution that copies of all the essays and reports intended for the *Transactions* should be sent to the Secretary of the English Agricultural Society prior to publication, giving him permission to print anything he liked in his journal after it had appeared in the *Transactions*.[57] This move, which Pusey eagerly accepted, was made easy by virtue of the fact that Spencer and Thompson were also members of the Publication Committee of the English (about to be re-named the Royal), whose own chairman, Pusey, was a close friend of Thompson, and shared Spencer's political views.[58]

Once more, therefore, the Yorkshire was giving valuable assistance to the national society as it was trying to establish itself. Indeed, in the first four issues of the Royal's own Journal (1839/40–43), roughly 15 percent of its material came out of the Yorkshire's *Transactions*, or directly from active YAS members. Of course, that was also beneficial to the YAS, for it ensured that much of its material would have a wider readership than could be obtained locally. By early 1842, the Yorkshire's membership stood at about 1000, whilst the Royal's had reached about 5400.

The rapid success of the *Transactions*, and of Thompson's policy of inviting the farming community to share its experience with him, resulted in the considerably heavier workload which justified the setting up of the Publication Committee in June 1840. Also, partly to cope with the extra work, and partly to handle the Society's rapidly growing general business, an Assistant Secretary was appointed in August 1840, at a salary of £50 per annum. The appointee was none other than M.M. Milburn, of Thorpfield, the winner of the premium for the report 'On the turnip crop on light land', and apparently himself a tenant farmer.[59] This appointment seems to have been quite exceptional for a major agricultural society; it was more usual to appoint as a society's secretary a person from the field of journalism, or, at any rate, rarely someone from within the farming community. Being himself a tenant farmer, Milburn was undoubtedly instrumental in keeping the Society's office-holders in touch with the needs of the ordinary farming community.

His appointment coincided with the third annual show at Northallerton. As a centre of the county's stockbreeding, the show had been approached with high expectations, which were amply fulfilled. Public attendance was about the same as at Leeds, although a much larger proportion of the total were members, and therefore the gate-receipts were less. Livestock attendance, on the other hand, was considerably higher. There were the same number of Shorthorn classes as at Leeds, slightly more of Leicester sheep and pigs, and 14 classes for horses (compared with 11 at Leeds and 12 at York). The turnout of implements, however, was disappointing and only two premiums were awarded: one of £5 to Mr Malthouse of Ripon for his extremely useful corn and turnip drill, and one to Busby of Newton-le-Willows for a set of heavy harrows. A number of other implements were interesting enough to attract the judges' attention, but they were not sure that these would actually work. For instance, there was a novel single-horse cart which the judges felt 'to be somewhat at variance with the acknowledged principles of mechanics'.[58] The Committee was determined to remedy this poor state of implement exhibition at the show, and it immediately resolved to stage an actual trial or working-demonstration at the next show, which turned out to be hugely successful.

Despite the relatively small net profit made by the Society in this third year – only £60 9s 1d (the decrease due largely to a fall in the number of new members) – the management remained sanguine. Moreover, it was now explicitly laying out its strategy, as follows:

I.   Prizes for Stock.
II.   Prizes for Essays.
III. Committees to facilitate the Introduction of Science into the Practice of Agriculture.[59]

The first of these, it felt, had been eminently successful in all three shows so far. The second, it was now admitted, had failed, for too few essays had been sent in by the Society's ordinary, farming members. But steps were already in hand, with certain members of the Publication Committee having undertaken 'to write to different gentlemen who had used the subsoil plough, and tried nitrate of soda as a top dressing; and to embody the information thus obtained in articles on these subjects'. The third element of the strategy, the promotion of science, was already being implemented, with the setting up of the Agricultural Geology Committee (on 27 August 1839) and the Agricultural Mechanics Committee (on 29 September 1840). The latter was initially founded as the Implements Committee, comprising Legard, Denison, H.S. Thompson, William Beckett and John Fairburn, with £80 at its disposal.[60] It is worth noting here that by October 1844 Thompson was clearly its chairman. When announcing the establishment of these two committees to the Society's members in the Address for 1840, the Council (as it now was called) declared that it

> has uniformly been of opinion, that one of the peculiar duties of the leading Agricultural Societies is to extract from the discoveries of science all that can be made useful to Agriculture.[61]

On the whole, then, at the close of its third year there was ample sign of determination, a workable strategy and good health within the Society. Even the membership had risen slightly over the previous year, now standing at about 1100.[62]

It must have been with a feeling of satisfaction therefore that Spencer retired from the Presidency. Why he did so raises a slight query, for it was suggested at the founding meeting, 10 October 1837, that he be elected for a six-year term. (This entry may have been erroneous, for the term for the new President seems now to have been set at three years without any apparent discussion of the matter.) At any rate, the change of incumbency did not make much difference to the running of the Society, for the new President, Lord Wharncliffe, did not participate greatly in its affairs, and during his frequent absences from meetings of the General Committee, Spencer continued to take the chair.

It is indeed remarkable that Spencer's meticulous and active involvement in the Society continued until the autumn of 1842. It may accurately be said, therefore, that Spencer was the *de facto* leader of the Yorkshire throughout its first five years, showing incredible dedication when one recalls that he was also the active first President of the Royal and the assiduous President of the Smithfield Club, holding other public offices too during that period.

At the AGM in August 1840, the entire General Committee (bar the President) had to stand down for fresh election. The new General Committee consisted of 27 members, and amongst those who were re-elected were Childers, Denison, Johnstone, Legard and H.S. Thompson. In short, with Spencer still at the helm (officially as Vice-President), the policy-making nucleus of the first three years remained in control of the Society. Under their determined direction, the Society would continue its ambitious programme.

The composition of the new General Committee was also noteworthy for its overlap with the Council of the Royal. This was stronger than ever before: twelve of the General Committee were now members of the Royal, and eight of these were also governors or officers within it. Spencer was now a Vice-President in both; and Childers, Sir Samuel Crompton (of Woodend, Thirsk), Sir John Johnstone (of Hackness, Scarborough), W.R.C. Stansfield (of Esholt Hall, Bradford), Thompson, Sir Edward Vavasour (of Haslewood) and Godfrey Wentworth (of Woolley Park, Wakefield) were all governors or officers, or both, within the Royal.[63]

At the same time, the Council expressed its confidence in the Agricultural Geology Committee by renewing its £75 grant. That confidence was apparently well placed, for the next issue of the *Transactions* (1840–41) carried a very impressive report by this committee, showing its understanding of fundamental geological and chemical issues, and their connection with agriculture. The *Transactions* were acknowledged to be a means of disseminating scientific understanding throughout the agricultural community. In addition to the 'Report of the Committee on Agricultural Geology' (which, at 103 pages must be one of the longest scientific reports ever to appear in an English agricultural journal), there were several communications from tenant farmers on manurial field trials which had almost certainly been carried out under Thompson's direction. The same issue also contained two brief farming papers by the Secretary and the Assistant-Secretary.

The Agricultural Geology Committee's report deserves some detailed analysis, for it was not only a magnificent piece of survey-work but probably the earliest serious criticism of the agricultural chemistry then being promoting by Liebig and his followers. The report appears to have been written by the Reverend William Thorp, an original member of the committee, who read the work before a gathering of members on the day before the Hull Show. The report also shows strong signs of Legard's and Thompson's hands; Thompson's influence is especially conspicuous in the extraordinarily detailed and up-to-date chemistry and in the fact that Spence's list of analytical services was again appended.

The opening paragraph is notable, for it supports the suggestion that the YAS was acquiring a strong scientific orientation around the time when the committee was set up in August 1839. It runs as follows:

> Next, indeed, to the knowledge of what is best to be done in practice, is the knowledge of the *reasons* why one mode of agriculture is better than another mode. Now these reasons are, in fact, *the science*; and the farmer who does not know a good and satisfactory reason, beyond the use of wont or hap-hazard experience, for adopting certain rotations of crops, for liming one sort of soil and not liming another sort and in short for all the various processes and operations, must be pronounced to know little more than half his own business. I think therefore . . . no more important subject can occupy the attention of the agriculturist, than an inquiry into the reasons why the chief processes of agriculture are more successful in some circumstances than in others; for if these reasons are once discovered and the facts connected with them established beyond controversy, like many of the facts in practical chemistry and practical mechanics, then the farmer will have a sure guide in his operations, and he will be as superior to the old farmer of hap-hazard experience, as the modern mariner is to the mariner of olden time who dared not advance out of sight of land, for fear of losing himself in the pathless ocean.[64]

There could be no clearer declaration of how far and firmly the Yorkshire's sights were being set. The path of farming was set for re-charting. It was to be a time of change, not reluctant change but a movement powered by science, managed by progressive landowners and large tenant farmers, and tried and proved by the whole farming community, all three now meeting within an institutional setting represented by the YAS.

The Report continues:

> Since the issuing of the Committee's first report, the lectures of Professor Daubeny and Johnston, and translations of the works of Liebig, Sprengel and Schoebler, and De Candolle, have appeared; and there is now being made, not only in England, but on the Continent of Europe, a general attempt to obtain first principles of agriculture by the aid of science, and to explain its phenomena by the known laws of matter, as exhibited in the sciences of geology, chemistry, and vegetable physiology; and in furtherance of these objects, the following Report has been drawn up. . . .[65]

All the scientific works cited here had become available (in English) only that year. A number of them were polemical – hardly standard textbooks – and several were highly innovative, in particular Liebig's *Organic Chemistry in its Applications to Agriculture and Physiology* (1840). The Agricultural Geology Committee were boldly entering the field of the latest, and what was quickly to become the most controversial, branch of chemical research. Their report must have been seen, then, as a research-document of high calibre.

The study had concentrated on a district extending from Pocklington in the north, down via Market Weighton to the Humber in the south; and from Beverley in the east to North Cave in the west (see map on page 15). The first part of the study took the form of a geological survey, describing soils, subsoils and rock formations both chemically and physically. On the basis of this, the report offered an explanation of why the Wolds generally required such frequent manuring (a major expenditure in that region), adding that 'it becomes then an important inquiry, whether any other manure* equally valuable may not be procured as a substitute, and at least cost'.[66]

This question occupied the second part of the report, which began by quoting Liebig, who had just issued an authoritative-sounding declaration that manures containing nitrogen and ammonia were the most effective of all. With this, the report did not wholly disagree, but it did suggest that Liebig and at least two of his English followers, Daubeny and J.F.W. Johnston, were wrong in asserting that the carbon or 'carbonaceous matter' of manure did not contribute to a plant's growth.

In adopting this position (that it was only nitrogen or, a little later, minerals which were of real use in fertilizers), Liebig was deliberately opposing the older Humus Theory of plant nutrition, according to which plants were supposed to get much of their carbon from decaying vegetable and animal matter in the soil. The most basic process underlying photosynthesis had been discovered, but it was still uncertain how much of its carbon a plant could acquire this way, and

---

* Manure other than bones, rape-dust and farmyard manure.

the mechanism was still highly conjectural. By 1840, the Humus Theory, and variants of it, had actually been receiving considerable experimental and theoretical support, especially on the Continent. The issue was now becoming a subject of vigorous debate, especially in the mid-1840s, when the Dutch chemist, Jan Gerrit Mulder (1802–80) came up with impressive chemical analyses and theory in support of 'humic acid', in opposition to Liebig's mineral theory.[67]

As one works through the English agricultural journals of the early 1840s, it becomes clear that their publication committees and their readers were both excited by, and critical of, Liebig's chemistry. Indeed, the reception of his work in Britain was so complex that we have not yet reached a useful appreciation. Some historians give the impression that English farmers (as well as Liebig's followers) immediately warmed to his recommendations for scientific farming, and indulged in an orgy of spending on mineral manures.[68] Others, slightly more soberly, have suggested that he was at least the chief figure whose ideas had a seminal influence on the whole movement.

At any rate, from working through the journals of the YAS and the RASE, as well as provincial newspapers and other publications, we can now say that from the very start there was a body of opinion critical of Liebig's ideas on how chemistry could aid (indeed revolutionize) farming in England. Liebig's book appeared in late 1840, and in June 1841 the *Quarterly Journal of Agriculture* carried an incisive critique of it, based partly on chemical knowledge and partly on close farming experience, by Dr John Madden.[69] In the same year there were critical comments in the *Durham Advertiser*, taking issue with J.F.W. Johnston's pro-Liebig articles therein, and then the YAS's *Transactions* entered the fray, with the Agricultural Geology report supporting the humic acid theory. This reminded Liebig (and Daubeny and Johnston and, by implication, all of Liebig's followers) that common farming experience went against them, criticising Liebig's mode of argument in his treatise and correcting him on the chemical function of gypsum when used as a fertilizer.[70]

Who authorized this remarkably trenchant and confident critique of the already renowned chemist? Although Thorp's was the only name given for the report's authorship, we can be sure that it was the work of the whole committee, which also included Sir John Johnstone, Legard and Thompson. Of these, Thompson certainly possessed a working interest in chemistry. We also know, from a later document, that Thompson was keenly anxious about Liebig's impact on English farming. In 1855 Thompson was to write, recalling the late 1830s and early 1840s:

> At that time a very general impression prevailed that British agriculture was capable of great development, but that there were no established principles to guide its advance. . . .
>
> The appearance of Baron Liebig's book was, therefore, naturally and deservedly hailed with great delight. All admired the masterly way in which he traced the elements of vegetable life to their original sources, pointed out their chemical composition, and followed them through the various stages of the plant's

development and maturity, until the process of decay had again reduced them to the elementary form. His main position, too, that in order permanently to maintain the fertility of cultivated land, it was necessary to restore to it all the substances contained in the various crops exported from the farm, was as new to agriculture as it was convincing, and its application to practical agriculture seemed as simple and easy as it has since been found to be complicated and difficult.

For the time, however, the whole secrets of the science of agriculture seemed to be laid open by the production of this master-key; nor could it well be otherwise. The accuracy of the chemical investigations which formed the basis of this work has never been questioned, and the reasoning with which the various results were united into one consistent and comprehensive scheme seemed so sound and satisfactory that the delighted reader was led on by easy steps until he reached an elevation from which it was difficult to avoid believing that the prospect before him included the whole *past, present and future* of agriculture.[71]

Further indication that Thompson might have had a hand in writing the report arises from the fact that he was conducting his own field-trials, accompanied by chemical experiments with Spence in the latter's laboratory in York, specifically to test Liebig's ideas. In 1845 this investigative work bore important fruit, with Thompson's discovery that soils absorb and retain alkaline bases (ammonia, sodium and potassium) whenever solutions of their salts (ammonium sulphate and potassium nitrate, for example) trickle through them. This discovery went a long way towards explaining a number of puzzling findings: for instance, why drainage water from land that had been fertilized with ammonium and potassium solutions itself contained no ammonia and little potash. What had happened to the ammonia and potash? Thompson could now offer an excellent explanation, and his work was published in several agricultural journals as a proud vindication of that ideology which fired both him and his Society.[72]

This discovery had tremendous import for the manufacture of fertilizers and, more to the point, it showed precisely why a patent fertilizer manufacturing scheme that Liebig set up in England (with the Muspratts, chemical manufacturers in Liverpool) in 1845 turned out to be such a disaster.[73] (see Appendix B.)

There can be no doubt that Liebig wished to revolutionize farming, particularly in England where he felt he had a high chance of success, with the support of his followers. He had also been introduced to influential and progressive landowners and agriculturists during his visits to England. By the late 1830s, moreover, his ex-pupils and supporters were occupying positions of influence within the BAAS, and with their encouragement he drew up a blueprint for the scientific revolution of agriculture, based upon his work as an analytical chemist. His book, *Organic Chemistry in its applications to Agriculture and Physiology* was thus his manifesto.

Liebig appears to have been under the impression that his agricultural revolution was proceeding smoothly (though slowly) until the mid-1840s, when one of his German ex-pupils working in London, August Hofmann (1818–92), informed him that opposition was brewing within the RASE, with Pusey the principal trouble-maker.[74] By 1846, he was acutely aware of heavy opposition to his theories amongst the English agricultural community. But what he did not realize was that there had been earlier critiques of his views, as in the YAS's Agricultural Geology Committee report. Likewise, historians of agriculture and of nineteenth-century chemistry (with the possible exception of G.E. Fussell) have not been aware of the informed criticisms of Liebig being produced by the landowner-agriculturists who were in control of the societies and other institutions (such as Rothamsted) which took upon themselves the task of bringing science to bear upon farming. As this *History* intends to show, this task was being shouldered at an early stage by the Yorkshire, followed by the Royal and by Rothamsted and other local societies such as the Bath and West (which appointed its own consulting chemist in 1854).

The chemical concern at the heart of the YAS become more intense in proportion with Thompson's ever-growing role within the Society. Thus, if we scrutinise the business of the Council during 1841–2, we find him being requested to pen the Annual address, delivered by the President at the AGM and be printed in the *Transactions*.[75] He was elected both to the Finance Committee[76] and the local organizing committee for the 1842 York Show.[77] Correspondingly, the chemical profile in the Society's business grew. Spence was now being paid directly by the Secretary, on Council's instructions, for soil-analyses on behalf of the Agricultural Committee.[78] The main lecture for the members at the York Show was a highly scientific and professional discourse on 'The chemistry of manures', given by T.H. Barker MRCS, Lecturer in Chemistry at the York School of Medicine, and Curator of the Yorkshire Philosophical Society.[79] Thompson, meanwhile, was beginning to report in the *Transactions* the results of a nationwide field-research programme on the use of nitrate fertilizers, that was being conducted by landowners, land agents and tenant farmers, and that he and Pusey (in the RASE) were coordinating.[80]

Barker's lecture, which was promptly printed in the *Transactions*, is note-worthy with regard to Liebig. In a number of ways, Barker took his cue from Liebig's *Organic Chemistry*, discussing some of the issues that Liebig had opened up (such as the chemistry of 'putrefaction'). Barker discounted carbonaceous manures (like dung) as major sources of plant-nutrition, and he emphasized the value of ammonical manures, as did Liebig in the first and second (1840 and 1842) editions of his book. But Barker was also advocating certain chemical ideas with which Liebig would soon disagree. For instance, Barker was too well acquainted with farming practice to deny that farmyard manure would ever be superfluous. Soon Liebig would say precisely that, as he would wax more lyrical on the virtues of mineral and manufactured fertilizers.[81]

Barker also made explicit the philosophy of agricultural science that was being promoted by Thompson and his friends:

If the farmer will assist the chemist with carefully conducted trials, the chemist will be enabled to afford such deductions as will render the subject capable of definite explanation. It is the combination of practice with theory, that alone can improve the science of agriculture; and it is impossible that either the chemistry of agriculture, or the practice of the art, can be carried on successfully without combination.[82]

Of course, Barker was here adopting a radical position so far as the farming community was largely concerned. Many farmers, certainly most small farmers in Yorkshire, as elsewhere, had yet to put much money into manures other than dung; and few would then have been planning their farming in terms of a chemical balance sheet. But that was the type of entrepreneurship that the policy-makers and managers of the YAS and the RASE were determined should become the way of English farming. As was Liebig. But men like Spencer, Thompson and Pusey, owners of land and leaders of men in birthright and in duty, were set upon mapping that way themselves. In the telling phrase that was to be coined by a close friend and fellow Publication Committee member of the RASE, Thomas Dyke Acland (himself the leading light of the Bath and West in the second half of the century), there should be an 'English Chemistry of Farming'.[83] And everything else about the progress of agriculture in England should likewise be Saxon.

The 'map' continued to be drawn in ever greater and more scientific detail in the *Transactions*. Volume 6 (1842–3) carried a major, throughly chemical paper on 'The economy of waste manures', by John Hannam who was also a contributor to the *JRASE*. Volume 7 carried a 'Report on experiments with guano', written by the Secretary; it also carried an excellent paper by Spence, on 'Analyses of grasses, soils, etc'. There were also a number of reports taken from the *JRASE*: 'On the solution of bones in sulphuric acid for the purposes of manure' by no less a figure than the Duke of Richmond; a 'Report by the Committee of the Morayshire Farmer's Club, appointed to inspect and to report on the experiments made in raising turnips by means of sulphuric acid and bone dust' (seminal in persuading farmers that bones treated with sulphuric acid, yielding degrees of 'superphosphate', were more effective than plain bones or bone-dust); and a lecture on 'The applications of physiology to the rearing and feeding of cattle', by Lyon Playfair (in which Liebig was cited warmly).

The scientific programme pressed on into Volume 8 (1844–5) of the *Transactions*, which contained a report of the Council dinner discussion at the 1845 Show, 'On the best mode of preserving and applying liquid manure'. (Since the fourth show it had become a regular event to choose a topic for discussion after the Council dinner.) The journal also contained another substantial paper by Hannam, 'An experimental inquiry into the theory of the action, and the practical application, of bones as a manure for the turnip crop' (taken from the *JRASE*). Several more communications were printed on the subject of bones treated with sulphuric acid, from the *JRASE*, with a note by

Pusey, as well as a comment by a Scottish tenant farmer which neatly indicates the stimulus that Liebig gave to agricultural chemistry, and the spirit of experiment that was abroad in farming:

> After reading Liebig's work on Agricultural Chemistry, about four years ago, I resolved to try the experiment of using dissolved bones, and procured 26 bushels of bones, 2 bottles of sulphuric acid at 1d per lb; about 190 lbs each. This mixture I applied to 9 acres of land, with 20 carts of dung per Scotch acre, and was highly satisfied with the result.[84]

Volume 9 (1845–6) contained more material along the same lines. There was a report on a Council dinner discussion initiated by a lecture 'On the use of guano' by J.F.W. Johnston, in which Thompson and Legard appear to have been the main discussants. There were several reports sent by members to Thompson on livestock-feeding experiments, from which it appears that he had been intensifying his efforts as central coordinator of the Society's field-experimentation programme (just as Pusey was doing in the RASE). And there were a large number of brief communications taken from the *JRASE*, showing how enthusiastically the RASE's members, high and low, were participating in its manurial experimentation programme.

Noteworthy in these *JRASE* papers now being re-printed in the *Transactions* was one by Pusey, on dung and artificial manure, in which he drew attention to the work of one of Liebig's main continental opponents, the French chemist and estate-owner, Jean Baptiste Boussingault (1802–87). Pusey, along with Lawes and Gilbert at Rothamsted, was finding Boussingault much more congenial than Liebig; the Frenchman's work was already being cited in the English agricultural literature in 1840 and was to be cited with almost wholesale approval from 1845 onwards. Pusey drew attention to how 'the two leaders in agricultural chemistry, Liebig and Boussingault, are at variance', particularly on the question of the need for nitrogen in manures.[85] This question was of central interest to the farming community, and it was examined in great detail within the YAS's *Transactions* and the *JRASE* as they grew ever more distrustful of Liebig's chemistry, and as their members sent in the results of their field-trials with the growing variety of manures on the market.

At this stage, we might suspend our appraisal of the Society's scientific programme and examine its other activities. The show had gone from strength to strength, with what was to prove an important innovation at the fourth Show at Hull (4 August 1841) in the form of a working trial of agricultural implements. The Council had written to many of the major implement manufacturers in England inviting them to exhibit their wares. A field was chosen adjoining the Hull and Selby railway. Trams were organized to transport visitors to and fro at a nominal charge. The actual day was fine and many people came. Yet, the Council felt, it was a decided failure technically 'as a trial of merit'. Many of the implements did not function as well as they could, largely because they were demonstrated by men who were not properly familiar with them. Furthermore, they were not kept functioning for long enough for the visitors to see for themselves how well they worked.[86] This technical failure (although from the spectators' point of view, it might have been entertaining enough) caused the Council to decide that in future the trial of implements would be limited to demonstrations in the show yard itself.

On other counts the Hull Show was a success, with a large attendance by townspeople as well as farmers. Gate receipts and dinner receipts were especially high on the actual day of the show (4 August) although less so on the preceding implements trial day. Incidentally, this was the first two-day show, in effect. There were large entries of livestock, although compared with the York and Northallerton shows the horses were disappointing (see Table 2.3 for livestock entries at the first five shows). Once again the country's top breeders walked away with most of the premiums for Shorthorns and Leicesters.

Despite the large public attendance, and its general success, the show itself incurred a loss – admittedly of only £86, but this was indicative of a problem that would almost cripple the Society later in its history, namely the cost of fitting out a new show site each year. (The Northallerton show had also incurred a small loss, of £60.)

Table 2.3: Exhibition livestock entries (number of animals) at the first five shows

	York 1838	Leeds 1839	Northallerton 1840	Hull 1841	York 1842
Cattle	68	72	116	110	124
Sheep	90	72	75	79	117
Pigs	38	17	22	36	43
Horses	105	79	95	80	100
Total	301	240	308	305	384

The fourth year as a whole saw a deficit of income against expenditure of £110.[87] The Council, however, saw no cause to worry, partly because they had fixed York again as the venue for the fifth show and there, they knew, they could count on a large attendance coupled with lower expenditure since they would again have use of some permanent buildings. Indeed, the fifth show, again held over two days (2 and 3 August) went off 'with great eclat'.[88] There was a record submission of livestock; the gate-receipts were almost as large as at Hull, and a very much lower expense was incurred for preparing the yard. This fifth show turned in a healthy profit of £225, leaving £930 6s 10d in the Treasurer's hands (exclusive of the £900 invested). The show's success was also due, it seems, to the indefatigability of the York Committee, of whom George Swann and H.S. Thompson were the principal members. Swann was appointed 'Steward of the Yard' (this appears to have been the first time that such an office was designated, being the equivalent of today's Honorary Show Director), and Council resolved 'That H.S. Thompson Esqre be admitted to the Show Yard at such hours as he may choose.'[89]

The process of choosing a venue for the sixth show differed from that of the previous ones, and was the start of a pattern that was to last until the 1880s. The economic advantage to a town of hosting the YAS show had become evident by now, in terms of the revenue it generated locally in trade, transport and supplies. So, either at the Hull show or soon afterwards, a deputation from Richmond waited on the Council and offered £150 plus other advantages if the Society would next visit there. But Thirsk and Doncaster also sent deputations, thus starting the annual competition for hosting the show. Doncaster won, for although their donation was the same as Richmond's, they offered a magnificent location for the Council dinner in the Banqueting Hall of the Mansion House, as well as an excellent site for the show and every facility for transporting people, livestock and implements to the site.

This show was a financial and technical success: the exhibition of implements 'although not perhaps so extensive as the previous exhibition at York and Leeds, was nevertheless excellent, and comprised some most ingenious and useful implements'.[90] It also saw one or two new features, in particular a joint meeting with a scientific society and the attendance of a representative from a foreign agricultural society. The joint meeting was held with the West Riding Geological Society, commencing at 2.30 on the day of the show (Tuesday 2 August) and chaired by the Earl Fitzwilliam who was at that time President of the West Riding Geological Society, as well as Vice-President of the YAS and of the RASE.[91] The meeting began with a scientific lecture, by the Reverend Thorp, and it is evident both from the general discussion which followed and from Fitzwilliam's comments that this was considered a highly proper activity at a YAS show.

Another new feature manifested itself in the discussion following the Council dinner. Two topics were chosen. The first was the breeding of livestock, introduced by Spencer. The other was 'The best mode of treating farmyard manures', notable for the easy yet accurate manner in which it was handled by H.S. Thompson and for the contribution made by a representative from the American Agricultural Association, a Mr H. Coleman. This appears to have been the earliest YAS Show attended by a representative of an overseas agricultural society. At the time, though, this was hardly significant. Much more important was the presence of key figures from the RASE; indeed, on high table at the Council Dinner sat Spencer, Pusey and several other Council members and officers of the national society, all apparently keen to learn what they could from the YAS.

Despite the successes of the shows, actual membership declined from 1841 onwards. In August of that year it stood at 960; by August 1843 it was down to 840; by August 1845 it had dropped further to 750; and at August 1847 it was 680. The membership figures continued to fall in the 1850s, reaching an all time low (since the founding months) of 480 in 1865.[92] At first glance, this would seem serious but there was little indication of anxiety in the Council, for several probable reasons. First, as so easily happens to any society, a number of those who join in the first flush of enthusiasm do not actually become committed and sooner or later default on their subscriptions. For the historian, this is an important cautionary point, for if one goes by membership figures alone one is likely to get an inflated and artificial impression of a society's character.

The RASE also had the same problem of members defaulting on their subscriptions. By 1845, indeed, the RASE's membership arrears had reached almost £7000. Both the YAS and the RASE appear to have taken the same measures to deal with the problem: they purged their lists of all those who were only nominal, non-paying members. The YAS seems to have taken this step rather earlier, in about 1840–41; the RASE did not act until 1848. The YAS also seems to have been more determined to keep the measure in force. As early as 1840 it was devising better ways to collect its subscriptions. At first it set up a sub-committee to appoint collectors in the market towns.[93] Then, at the Council Meeting at the Doncaster show it appointed an official collector for the Society, one John Watson of York, who was to be paid 'one shilling in the pound for collection of subscriptions inclusive of the expences and have £1 1s 0d per day when employed for the Society at the annual Show in addition to his expences'.[94]

A second reason for Council's apparently cool handling of the decline in subscribers was the increasing financial contribution of the show, whose profitability was clearly going to depend most directly upon the attendance of the ordinary public. Added to this, the show was clearly the major symbol of the Society, and it was the principle concern of Council as a whole, even as the several sub-committees remained busy on their own projects. By 1843, the YAS show had become known as the 'Great Yorkshire Show' – apparently by popular acclaim, rather than official edict.[95] It has proudly retained this title ever since, to the extent that it was argued that the Society would not want a Royal Charter, since that would oblige it to call itself the 'Royal Yorkshire Show', which would be less distinctive than the 'Great'.

The core of men managing the YAS changed slightly in 1842. Until that year's show, Spencer had continued to play a very active role, often chairing the meetings of Council and participating in the work of the Publication and other Committees. But thereafter his active involvement declined, perhaps due to ill health, and in the remaining three years of his life he did not resume a direct role except in the running of the show. His departure was followed by a significant development in the power structure of the Society. Increasingly, council meetings were to be presided over not by a landocrat, but by the likes of Thompson, Legard and other gentry. Earl Spencer was the only aristocratic President in the formative years to participate fully, sometimes on a week-to-week basis, in the management of the Society. It should be noted, though, that the third President, the Earl of Zetland, and the fifth, Lord Wenlock, did on occasion chair Council. (See Appendix A for list of Presidents.)

At the end of 1842 Howard resigned his post as Secretary. Clearly, he had done an excellent job, for a subscription was opened by the Council to purchase a piece of plate to present to him at the forthcoming annual show, and Spencer headed the committee to organize the matter. His successor was Matthew Milburn, at £70 per annum.[96] The Assistant-Secretary's post was not filled, possibly because Thompson now offered to undertake officially the editorship of the *Transactions*, so relieving the Secretary of some duties.

It would be reasonable to suggest that from this moment (December 1842) onwards, Thompson was the *de facto* chairman of the Publication Committee. This would explain the powerful scientific orientation of the *Transactions* from then on, as well as the increasing use of material from the *JRASE*. Thompson was also on the latter's Journal Committee and had easy access to its material. Indeed, the policies of the two Publications Committees were steadily converging, with the RASE's initial dependence upon the *Transactions* now turning to a greater reliance by the YAS on material from the national society. Thus, in 1844 Thompson was given a totally free hand by Council

> to make any arrangements with the Royal Agricultural Society for the republication of their Transactions, with the limit he proposes of not increasing the cost of this Society's Transactions to more than £100.[97]

The minutes of the Council meetings during 1844, 1845 and 1846 also reveal the depth of the Society's commitment to science, particularly chemistry. In October 1844, Spence was appointed official Analysing Chemist to the Society by a Council which needed no persuading on the point.[98] In October of the following year, the Council took steps to establish a formal link with the Chemical Association of Scotland*, and secure the services of its chemist, J.F.W. Johnston, for the Wakefield show and AGM.[99] The Chemical Association does not seem to have responded with enthusiasm, for in the following March (1846) the Council resolved to dangle a financial carrot before it, of a £5 subscription 'in case they will allow their chemist to deliver a lecture in the first week of August'.[100] The Yorkshire got its lecture (discussed above), the Chemical Association got its carrot, and the Yorkshire had achieved wider contact with the agricultural community at large.

---

* In his work for the Highland and Agricultural Society, Johnston quickly demonstrated the value of soil and manure analyses. Members of the society then felt that the Society should operate its own laboratory. A committee was appointed in 1842 to look into this proposal, and although its worth was recognized it was turned down because of expense. The plan's proposers thereupon set up the Agricultural Chemistry Association of Scotland, appointing Johnston its chemist in 1843. Johnston worked for the Association until 1848 when it was dissolved. One reason for its dissolution was the disparity between Johnston's view of the type of science it should promote, and its subscribers' view. Johnston wanted a rigorous, fundamental-research programme in search for the general underlying principles of plant and animal chemistry; whilst the subscribers, who were mostly farmers, sought a more immediate and practical orientation. However, the Association bore fruit, for not only did Johnston carry out numerous analyses for the farming community but its dissolution actually brought about the very development that had been called for within the Highland back in 1842. The Highland now reversed its earlier decision and appointed an official chemist of its own: Dr Thomas Anderson, Regius Professor of Chemistry at the University of Glasgow. He held the post until 1874. He was succeeded by his assistant, James Dewar, who shortly afterwards left the Highland for the Jacksonian Chair in Chemistry at the University of Cambridge, where he made a brilliant career.

Amidst all this, what was happening to the interests of the small farmer? All the evidence indicates that his interests were being borne in mind. At the annual meeting in August 1846, the Council felt that the Society had come of age, not least in proving its utility to the ordinary farmer. Its 'Address' was deservedly self-congratulatory, and revealed the resolve that successive General Committees and Councils had had in pushing through their policies. The 'Address' opened as follows:

> At the conclusion of the first circuit of the three ridings, the experiment of a Yorkshire Agricultural Society might be said to have been firmly tried, and no better proofs of its success could be desired than the steady support of seven or eight hundred subscribing members and the attendance of some thousands of visitors at each of its annual exhibitions. The Council could therefore with confidence invite the tenant farmers to participate in advantages which were no longer prospective or theoretical, but already realized and within their reach. Before, however, the great body of the occupiers of the soil could partake of, or even appreciate, the benefits arising from this annual gathering of the leading farmers of the county, it was necessary to remove some long established prejudices and to combat many plausible objections which were brought forward as serious drawbacks from the utility of such meetings. One or two successive addresses were accordingly occupied in shewing the fallacy of the arguments commonly used in depreciation of agricultural exhibitions, and in justifying the course adopted by the Council of expending a large portion of the available funds in prizes for cattle and other livestock; even though the leading object of the Society had always been to afford information and assistance to those most in want of it, viz. the small farmers.[101]

The Council was convinced that the Society had substantially affected the agriculture of the county, claiming that the newly-created agricultural societies in Northallerton, Doncaster and Wakefield had been direct consequences of its shows in these towns. It also felt that the small farmer had benefitted from being able to see for himself, as never before, the wide range of implements and machinery available from all over the country at the annual show. By having reliable information set before him on a range of topics, such as manures, crop-rotations, tenant-rights and other 'practical truths', the small farmer could see obsolete practices exposed for what they were.

Of course the historian has to handle such convictions with scepticism. Was the Council being overly optimistic? Probably not, for there is no evidence to suggest that the Society had not been serving the needs of the farming community. On the other hand, there is considerable positive evidence: tenant farmers, land agents and landowners were now participating in the field trials that Thompson was coordinating; attendance at the show had been growing strongly; and many implement manufacturers undoubtedly believed that it was worth their while to transport their wares to the show. (By the mid-1840s, the RASE's show was also heavily supported by implement and machinery manufacturers all over the county.)

Besides, it seems that Spencer, Thompson and their like at the nucleus of the

Society had a genuine concern for the ordinary farmer and farm-labourer. Thompson himself was to be recalled as a model landlord,[102] and in his own writings for the *Transactions* and for the *JRASE* he rarely missed an opportunity to draw attention to the practical needs and rights of 'hard-working, deserving tenants'.[103]

The 1846 Council Address, which was very probably penned by Thompson again, touched upon a controversial issue which we have already seen was a headache for the Council and show committees: the display of implements and their premiums. The Council was uncertain how best to manage this feature of the show, but nonetheless the Council steadily raised the premiums for implements, and by the time of the Doncaster show it was finding a suitable means for actually testing the workings of farm machinery. At the Doncaster show itself, for instance, some of the ploughs and 'scarifiers' were tried out on a field of clover stubble, which also enabled the judges to try out a new and useful device – the dynamometer, for which a special premium was awarded. The trial of implements at the next show, in Richmond (1844), was more elaborate. At the recommendation of the Implement Committee the trial began on the Friday before the show (itself held on Tuesday 7th August), but most of it was actually postponed until much later, on the 22 October, when 'the stubbles were available, and when a much smaller concourse of people would be likely to be present'. Moreover, at the suggestion of many implement manufacturers, medals were struck by the Royal Mint and these were awarded either instead of, or as well as, certain premiums. Implement manufacturers were present from all over the country and a few (Ransomes of Ipswich, Dean of Birmingham, Barrett, Exall and Andrews of Reading) came from further afield. It seems that they were all satisfied with the system, 'and declared that in no place was ever so full and fair a trial given'.[104] This comment had double significance, for it also suggests that since most of the awards went to Yorkshire manufacturers and inventors, and the Gold Medal for the best assortment of implements to Crosskill of Beverley, Yorkshire manufacturers must have been amongst the finest in England.

The Richmond system was repeated at the Beverley show (1845) with great success. Indeed the pre-show examination of the implements lasted for three days (the Friday, Saturday and Monday prior to the show), and the main trial again took place in October. Council was at last satisfied 'that what has hitherto been so much desired has at length been accomplished, viz. a full, deliberate and careful test of the merits of the various field implements submitted to competition'.[105] This success was no doubt due in part to the tremendous effort made by the Lord Mayor and Corporation of Beverley to host the YAS show, an effort which is understandable if one recalls Beverley's economic and geographic importance at that time. Indeed, so keen was Beverley to host the show that the deputation it sent to the YAS Council in August 1844 established the pattern of soliciting the show for the next few decades. Henceforth, deputations from towns all over the county would wait upon the Council at each show, offering a package of provisions and promises to secure the next venue. So, for 1845

Beverley offered, in addition to a donation of £150,

1st. Fields for the Show, ten acres sufficiently fenced.

2nd. The use of the Beverley Agricultural Society's pens for sheep and cattle, and will provide additional pens if necessary.

3rd. Provide a police force to place at the disposal of the Society.

4th. Room to dine 1000 persons, with kitchens and small rooms behind, suitable for meetings.

5th. Guarantee the carriage of stock, implements, etc. from Hull to Beverley and back to Hull free of expence to this Society.

6th. Ground for the trial of implements with horses and materials for the same.[106]

At the Wakefield show (1846) even more time was devoted to the implements trial: those that could be tried out in the show yard were put through their paces over three days, again prior to the show day itself, and a further three days in October were set aside for the heavier implements and machinery. The Scarborough show (1847) saw a slight diminution in the system, since fewer exhibitors actually turned up than had indicated, but the trial was still a success. And finally (in this analysis of the first ten shows) the great joint RASE–YAS show at York in 1848 fully vindicated the time and money spent by the Council in promoting the demonstration of implements.

Despite this achievement, there were criticisms of implement trials both nationally and locally, which kept some societies which were large enough to organise trials from actually doing so. It was pointed out that some implements were more efficient on hard, dry soils whilst others were designed for wet ones. Then, too, as J.C. Morton was to complain in the 1860s, the prize-system at these shows tended to mean that the winner took all. An implement or machine which won a first premium would be noted and bought eagerly, whilst the runner-up which might be only marginally less efficient would be forgotten. As the 1846 Council Address indicated, the YAS's managers (who preferred to call themselves 'Directors') took such reservations seriously; and they seem to have handled the whole issue with conviction. At any rate, the Society did not have to face the sort of crisis that the RASE did at its 1860 Canterbury show, where there was a virtual revolt by machinery manufacturers. Nor did it immediately abandon its implement premiums, as did a number of other societies.

Another feature to emerge in the course of the 1840s was the changing nature of the YAS's relationship with the RASE. We have seen that the *Transactions* increasingly carried material from the *JRASE* from about its seventh issue onwards, thus reversing the dependence of the earlier years. We have also seen the increasing overlap between their office-holders, their Councils and, perhaps most significantly of all, their Publication Committees. We have also noted that H.S. Thompson was the principal intermediary between these committees, and that he and Pusey were coordinating very similar sets of field-experiments and held similar cautionary views on Liebig's agricultural chemistry. Thompson and Pusey also attended each other's shows; Pusey was almost certainly present at several, including that at Doncaster, while Thompson so regularly attended the RASE's that by the late 1840s he was writing the annual 'Implements Report' of the RASE's show for the *JRASE*.

It was hardly surprising, therefore, that the idea of a joint Yorkshire-Royal show began to be mooted. Precisely which society initiated the idea is uncertain. It might have been the YAS, for its Council was already discussing the plan in the autumn of 1846 (two years before it actually took place).[107] Moreover, the YAS Council seems to have been eager to entice the RASE up to York, where the event finally took place, for they offered £500 (the whole of the Society's profit for the year of August 1845–August 1846) as a donation 'in the event of their holding their County Meeting for 1848 in Yorkshire'.[108] Subsequent monies also seem to have been transferred to the RASE.* The importance of such a visit by the now much larger national society to the local one was also evident from the composition of the deputation sent to handle the negotiations in London: Childers, Johnstone, Stansfield and Thompson – all four members of the inner core of management.

Once the agreement had been clinched, the Council exerted itself to make the show (the tenth anniversary of the original show) the most successful yet. Crucial to this effort was the detailed planning carried out by the Thompson-led nucleus of the Society. The Council meetings, from October 1846 until the eve of the show in August 1848, at which the great event was steadily planned, were dominated by Childers, Johnstone, Legard and Thompson, with major decisions being made even when attendance was below the quorum. Moreover, one of this group invariably chaired Council, due to the frequent absence of the Society's President (Lord Wenlock for 1845–6, and the Earl of Harewood for 1846–7), except in the final year of planning. That year, the first non-aristocrat landowner held Presidency: Sir John Johnstone.

As we have seen, Johnstone had been an ardent colleague of Thompson's since 1839, when they had both been founding members of the Agricultural Geology Committee. He had been a frequent attender of Council, and undoubtedly shared Thompson's ideas about the policies of the Society. As he was no doubt intended to be, Johnstone was a most active President, chairing most of the Council meetings during his office, taking part in the planning, giving his support to the still expanding programme of agricultural experimentation which now came under the direction of a new Experiments Committee (comprising Johnstone, Legard, Thompson and Wiley).[109] Johnstone also helped to affirm Thompson's central role within the Society.

---

* It is difficult to determine exactly how much the YAS paid to the RASE to hold the 1848 York Show. If one examines the minutes of the YAS Council one finds that, in addition to the £500, Council was voting additional monies for specific premiums at that Show. (See YAS Council, 11 Nov. 1847.) As for the record of actual payments there are discrepancies. On 15 June 1848 the YAS Council authorized an immediate payment of £100. That left £400 to be paid, apparently on or about 1 August. But the RASE accounts for the half-year ending 31 December 1848 itemize only £350 as received. (See *JRASE*, 1849, *10*:ix) Furthermore, an editorial addendum to an article (*JRASE*, 1848, *9*:279) mentions only £300 as the total grant from the YAS.

1   Print of the Black Swan, Coney Street, York, by John Clark, 1804, the venue for the early meetings of the Society, demolished in the 1950s

2   Selection of early show catalogues

At a Meeting,
Held at York, on Tuesday, October 10, 1837,
Earl Spencer in the Chair;
It was resolved,

1.— That a Society be formed called the "Yorkshire Agricultural Society," the object of which shall be to hold an annual Meeting for the Exhibition of Farming Stock, Implements, &c., and for the General Promotion of Agriculture.

2.— That such Meeting shall be held successively, in different places in the County, on the last Wednesday in August, in each year, and that the First Meeting be held at York, in August, 1838.

3.— That every subscriber of One Pound annually, be a Member of this Society

4.— That Donations for forming a Fund to carry into effect the Views of the Society be received by the Treasurer.

3   First page of the minutes of the founding meeting of the Society

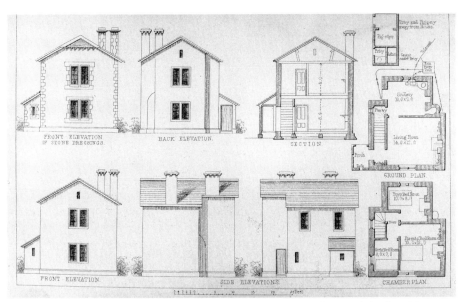

4   Cottage plans from a report, 'Prize Plans for Landowner's Cottages', in the 1860 *Transactions*

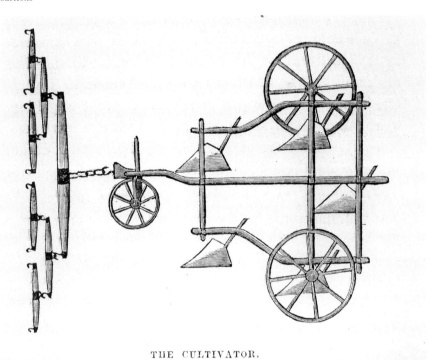

THE CULTIVATOR.

5   First illustration of machinery in the Society's journal. From a 'Report on the Turnip Crop on Strong Land' in the 1839 *Transactions*

THE ROYAL AGRICULTURAL SOCIETY'S MEETING AT YORK.

THE CATTLE AND IMPLEMENT SHEDS.

1848.

[COUNTRY EDITION.] THE ROYAL AGRICULTURAL SOCIETY'S MEETING AT YORK.—THE DINNER PAVILION, FROM THE NEW-WALK.—(SEE PAGE 32.)

6 Joint meeting of the Yorkshire and Royal agricultural societies at York, 1848 (*The London Illustrated News*)

Exhibited by H. Bushell, Agricultural Engineer

Stand 9, The Great Yorkshire Show,

Stockton on Tees, 1863

	£	s.	d.
Patent Self-Raking Reaper : : : : : : :	35	0	0
Patent Eclipse Reaper, to cut 5 ft wide with tilting platform (new patent)	16	16	0
Royal Prize Mower, to cut 4 ft wide : : : :	21	10	0
Great Yorkshire Prize Combined Reaper and Mower to cut 4' 6" :	26	0	0
Double Action Haymaker, with patent screen. For trial : : :	14	7	0
K0 Chaff Cutter, hand power : : : : : :	2	15	0
K12 ditto, with pulley for power : : : : :	10	0	0
Patent Pulper : : : : : : : :	4	10	0
Patent Gardener's 30-knife Turnip Cutter : : : :	4	10	0
Ditto 14-knife : : : : : :	4	10	0
Ditto Double action for beast and sheep : : :	5	10	0
No. C Linseed Cake Breaker : : : : : :	2	0	0
No. 3 ditto will break to any size : : :	3	10	0
No. 4 ditto ditto			
with 2 pairs of rollers for crushing to dust : : :	4	14	0
No. 1 Bean Splitting Mill, ditto : : :	2	2	0
No: 2 ditto ditto for power :	3	5	0
No. 0 Mill, for all kinds of grain : : : : :	3	5	0
No. 3 Roller Mill, ditto : : : : :	3	10	0
No. 4 ditto for hand or power : : : :	7	10	0
Barley Horner : : : : : : :	4	10	0
Cartwright's Patent Chain Harrows, 7½ ft wide : : :	3	15	0
New Patent Triangular Iron Chain Harrows : : : :	4	0	0
Set of 3 and 4-beam Bedford Seed Harrows : : : :	3	3	0
Set of 3 ditto, 10 ft wide, heavy for general purposes :	4	4	0
Set of 3 ditto, Excelsior Seed Harrows : : : :	3	3	0
Set of 3 ditto ditto for general purposes :	3	10	0
Set of 3 ditto ditto very strong : :	4	4	0
Horse Rake, light leverage : : : : : :	7	0	0
Hay Sweeps : : : : : : : :	1	10	0
Cultivator : : : : : : : :	7	0	0
R. Plough, with steel breast : : : : : :	4	2	0
RB. ditto ditto : : : : : :	4	5	0
RC. ditto ditto : : : : : :	4	9	0
No. 1 Improved Wood Plough, with iron head : : :	1	12	0
No. 2 ditto ditto ditto : : : :	1	15	0
Winnower : : : : : : : :	8	10	0

PHOTOGRAPH

OF TWO FINE WHITE TWIN CATTLE (OX AND HEIFER),

CHALLENGED ALL ENGLAND, AND NOT ACCEPTED, FOR £25 ASIDE.

Bred and Fed by Francis Carr, of Heslington, York.   Calved 6th June, 1860.

OBTAINED THE TWO SECOND PRIZES, OF £5 EACH, FOR FAT CATTLE AT YORK CATTLE SHOW, IN DEC., 1863; AND ALSO WON THE TWO FIRST PRIZES AT THE LEEDS SMITHFIELD FAT CATTLE SHOW, OF £10 EACH. THE OX HAD ALSO AWARDED TO HIM THE MAYOR OF LEEDS' SILVER CUP, VALUE £21, FOR THE BEST BEAST IN THE YARD, DEC. 10, 1863.

8   1860 prize-winning cattle

Photo by]   [G. H. Parsons

Fig. 4.—Shorthorn Bull, "Shenley White Ensign" 152,033.

Winner of the Y.A.S. Champion Prize for the best Male above 1 year, Leeds Show, 1921. The property of Mr. F. B. Wilkinson, Cavendish Lodge, Edwinstowe, Newark. Bred by Mr. C. F. Raphael, Porter's Park, Shenley, Herts. Born 1st August, 1918.

9, 10, 11   This and the following two photographs are of Yorkshire prize-winners, taken from the 1922 *Transactions*

Photo by]   [*G. H. Parsons*

Fig. 5.—Shorthorn Heifer, "Mischief" (Vol. 65).

Winner of Y.A.S. Champion Prize for the best Female above 1 year, Leeds Show, 1921.
Bred by and the property of Mr. John H. Toppin, Musgrave Hall, Skelton, Penrith.
Born 27th September, 1918.

10

Fig. 6.—Dairy Cow, "Ringlet."

Winner of the Yorkshire Herald Challenge Cup for the best Cow in the Dairy Cow
Classes, and Leeds Ladies Challenge Trophy for the Champion Cow or Heifer for
Dairy Purposes of the Shorthorn Breed, Leeds Show, 1921. The property of Messrs.
John and Norman N. Lee, Stonelands, Arncliffe, Skipton-in-Craven.

11

Yorkshire Agricultural Society's Potato Show, York,
5th November, 1925.

12 Yorkshire Agricultural Society Potato Show, York, 1925

Photo by]   *["Leeds Mercury"*

Fig. 3.—CLEVELAND BAY STALLION, "BEADLAM BRISCO" 1734.

Winner of the Cleveland Bay Horse Society's Special Prize for best Cleveland Bay
Stallion or Colt, Leeds Show, 1921. The property of His Majesty the King,
Buckingham Palace. Bred by Mr. George Scoby, Beadlam Grange, Nawton, York-
shire. Foaled in 1911.

13 Yorkshire prize-winner, from the 1922 *Transactions*

Already, Thompson occupied key positions in the sub-committee structure of the Council, and although it was a rule of the Society that one-third of the Council should stand down each year for re-election, not until 1868 did Thompson ever stand down. Other members of the management-nucleus did, and were not re-elected; at the AGM. on 5 August 1846, Charge, Childers, Maxwell and Swann were all replaced. Thus, uniquely among the Society's founders for a period of over 30 years, Thompson was a continuous, elected member of Council, except when he served as a Vice-President (1862-5) or as President (1861-2). In the run-up to the 1848 show at York his uniqueness was further recognized; despite there being a very active President that year (Johnstone), it was still resolved uncontentiously that the prestigious annual address for the big event should, as usual, be penned by Thompson alone.[110] There could be no doubt who was now the leading light of the Yorkshire: the thirty-nine year old Harry Thompson.

The joint RASE-YAS show at York in 1848 was a great event, surpassing all reasonable expectations. [See Plate 6]. Media coverage presented it largely as the RASE's show, which in terms of pulling in the public it might have been (although this is debatable and will be touched upon below). There can be no doubt, however, that the groundwork for its success was laid magnificently by the YAS and the citizens of York, working with a strong sense of mutual interest (illustrating the point about town and country made in Chapter 1). A county committee was set up in York to raise a public subscription and to coordinate the on-site construction for the show. M.M. Milburn (the YAS Secretary) and J.L. Foster (an ordinary YAS member) were secretaries of this committee. The YAS's treasurers, Messrs Swann, Clough and Co., agreed to handle the public subscription, which was opened with a donation of £100 by the Lord Mayor, George Hudson (himself a founder member of the YAS).

Additionally, other agricultural and agriculture-related associations contributed towards the event, from the humble donation of £10 by the Whitby Agricultural Association and the £25 donation by Scarborough Town right up to the efforts of the York Horticultural Society which decided to hold its own show at the same time, on a site adjacent to the principal showyard. Final preparations began a week before the three days of the show (Tuesday to Thursday, 11 to 13 July) with the arrival of implements and seeds. The site for the show, some 180 acres on Bootham Stray, had been admirably chosen, for its nearness to the Scarborough railway allowed branch lines to be laid directly to it. This site, however, could not be used both for exhibiting the implements and livestock, and putting the implements to trial. So, an additional piece of land at a short distance from the show site was provided personally by Thompson for this purpose.[111] The working trial of all the implements took four days of exhausting judging – from Friday to Monday. One indication of the quantity of work to be done is that on the Saturday the judges of the implement trials were working until 11.00 p.m., and on the Monday they were at work again at 4.00 a.m.

The exhibition of implements at York was far larger than that at any previous

YAS show, and seems to have been the greatest display that even the RASE had organized. Indeed, it may be said that the introduction of so many types of implement and machinery to the county was the principal contribution of the RASE to this show. The presence of the RASE also brought to the attention of the Yorkshire farming community the virtues of livestock other than those exhibited at the YAS show: Herefords and Devons, Southdowns and Longwools.

On Tuesday 11 July the Implements Yard was opened to the general public, admission 2s 6d, open from 8.00 a.m. to 6.00 p.m. On Wednesday, when the livestock was judged, the public were admitted also to the Livestock Yard, after the judging at 6.00 p.m. This Wednesday especially saw a huge public attendance, for HRH Prince Albert arrived to spend a day at the show. Thursday, the final day, must have been the most relaxed, for there was no more judging to do and the site was open from 6.00 a.m. On this final day, too, it seems that agricultural labourers turned up in large numbers, wanting 'to make a day of it' and 'have a real good look at the implements' (as Thompson happily noted), for they were prepared to pay 2s 6d for a whole-day admission rather than 1s for half the day.[112]

Science was also part of the show's business and two lectures were given on the subject. The first was delivered by J.F.W. Johnston 'On the application of science to agriculture', at 4.00 p.m. on Tuesday in the De Grey Rooms of the City Council, to which members of the RASE and the YAS and their friends were invited. The Earl of Yarborough, the President of the RASE, was in the chair and there were probably several hundred persons present. One comment in Johnston's lecture is particularly worth noting, for it illustrates the tremendous interest in science – and particularly in chemistry – that had flowered among English farmers in recent years, and which the YAS was determined to cultivate. Johnston was comparing the agricultural literature of 1838 with that of 1848. In 1838, he recalled,

> the strongest of the agricultural periodicals that ever touched upon the subject at all for the most part undervalued the worth of natural science to the farmer, and ridiculed the pretended value of chemistry.

But now, in 1848,

> the weekly journal was considered badly conducted in which every number did not embody some scientific and especially some chemical information. Scarcely a provincial paper which boasted of an agricultural corner, but indulged freely in chemical nomenclature as being more agreeable to the taste, and within the easy comprehension, of almost every farmer.[113]

The second scientific lecture was given by Professor Symonds of The Royal Veterinary College, London, 'On calving and lambing'. This too was excellently attended and one can imagine that lively discussion continued during the Council Dinner immediately afterwards. There was also at least one other lecture involving science at the show, for at twelve o'clock on Tuesday the controversial farmer and lecturer J.J. Mecchi (of Tiptree Hall in Essex) spoke 'On the best mode of procuring manure' to a meeting of the York Farmers' Club, in the Merchants' Hall in Fossegate (incidentally the venue for the YAS's sesquicentennial celebration in October 1987). So, amidst the hustle and bustle of the great York show with its fierce competitiveness for gold and silver medals and premiums worth up to £50, there were oases of sober scientific contemplation. As Spencer had pronounced, the RASE, and no less the YAS, were in the vanguard of scientific progress.

The historian ought not to leave this York show without trying to convey an impression of its festivity. Perhaps the greatest single contribution to this aspect of the show was made not by the RASE or the YAS, but by the York Horticultural Society, which had erected a beautiful radiating pavilion or marquee (with a circular central portion and nine wings) adjacent to the showyard for its own annual show, which began on Tuesday. This flower show by the York Horticultural Society was not far short of a glittering pageant; it attracted thousands with its spectacular sights and gorgeous scents, manifesting a passion not only among the aristocracy of Yorkshire and burghers of York but also among the leaders of the YAS.

Among the patrons and Vice-Presidents of the York Horticultural Society were a good number of the YAS's own office holders, past and present: the Earls of Carlisle and Zetland, Earl Fitzwilliam, the Lords Feversham, Hotham, Howden, Morpeth, Wenlock and Wharncliffe, Robert Denison, Arthur Duncombe, George Lane Fox, Sir John Johnstone, Sir Thomas Legard, R.F. Shawe, and others, all eager to indulge in this private passion while publicly promoting agriculture. It is quite likely that this interest, coupled with the huge popularity and profitability of the flower show, left a lasting impression upon the YAS, sowing the seed for the idea of a horticultural section at the Great Yorkshire. In the future this idea was to be sporadically put into practice, becoming a permanent fixture of the show in the twentieth century.

This York show marked the apotheosis of the YAS's own efforts within its formative period, confirming the Society's founding ideology and policy. The immediately subsequent YAS shows (the second at Leeds, in 1849, and the 1850 show at Thirsk at the heart of the Shorthorn rearing area) capitalized admirably upon the success of York, evincing a real commitment by Yorkshiremen to their county show, 'The Great'.

To take us up to the mid-century, it remains to examine the furtherance of the YAS's science policy. While preparing for the York show, Thompson had been soliciting the results of trials with a variety of manures, including the much-heralded Liebig-Muspratt patent manure for wheat (whose efficacy he had reason to doubt because of his and Spence's discovery of the selective absorbency of soils). By 1847 Thompson was also in possession of strong evidence that Liebig's manure was worthless, which he quickly printed in volume 10 of the *Transactions* (1847–8). The evidence was sent in by Robert Turnbull, land-agent on Sir John Johnstone's Hackness Estate, who wrote directly to Thompson:

> At the request of Sir J.V.B. Johnstone, I forward you the results of a set of careful experiments made on the Hackness estate in 1846. The main object was to ascertain the value of Liebig's patent manure, as compared with guano and other fertilizers, as tillage for wheat.[114]

Turnbull, perhaps under Johnstone's supervision, had conducted a careful and scientific study of a variety of manures, simultaneously monitoring plots which had not received any manure. The data had been recorded scrupulously, and it all weighed heavily against Liebig. On some plots, Liebig's rather expensive manure had not shown any advantage over ordinary dung; on other plots, Liebig's manure produced about the same yields as no manure whatsoever; and on one plot treated with Liebig's manure 'the crop would probably not have been worth the trouble of reaping, if it had not received a top-dressing with guano, in April'.

If Turnbull's communication was damaging to Liebig, the extraordinarily lengthy editorial comment appended by Thompson was even more so, for it showed that Liebig's Mineral Theory (of plant-nutrition and fertilization) could be challenged both in theory and practice. Thompson drew attention to, and supported, the research being conducted by the man who, more than anyone else, was to demolish Liebig's credibility among English farmers: John Bennet Lawes, of Rothamsted.

At the heart of Liebig's Mineral Theory was his insistence that agricultural land did not require nitrogenous manures, but only inorganic or mineral fertilizers devoid of nitrogen. On this issue, Liebig's own ideas had changed. In the first (1840) and second (1842) editions of his *Organic Chemistry* he had warmly recommended nitrogenous manures as a *sine qua non* of progressive farming.[115] But in the third edition (1843), he changed his mind, apparently as a result of an agricultural tour of England during 1842, and now denied their usefulness.[116]

From 1845, this new position of Liebig's was being tested by key figures within the English farming community: by Johnstone and Thompson in the YAS; by Pusey and his fellow gentry in the RASE; and by Lawes and his chemist, Joseph Henry Gilbert, at Rothamsted. Lawes's first paper to argue that Liebig's theory of fertilizers was nonsense, and his patent manures worthless, appeared just at the time when Thompson was getting farming reports to the same effect.[117] Thus, he saw the Hackness Estate field trials as evidence to support Lawes's insistence

> that nitrogenous manures are of the first importance as far as the wheat crop is concerned, and that if they are deficient, mineral manures cannot by any means supply their place.[118]

The same issue of the *Transactions* carried, again, a number of papers borrowed from the *JRASE*, including a brief essay by Pusey 'On a new means of preparing bones for manure', in which Liebig was also singled out for attack. Pusey had been doing his own experiments on various bones-plus-sulphuric-acid manures, and he could now assert that Liebig's method of manuring was both ineffectual and expensive, concluding that 'the whole doctrine of manuring plants with ingredients of their ashes (i.e. the Mineral Theory) is rendered very doubtful by Mr Lawes's careful experiments'.[119]

The mention of Lawes in this volume of the *Transactions* introduces yet another link in the network of contacts which the YAS were building up within the national farming community. John Bennet Lawes was the owner of the Rothamsted Estate in Hertfordshire, where he had farmed since 1834 and where he had conducted agricultural and chemical experiments since 1836. At first, these experiments had been on a very small, pot-plant scale, but in 1841–2 they became more extensive. One result of his early experiments and his farming experience was his patented manure (June 1843), which was manufactured on a large scale, thus laying the basis of the superphosphate industry in Britain.

By the mid-1840s the research being done at Rothamsted was filtering through to the agricultural community, and the exclusive vehicle for this was the agricultural periodical, above all the *JRASE*. By the mid-1850s, Lawes's research was highly regarded by the English agricultural community, and, increasingly, English farmers looked to Lawes and not to Liebig for guidance in their 'progress with science'. Lawes was to become a figure of great authority in the English agricultural community.[120] It is thus significant for this *History* that in the 1830s he forged an enduring friendship with two of the YAS's founding members, Robert Denison and H.S. Thompson.

These three men had undertaken several 'practical agricultural tours' through Britain in the 1830s, in the manner made fashionable by the indefatigable Arthur Young in the days of the first Board of Agriculture.[121] Thompson became a frequent house-guest at Rothamsted, returning almost annually to see for himself the progress of Lawes's and Gilbert's experiments. In the mid-1850s, when Thompson succeeded Pusey as chairman of the RASE's Publication Committee he gave Lawes virtually open access to the *JRASE*, even allowing him to send manuscripts directly to the printer without passing through his own editorial hands.[122] Thompson gave Lawes public support most readily whenever it came to rebutting Liebig and his followers. (See Appendix D for Thompson's editorial communication with Rothamsted.)

This scientific interest within the YAS, which had pre-dated that within the RASE, supplied the early resources for the RASE's own policy, which pre-dated the policies of any other local societies whose histories we know, such as the Bath and West.[123] In January 1848 the YAS Council set up its Experiments Committee to plan, coordinate and implement its agricultural-chemical experimentation programme, a move which was mentioned in the Annual Address (hardly surprising, since Thompson had written it), as follows:

> The Council have already stated their desire to lose no opportunity of increasing the Society's usefulness; and, after attentive consideration, they are of opinion that no method holds out greater promise of useful results than a well devised system of experiments, planned by the Council and carried out by such members of the Society as shall profess their willingness to aid in forwarding these views.

Agricultural science is not yet in a position to lay down fixed rules for the guidance of the farmer; but it may and does throw out valuable suggestions, which it would be equally unwise to reject or adopt, until after repeated and careful trial.[124]

So Council now organized a register of members who would be interested in participating, from which the Experiment Committee

will select a limited number of names for each experiment, having regard to the position of their farms and the nature of their land; and will furnish them with such instructions as may be thought necessary for ensuring uniformity of management.[125]

We do not know what proportion of the Society's nearly 700 members put their names on this register, but we can be certain that there were sufficient names to match Council's expectations, for within two years they were able to amass a large amount of data on a variety of manures for the all-important turnip crop, printed in the 1849–50 *Transactions* as a lengthy report.[126] The report's conclusions, principally that phosphate and ammonia were the most needed fertilizers for the turnip, also found their way into the 1850 Council annual address as a proud demonstration of the utility of science when conducted by agriculturists themselves, as opposed to its futility when conducted by impractical chemists like Liebig. In effect, the YAS was proposing that the 'English Chemistry of Farming' (to anticipate Acland's phrase) was coming of age. Moreover, the YAS was now being looked upon by other local societies elsewhere in England as an exemplar of what they could achieve. For instance, one William Miles, a prominent member of the BWES, brought out a pamphlet in 1851 outlining what his society could do, drawing his inspiration from the YAS and the North Lincolnshire. The YAS, he noted,

gives prizes for above 40 classes of stock, and for about the same number of implements, to which latter object it devotes £150. It has a paid secretary, a very intelligent land agent; this is essential for a Society that aims at something more than a Christmas market show; and it publishes annually a small volume, containing (by permission) some of the most useful papers in the Journal of the Royal Agricultural Society, which is forwarded to all its members free of expense. This is a very important feature in the Society.[127]

Within a couple of years, indeed, the BWES was to receive a new lease of life under the stewardship of T.D. Acland, who ran the Society along the lines of the lessons that Miles drew from the YAS.[128]

To round off this analysis of the YAS's work up to the mid-century, we should look briefly at a difficulty that the farming community was experiencing in 1847–50, when there was another depression in prices. Partly as a result of the repeal of the Corn Laws, with the inauguration of a free trade policy towards foreign grain, but also due to other factors, the price of English wheat fell heavily from 54s 8d per quarter in 1846 to 38s 6d in 1851. Other grain prices also fell, with the result that farms were abandoned nationwide and especially in the heavy arable areas. Members of the YAS Council were actively concerned about these difficulties, and they acted accordingly both in private (in aiding their own tenants) and in public. In the latter respect, they adjusted the emphasis of reports which they now chose for the Society's essay-prizes: in 1848 they offered a prize for the best practical Report on 'The Management of Manure', and in 1849 on 'The System of Husbandry which requires the least amount of horse labour', since these were two aspects of Yorkshire farming where improvements really would save money. Council (and principally Thompson) also gave out practical advice in its annual addresses during this period, the 1849 Address being especially notable for the easy way in which it gave a thoroughly scientific explanation of the economic management of farmyard manure.[129] Council undoubtedly saw in science the principal salvation for the farmer, for it would show how farming skills could be put to economic gain. The addresses of 1849–51 spelled out the practicable lessons that could be drawn from the scientific theories that the YAS's Experiments Committee were testing.

The *Transactions* also contained material informing the Yorkshire community of national developments. Most notably, a report by Philip Pusey, 'On the progress of agricultural knowledge during the last eight years', was a magnificent piece of work. Pusey cast his net widely in surveying the weaknesses and strengths, the problems and solutions, of farming in England. He also knew his chemistry, for his report was crammed with details of the theories of the leading agricultural chemists – Liebig, Boussingaullt, Sprengel and Lawes – and of the field-trials that had been conducted to test them out, with such disastrous results for Liebig (said Pusey). But Pusey was also arguing a case – for 'high farming'. In his view, the hallmarks of the most progressive and profitable farming were the systematic improvement of the land by drainage, the use of economical fertilizers such as marl and lime and bone-dust, better farm buildings, the scientific management of roots, the feeding of oil-cake to livestock, and more appropriate crop rotations. Moreover he warned:

> We ought to hear no more of the extravagance of High Farming. Your real spendthrift farmer is the man, penny wise and pound foolish, who gives whole turnips to tegs and indulges in the luxury of couch on his fallows.[130]

And, ever present in the farmer's mind, the cost is considered. Pusey declares that

> Ten pounds an acre is a floating estimate of the proper capital. Farming myself of course high, I cannot bring my own investment to more than six pounds an acre, a sum which I believe, with sheep farming at least, to be an ample allowance for the highest possible farming.

This paper by Pusey, published simultaneously in the *TYAS* and the *JRASE*, was possibly the most masterly and influential piece of mid-century English agricultural analysis. It was to be quoted and re-quoted, and even re-printed, in many other journals. Its conclusion was quoted with particular relish, for Pusey captured brilliantly the exquisitely English spirit of agricultural progress, a spirit which was precisely at one with the ideology of the RASE and the YAS:

> Books will not teach farming [boomed Pusey], but if they describe the practices of the best farmers, they will make men think and show where to learn it. If our farmers will inquire what is done by the foremost of them, they will themselves write such a book of agricultural improvement as never was written elsewhere, in legible characters, with good straight furrows, on the broad page of England.[131]

There could be no finer rhetoric grounded in the practice and patriotism of the progressive part of the landed gentry, encapsulating the efforts of the YAS as well as the RASE up to mid-century.

3 THE 'GOLDEN AGE', 1850–75

'They did not have to make money. It was brought home and shot down at their doors.'

J.G. Cornish, on the ease of farming in the 'Golden Age'.[1]

This chapter follows the YAS from the mid-century up until the late 1870s. There are two reasons for this periodization: one reason relates to the character and fortunes of English farming in general, whilst the other concerns the YAS itself.

Without doubt, English agriculture underwent fundamental changes during this period, and these changes were part and parcel of the general upswing in the economics of agriculture which lasted until the late 1870s and which have earned (from Lord Ernle) the not entirely misleading tag, 'The Golden Age' of modern English farming.[2] These changes were various, and are quantifiable as a result of the systematic collation of agricultural statistics since 1865–6, instigated by the YAS, the RASE and several other societies and associations.

The total cultivated acreage in England and Wales began again to expand from the start of the 1850s and continued to grow for at least two decades. More fundamentally, the pattern and balance of farming shifted after the mid-century. In broad terms it may be said that as much more capital was put into agriculture, so the exceptional became the commonplace and the ideas of the so-called classical Agricultural Revolution became the norm.[3] More specifically, it may be said that whereas before the third quarter of the nineteenth century the basic end or goal of almost all farming – and certainly of mixed 'high farming' – had been to profit from grain crops, from the mid-century onwards the goal tended more and more towards the profiting from livestock.

In the 1840s an increased yield of grain had been held as the *raison d'être* of high, and in fact all mixed, farming. As Pusey put it:

All these breeds [of cattle and sheep] are now fatted chiefly not on grazing pastures, but on arable ground. The origin of this practice was no doubt the production of meat for an increased population; it is continued and extended, not from a view to profit in the sale of the meat, but for the production of dung and the consequent increase of the corn-crops.[4]

In keeping with the deeply entrenched teleology of grain, it was widely held that the cost of stall-feeding cattle through the winter (a system that Thompson experimented with and was very keen to promote) could not be recovered from the sale of the fatstock the following spring, but only by crediting the grain-side of the whole mixed enterprise with the dung which had accumulated and had been conserved in the stalls and covered yards. In fact, it is likely that fatstock prices were generally insufficient to cover the purchase of store-beasts and oilcake and yet still yield a profit. It is also probable that stall-feeding came to be practised widely during the 1840s only as the price of wheat was high enough to justify the production of rich dung.

In short, and to simplify, whilst protection lasted, the price of grain covered and justified losses on the stall-fed livestock. But after the repeal of the Corn Laws, grain prices dropped again. In 1851–2, 1858 and the mid-'60s, wheat was actually cheap enough to be fed to livestock, and even to pigs, on a large scale. Increasingly, such seeming extravagance made economic sense, for from the mid-century onwards demand for meat and other livestock products rose steadily as the urban (and the total) population expanded, as wages rose in real terms with an increasing differential between industrial and non-industrial incomes, and as consumption of livestock-dependent consumer materials such as wool and hides increased. Between 1853 and 1878, according to the indefatigable analyst and informer on all things agricultural, Caird, the capital value of British livestock soared by some 80 percent.[5] Between 1853 and 1873, meat prices rose similarly on the metropolitan market: mutton by 85 percent, beef by 58 percent.[6]

Such developments in demand and price forced fundamental changes in the pattern of farming. So, during the period from 1850 to the late 1870s, cereal acreage declined, although there were exceptions in 1870–3 and 1878 when abnormal price-rises temporarily induced larger arable crops. The actual number of cattle and sheep rose, although there were periods of temporary decline, as when the hill flocks of breeding ewes suffered in the hard winter of 1859–60, and when the summer droughts of 1864 and 1868 entailed heavy losses and liquidation-sales, while 1865–6 saw rinderpest. Supply could not meet demand and the gross output and profitability of livestock products rose, while those of arable dropped,[7] and arable was increasingly laid down to pasture.[8]

These changes followed marked gradients over the whole period, so that it is clear that the economic and the technical features of English farming were changing – and had to do so to sustain profitability.

One aspect of these changes is worth discussing more closely, for the Yorkshire, and Thompson in particular, seems to have played a determined role in promoting it. This was the conversion of arable land to permanent pasture. The partial evidence that we possess indicates that this conversion was under way in the early 1850s. Nonetheless, it went against the grain of the English farmer. Many farmers had been reared to regard the wheat crop as sacrosanct, believing in the wheat price as *the* index to agricultural (and national) prosperity. Moreover, it was easier to feel an income through arable than through stock: the returns came in to the arable farmer throughout the year with two, or more, cash-crops; he could, as it were, 'live from hand to mouth on comparatively less capital', as a Cumberland landowner observed in 1873.[9] By contrast, the stock-farmer had to lay out capital for a more extended period before he could get his stock on the market, which would be in August/ September, or June/July if he had been feeding with oilcake.

Furthermore, farmers were able to cling onto arable long past the demise of its profitability because of the incredible elasticity at the heart of mixed farming, in the interplay and counter-balancing of the arable side and the livestock. In general, throughout this period when grain prices dropped livestock-product prices rose, and this held true even at times of abnormal fluctuation.[10] Many farmers were therefore able to tinker with the mixed-farming pattern, retaining their psychological entrenchment in grain even though by thè late '60s and certainly the early '70s 'informed opinion' (like Caird's) was in favour of a radical swing away from arable and stall-feeding to fattening stock on grassland, and finishing speedily with oilcake.

Once the experiment was tried, however, it generally proved convincing. And this, along with the other developments mentioned above, accelerated in the late '70s, when grain prices fell catastrophically and another protracted period of agricultural depression set in.

An accurate summary would allow that while at the mid-century mixed high farming (i.e. fairly capital-intensive arable and stock) had been canvassed in such journals as the Royal's and the Yorkshire's as the path of agricultural progress and future prosperity, by the late '70s that system was breaking up and the livestock side, sustained no longer on roots but on pasture, was being pursued as the path for maintaining the prosperity of the previous quarter-century. That prosperity was not, in fact, maintained in the final quarter.

This, then, is the change in English farming which supplies the rationale for this chapter's periodization.

The local rationale – based on what was happening within the YAS – relies on two main developments. After 1854, the *Transactions* ceased to be a major instrument of policy. Already, in the late '40s, much of its material was being taken from the *JRASE*, and in the '50s this became almost standard practice. After 1854 (vol. 16) the actual size of the *Transactions* diminished. Until then, it had been a fairly substantial volume, but it shrank to about 60 percent of its size and held fewer original reports and less science, not recovering its early focus and scale until the late 1880s. (See Appendix C).

The main reason for this was twofold: the *JRASE* was going from strength to strength, receiving material not only from its own much larger national readership, but also from eminent agriculturists and agricultural chemists abroad.[11] Connected with this was Thompson's ever-growing work-load, that was suddenly increased in 1855 when, on Pusey's death, he succeeded as chairman. As chairman of two journal committees, one operating from York and the other in London, Thompson had to make a clear choice. The lion's share of his editorial attention had to go to the journal which could most effectively implement his policies and proclaim the ideology that he (along with Pusey and Legard and Johnstone) was committed to. It had to be the RASE's *Journal*. It was his duty to the nation.

As the decline of the *Transactions* marks the opening of this chapter's period, so the decline of Thompson marks its close, bringing to an end a chapter of the Society's life. As Earl Cathcart observed, 'The leadership of this important and most flourishing Society was virtually in Mr Thompson's hands, until the year 1870, when the pressure of other work, and perhaps failing health, to the regret of all, led to his virtual retirement'.[12]

The activities of the Society during this third quarter of the nineteenth century paralleled the expansion and increasing prosperity of agriculture nationally. Indeed, it may be said that this was the most uniformly buoyant and financially successful period in the Society's entire history – its own Golden Age. This is evident in the development of the show, in the Society's finances, in the greater workload of its Council and its Secretary (especially after 1864 with the appointment of Thomas Parrington), and in its ever growing prestige.

To start with the development of the show in this period, we find that the profits from the show in the 1870s were about one order of magnitude greater than in 1850. Thus whilst the Leeds show in 1849 returned a profit of £408, and the Thirsk show (1850) one of £369, the profits from Driffield (1875), Sheffield (1874) and Harrogate (1873) were £2910, £4498 and £3251 respectively.[13] Some of the later features of the show were basically developments of what had been tried previously. For instance, the implements section continued to grow until the mid-1860s. After the 1851 show, at Bridlington, there would be two catalogues, one for implements (selling at 4d per copy), and the other for stock (selling 6d per copy). The size of the show by then can also be gauged from the size of the print-run of the catalogues – 1800 copies for Bridlington. The value of premiums offered for implements and machinery remained at a steady £200 between 1850 and 1866, and during these years there was a steady increase in the influence of the Implements Committee, which by 1860 was deciding upon all the premiums, for livestock as well as for implements, and was the most powerful of the several sub-committees of the Council .

Examining the show's development, we find that in 1850 an attempt was made to capitalize upon the success of the York (1848) show by setting up a new Floral and Horticultural Society expressly 'to follow the meetings' of the YAS. The idea seems to have been initiated by the former society, and the YAS Council approved, 'provided that their arrangements are of such a nature as not to interfere with the shows or business of this Society'. The YAS Council also declined to act as the council for the proposed society, and thereby it seems unwittingly to have thwarted the proposal.[14]

The YAS Council preferred, it seems, to initiate its own projects, and the 1850s did see a number of experiments with the show. For instance, there were extra livestock classes at the 1853 show at York, including, for the first time at a YAS show, an extra class for 'cattle of any breed' and a £10 premium for the best agricultural balance sheet. Subsequent shows indicate that the Society was keen to experiment with adapting the numbers of classes and premiums in keeping with each year's locality. The 1855 show at Malton, for example, boasted an extensive poultry section, with 35 classes of premiums, apparently to suit that locality's strength in poultry small-holding. The 1859 show at Hull was also poultry-proud.

A bolder experiment was the winter fat stock and poultry show at Leeds on 6–9 December 1853, which Council agreed to hold in addition to The Great Yorkshire Show that July, apparently as an attempt to tap a possible urban demand. This winter show was a smaller event than the annual show, although its premiums were worth £299 and it seems to have been well attended, especially by school children who were admitted at half-price on the last day. In fact, the experiment was not repeated – its financial result did not seem to justify the effort. As a single experiment it was notable not only as an indication of the Society's growing confidence, but also as a continuation of that founding intent to cater for urban as well as strictly farming interests. Besides, the Leeds Corporation seems to have appreciated the effort, for they subsequently footed the bill for two new categories of premium at the annual show: for flax and for wools.[15]

From the 1853 show at York, it was decided that the show proper (i.e., aside from time set aside for implement trials) should take up two full days. Almost all the previous shows had occupied only one full day for public exhibition of the whole showyard (aside from the days for working trials). And it is likely that this decision was taken simply in response to increasing public attendance and Council's realization that gate receipts could be the principal income for the Society. For the same reasons, it was resolved to hold a three-day show at York in 1862, and thereafter the show proper has remained a three-day event (although, on occasion, it has been suggested that it occupy four days).[16] This development was also caused in part by the increasing enthusiasm shown by the towns of the county who wished to host the show. Their bidding became increasingly competitive, and they indicated a preference for a longer show. Thus, for the 1853 show, the cities of Ripon and York each offered

1. £200 for a one-day Show, £300 for 2 days.
2. A 7-acre field for the Showground.
3. A 4-acre field for implements trial.
4. Horses for the implements trial.
5. Dining room for 200.
6. Rooms for the Society's meetings.[17]

Accompanying this extension of the show's duration, the value of the premiums rose steadily. At the 1854 show at Ripon the premiums and medals were worth £644 10s 0d; at the 1858 show at Northallerton they were £700; in 1862 at York, £900; in 1868 at Wetherby, £1400; in 1872 at Malton, £1530. At first, it was the Society which financed these premiums, but from 1856 onwards, outside sources became more and more significant. Thus, in December 1855 the Rotherham Local Committee donated premium monies for the new class of 'Mountain Woodland or Penistone Sheep' whilst the Leeds Flax Society again made a generous donation for flax prizes. For the 1858 show, individual members of the Council started to donate towards the schedule of premiums:

Lord Bolton (the President) gave £25 for the best implement; H.B. Pierse £20 for the best cattle of any class; W.E. Duncombe £20 for the best hunter under seven years of age; and R. Bentley £30 for the best labourer's cottage.[18] For the 1862 Show at York, H.S. Thompson offered £50 'For the best essay on the improvements which have taken place in Yorkshire farming since the formation of the YAS in the year 1837'.[19] Most of these personal donations were one-off contributions, but those made by Bentley and by Thompson reflected a wider concern within the Council. Bentley's £30 premium for labourers' housing was followed up by the Council itself in 1860, when it set up a specialist committee to manage a competition for cottages and farm buildings, the awards to be made at the 1861 RASE show at Leeds (when the YAS did not hold its own show again). The establishment of this committee is noteworthy not only because it bore testimony to the YAS's genuine concern for the farm labourer, but also because of its composition. H.S. Thompson, Shawe, and George Legard were all members, indicating their continuing, central role within the Society, as was J.D. Dent (who was to take over Thompson's posts in both the RASE and the YAS in the 1870s).

As for Thompson's prize-topic, it long had been a personal concern of his that the YAS should reach out to the ordinary farmer and help effect real progress. In the end, however, no award was made, despite the addition of a £10 Gold Medal. Only one report was submitted, and this was far from what Thompson wanted, namely 'a statement of precise facts and statistics of the progress of production and the means employed in the several districts of the County'.[20] It might be added that perhaps only Thompson himself possessed sufficient knowledge of the whole of Yorkshire agriculture, and sufficient literary talent, to produce such a report. But heavily involved as he was by the early 1860s in both the RASE and the YAS, in addition to managing his own estate at Kirby Hall, his own business interests in the North Eastern Railway Company and his activities on behalf of the United Companies Railway Association, as well as the duties of High Sherriff of Yorkshire (in 1856), he simply would not have had time. It should be added, nonetheless, that perhaps the title of the topic was insufficiently catchy to whet the interest of money-conscious farmers; for when the scheme was re-introduced in 1871 by the Secretary (who was then Thomas Parrington), modified and under the title of 'The best examples of *profitable* farming in Yorkshire', it reportedly created considerable interest.

The Society's finances grew steadily, and its surpluses were invested in the railways. In December 1852, £400 of the handsome profit from the 1852 Sheffield show was 'offered to the York and North Midland Railway Company at $3\frac{1}{2}$% for 5 years' in the names of the Society's trustees, thus bringing the total of the YAS's debentures in that company to £1200.[21] In 1857, on the expiry of the five year term, the debentures were left there and were augmented steadily during the next 18 years or so: a further £1000 in 1872,[22] another £1000 in 1875.[23] But with its rapidly increasing wealth, the Society also had to manage its finances more professionally. In 1860, indeed, certain inadequacies in its financial management were giving cause for concern, and with apparent urgency a Finance Committee was set up to conduct a preliminary investigation. At the end of 1860, this committee comprised four of the most active Council members, namely the Right Honourable Admiral Duncombe, J.D. Dent, H.S. Thompson and Basil Woodd. These men were given a brief to go into every aspect of the YAS's finances, to engage for their own purposes a professional auditor, and to make recommendations for the future.

There remains insufficient evidence from this period to say what exactly precipitated the creation of this Finance Committee, but soon it was attempting to exert a firm grip upon every aspect of the YAS's expenditure. It determined how much the Council could afford to offer in premiums for the show (a decision hitherto in the hands of the Council or the Implements Committee), and persuaded the Society's management to pass a resolution that 'no payment of the amount of £5 and upwards shall be made except by cheque on the recommendation of the Finance Committee, and all cheques shall be signed by the Chairman of the Finance Committee and the Secretary'.[24] However, it seems to have proved impossible to exert a tight enough control over the growing complexity of the Society's finances, for in 1863 or 1864 a new anxiety arose, involving the Society's Secretary in particular.

The Secretary at that time was John Hannam who, like his predecessor Milburn, apparently first attracted Council's attention by his literary contributions to the *Transactions*.[25] Hannam had been appointed in June 1854 after Milburn's sudden death. Undoubtedly he was an excellent candidate for the post, being a land agent (based at Kirk Deighton) and something of an authority on agriculture in general. The date of his appointment itself indicates his eminent suitability, for it happened to coincide with a period when Council was expressing an anxiety about the character of agricultural employees in the county.[26] In fact, immediately prior to appointing a successor to Milburn, Council enacted a new rule 'that the Secretary do give security approved by the Council to the amount of £500'. Hannam was able to pay, and was then appointed.

He appears to have done his job at least adequately until 1863. In that year however, he seems to have been late by several months in crediting the Society's bank accounts with payments from the show. Thus, it was found by the Finance Committee that 'he was retaining in his own hands on the 31st Dec. 1863 a sum of money belonging to the Society amounting to £173 15s 0d'. This did not actually amount to theft, for the Finance Committee concluded that

> they entirely acquit Mr Hannam of any defalcation in the funds of the Society, but they desire to impress on the Council the fact that he has not paid the attention he should have done, and has failed in being punctual in the payment of accounts, which is so essential to the well-being of the Society.[27]

The two principal members of the Finance Committee, Dent and Duncombe, assumed responsibility for the situation and tendered their resignations. Hannam also offered to resign and his offer was accepted without demure, but Dent and Duncombe were given a vote of confidence by Council, and stayed on.

These two men were to render a most valuable service to the Society as central policy makers and officers in the remainder of the 1860s and the 1870s: Duncombe served as President in 1865-6, and Dent in 1872-3.

Whatever blame might have been laid at Hannam's own door, the historian has to suggest that the causes of the crisis in 1864 were not entirely of Hannam's own making. First, it appears that the Finance Committee set up in 1860 had been paying almost all of its attention to items of expenditure, and insufficient attention to items of income. Second, as the Society's affairs were becoming more complex, the duties and authority of the Secretary could not keep pace with change, with the result that several aspects of mangement and finance were of nebulous allocation. Exactly what were the duties and responsibilities of the Secretary?

This question appears to have been asked by the Council when appointing the new Secretary, Thomas Parrington (from Normanby, near Middlesborough), for several new financial specifications were attached to his job-description, whilst at the same time he was given much greater responsibility. For instance, the Secretary was now to be the sole collector of subscriptions. This development – clearer duties and greater responsibility, coupled with the choice of Parrington – marked the beginning of a more professional secretariat within the YAS. Henceforth the Secretary would play a direct role in the strategy of the Society.

Parrington's influence was quickly felt. His first task was to write to the Duke of Devonshire, who had already been voted the Society's President but had not yet been informed of his election by Hannam.[28] Parrington next had to make up the defects in the Council's minutes and the Society's accounts, which had been somewhat neglected in 1863-4. He then turned his attention to the problems of the Society's membership, which had become considerable but whose seriousness had been masked by the success of the shows. By April 1865, the Society had only 479 annual members, of whom 165 were in areas of subscription. Parrington wrote to all of those in arrears with their fees and to a further 200 gentlemen of the county, inviting them to join, with conspicuous success. By July he had recruited 70 new members,[29] and by December he had been able to reduce the number in arrears to only 43, whom he recommended should be struck off the membership list.[30] Moreover, by early 1866 Parrington appears to have taken in hand much of the planning of the annual show, which now entered another phase in its development.

As has been detailed already, the show had been developing steadily during the 1850s and early 1860s, and much of the credit for this must go to those founding members who from the first had served as stewards, judges and planners. In the mid-1860s, however, a number of the old guard retired: in December 1865, Childers withdrew from Council, and Samuel Wiley resigned as 'Director of the Showyard' (a title which was not yet formally created).[31] At the same time, new figures were replacing them: Dent, Duncombe, Major Gunter, Earl Cathcart, Sir George Wombwell and William Rutson in particular. And now Parrington. These changes in personnel brought about changes in the management of the show and in the very constitution of the society, for at a Special General Meeting in December 1866, with Sir George Wombwell in the chair as President, a new set of 'Rules of the Society' was drawn up.[32] The significant differences between these new rules and the original ones were simply a greater recognition of the powers of the management committee (called 'Council' in these new Rules, 'General Committee' in the old ones), and a greater degree of attention to the show itself, reflecting its proven economic as well as ideological significance to the Society.

In December 1865, Council decided upon a new county rotation for the show, with the first round as follows:

1866 at York
1867 in the North Riding
1868 in the Northern division of the West Riding
1869 in the East Riding
1870 in the Southern division of the West Riding
and so on.

This rotation simply reflected the size and commercial wealth of the West Riding, which deserved two out of the five allocations; but it is also possible that in insisting upon York once out of five occasions the Council had in mind the large public attendance, and profit, that the city could guarantee. This five-part system remained in force until the end of the century, at which stage the Society became desperate to check the financial haemorrhage of the show, which by then was making massive losses on several occasions. (See Chapter 4).

Other decisions concerning the future of the show were taken around this time. These included the appointment in 1869 of the Society's first Veterinary Surgeon, Professor Spooner, Principal of the Royal Veterinary College in London, who was to remain in attendance throughout each show[33]; the hiring of a warehouse in York to store the Society's 'rolling stock' for the show[34]; and the abandonment of premiums for implements, which by the late 1860s had apparently outlived their usefulness for the Great Yorkshire.[35]

Thanks in part to better financial management and in part to Parrington's enthusiasm, but also reflecting the general bouyancy of agriculture, the shows in the late '60s and the first half of the '70s were eminently successful, despite several formidable difficulties. The first of these was the cattle plague or 'rinderpest' which broke out in 1865, and rapidly caused havoc in cattle markets throughout the country. Council decided that there could be no cattle at the 1866 show at York, nor in 1867 at Thirsk, yet these two shows were still remarkably successful, largely because of the attendance of the Prince and Princess of Wales at York, and the horse racing at Thirsk. The horse racing was a special part of the festivities at Thirsk that year, and the RASE followed this development with considerable interest, for the RASE's Secretary applied to Parrington 'to supply the RASE with a telegraph, the same as those used by the Society, to make known the winning numbers of Horses'.[36]

By the late 1860s, the sheer logistics of the show were becoming more formidable than ever and a system of inviting tenders from local and national contractors and suppliers to provide certain facilities began to develop under

Parrington's efficient and ever-watchful eye. Thus, for the show at Wetherby in 1868 (held on Major Gunter's estate), and for the next five shows, Parrington signed a contract with Messrs Piggot of London to supply waterproof canvas for all the shedding and stabling:

	£	s	d
3500 ft of canvas at 25 ft wide	189	11	8
1000 ft of canvas at 18 ft wide	50	0	0
Total	239	11	8

Messrs Todd and Co., of Thirsk, were contracted to supply all the showyard fittings for £450.[37] The printing of catalogues also became increasingly open to competitive tender: for Wetherby, the 5000 catalogues cost £59 10s 0d, but due to competitiveness, the cost fell to £42 10s 0d for the Harrogate show (1873). Parrington's zeal was readily rewarded by Council: in 1868, Admiral Duncombe persuaded Council to give him a hefty £50 gratuity (almost 6 months' salary), and with effect from January 1871 his salary was raised handsomely from £105 to £200 per annum.[38] Mention should also be made of the regular foreman of the showyard, Mr Thomas Kilvington, whose magnificent behind-the-scenes effort for the Thirsk show (1867) earned him a Silver Medal, and on whom the Society would rely greatly during the next 21 years.

For the 1867, '68 and '69 shows, the local committees offered remarkably generous contributions towards the cost of premiums. When the deputations from Malton, Scarborough, Thirsk and Whitby waited upon the Council at York on the Knavesmire showground, in 1866, to bid for the next location, the high-powered Thirsk deputation offered £500 for special prizes in addition to what was then the standard offer (£250 towards the Society's coffers, an adequate site, fencing, policing, etc.). This allowed the Society to offer only £397 of its own money for premiums. For the Wetherby show the following year, the prize monies offered by the local committee and other local sources were so generous that of the £1400 given away as premiums the YAS provided only £420. To cap this generosity, when the Beverley deputation waited upon Council in 1868, in rivalry with a deputation from Hull, it announced that it had already raised a local subscription of £1000 'to devote to the interests of the Society' should Beverley be chosen.[39] The show was being wooed as never before. And conspicuously, towns which are no longer centres of trade and manufacture but which were so in the mid-late nineteenth century – like Beverley – showed most enterprise and extravagance in that courtship. What is more, they did not disappoint.

The 1869 Beverley show was the most financially successful in the Society's history up until then, the total income being £2558 10s 10d, £1163 higher than at Wetherby, allowing the Society to make a profit of £700 after all payments had been made.[40] Furthermore, it seems that Beverley's success gave the Society such a boost that it initiated a greater feeling of confidence in Council with regard to the annual show. The Society now began to increase its rolling stock considerably and allocate greater sums for premiums. In mid-1871 its ready cash amounted to £2031 17s 6d in its bank account. Again, it should be emphasized that underlying this buoyancy were the scrupulousness and professionalism of Parrington.

With the disappearance of premiums for implements after the 1860s the priorities in premiums underwent several changes. Sometimes, the order of prizes reflected the priorities of the YAS Council, acting always in conjunction with the local committee. At other times, the order clearly related to the specialist interests of the host town. In this latter vein, mention has been made of the poultry premiums at Northallerton (1858) and Hull (1859). Even more conspicuous was the pre-eminence of premiums for horses at the 1872 Malton Show: out of £1530 for prize monies, a full £800 went on premiums for horses, £370 for cattle, £235 for sheep, £105 for pigs, and £10 each for wools and for shoeing smiths. The sources of this prize-money in 1872 are also noteworthy:

	£
The YAS	1030
The Malton Local Committee	105
Lord Middleton's Hunt	100
The Rt Hon. Fitzwilliam MP and James Brown Esq.	75
Scarborough Agricultural Society	35
Appleton Agricultural Society	30
Earl Fitzwilliam	25
Earl Feversham (President 1872)	30
Lord Londesborough	20
Sir Harcourt Johnstone Bart, MP	25
Town of Pickering	25
Ryedale Agricultural Society	25
Mr C.J. Russell	5

We can thus see that smaller, more localized, agricultural societies were keen to be associated with the Great Yorkshire when it was held in their locality. But during the early 1870s the local hunts were even keener. For the 1870 show at Wakefield, of the total prize monies of £1529, £282 5s 0d was donated by the Badsworth Hunt.[43] And for the tremendously successful 1871 show at York, three hunts chipped in: the 'Hunting Gentlemen of Leeds' donated £120, whilst the Master and Members of Bramham Moor Hunt and of the York and Ainsty Hunt gave 50 guineas each.[44] Going by premiums alone, the Great Yorkshire was becoming something of a hunting show.

But that was not, of course, the whole picture, for independent reports of the show (such as those in the county newspapers) testify to its overwhelming importance as an agricultural display. Even the implements section remained impressive, despite the scrapping of premiums, for although this caused fewer exhibitors to attend, those who did attend each exhibited more appliances. (See Table 3.1.)

Table 3.1: Entries of agricultural implements at YAS shows, early 1850s to early 1870s

Year	Place of show	No. of exhibitors	No. of implements
1853	York	87	650
1854	Ripon	75	600
1855	Malton	88	733
1856	Rotherham	93	707
1857	York	102	983
1858	Northallerton	94	721
1859	Hull	141	1026
1860	Pontefract	119	896
1862	York	147	1566
1863	Stockton	107	977
1864	Howden	109	996
1865	Doncaster	123	1323
1866	York	150	1885
1867	Thirsk	101	1038
1868	Wetherby	103	1200
1869	Beverley	111	1406
1870	Wakefield	107	1564
1871	York	106	1483

Despite the reduced number of entries, the implements section did not seem to suffer in quality. The 1870 show at Wakefield, for instance, had 107 stands of implements, a number of which had won awards nationally – and particularly at the RASE show. Foremost among the Yorkshire exhibitors were:

Mr A.C. Bamlett (of Thirsk) with a variety of award-winning reapers and mowers.

The Beverley Iron and Waggon Company, 'extensive exhibitors of a vast variety of implements', who were clearly first-rate innovative designers, one of whose exhibits was 'a three-horse reaping machine . . . with double self-acting or reversible swathe delivery . . . especially adapted to the Yorkshire Wolds'.

Mr Henry Bushell (of the Implement Depot, York), who alone of the principal Yorkshire suppliers was exhibiting implements by manufacturers from outside the county. This firm, established in 1858, first exhibited at The Great Yorkshire in 1863 and, apart from during the First and Second World Wars, has continued to do so ever since. They began to manufacture their own implements in the late 1870s.

Messrs W. Crosskill and Sons (of Beverley), who exhibited 'improved clod crushers, carts, . . . waggons [sic], an improved Archimedean root-crusher, a three-horse reaping machine, an improved single rollerbone mill, etc'.

Mr W. Sawney (of Beverley) who had 'as usual one of the largest collections of implements', including reapers, winnowing machines, ploughs, drills, cutters, etc.

As for exhibitors from farther afield, we are told that there were 'some of the most celebrated makers from distant parts of the country, as well as makers of traction and other engines'.[45] The names included:

> *Clayton and Shuttleworth* (of Lincoln), with portable steam engines and thrashing and finishing machines.
>
> *Messrs Ruston, Proctor and Co.*, *Messrs Foster and Co.*, and *Messrs Robey and Co.* (also of Lincoln) with steam engines, steam threshers, ploughs and other prize-appliances.
>
> *Messrs Ransome and Sons* (of Ipswich).
>
> *Messrs Hornsby and Sons*, and *Coultas* (both from Grantham) with steam-driven corn and seed drills.

The 1871 show at York was the most financially successful in the Society's history to that date, its receipts of £2870 6s 5d outstripping even those of Beverley, which had taken £2552 11s 4d. It is noteworthy that in Parrington's opinion, York's success was due largely to the facilities offered by the North Eastern Railway.[46]

We have seen (in Chapters 1 and 2) how the development of the agricultural show depended in a variety of ways upon the services provided by the railway companies. It appears that this relationship was unproblematic during the 1840s and '50s and much of the '60s, largely due, one might guess, to Thompson's business interests in the northern rail network. But occasional tensions developed between the planners of The Great Yorkshire and the railways. For instance, at the end of 1867 the Midland, the Great Northern and the Yorkshire Railway Companies withdrew their by-then standard facilities of special rates to the YAS, causing Parrington to write to them in some alarm, 'urging . . . the claims of the YAS to the same privileges as conceded to the RASE'.[47] Fortunately, there were still one or two railway entrepreneurs on the YAS Council and one of them, Robert Tennant, who was a director of the Great Northern, seems to have persuaded the companies to restore the YAS's privileges in time for the show at Wetherby.

Even so, problems still remained. The YAS Council felt that the passenger platform at the North Eastern Railway Station at Wetherby was in such a dangerous condition that it could not sustain the hordes of visitors who would descend upon the town on the days of the show. They wrote in haste to the NER, requesting repairs, which seem to have been carried out. In the last quarter of the nineteenth century the problem of unsafe railway platforms would loom large in the anxieties of the show's organisers.

But on the whole, well into the 1870s, the YAS had abundant reason to be grateful to the railway companies who, sometimes with a little prompting, continued to arrange special trains, lay down sidings and offer discounted prices for passengers, livestock and implements going to and from the show. For the 1872 show at Malton, for example, Parrington was able to secure the cooperation of no less than six railway companies: the North Eastern, the Great

Northern, the Midland, the Lancashire and Yorkshire, the London and North Western, and the Manchester, Sheffield and Lincolnshire Railway Companies. For the 1873 show at Harrogate, Parrington persuaded the railway authorities to construct a special siding close to the showyard on The Stray which undoubtedly helped towards making this first Harrogate show a record-breaking event – which in turn laid the foundation for the tremendous tradition of warmth and mutual gratitude maintained between the borough of Harrogate and the YAS, culminating in 1949 in the location of The Great Yorkshire's permanent showyard at Harrogate.

Rounding off this account of the YAS show during the Society's 'Golden Age', the 1873 and '74 shows added to the feeling within the Council that The Great Yorkshire was the goose which laid the Society's golden eggs. The 1873 Harrogate show was 'the most successful and attractive ever held by the Society' until then, with almost 39,000 members of the public paying for admission, and receipts from exhibition fees, gate money, grandstand seats, catalogues, and rental of refreshment booths totalling £3251 17s 0d (£400 more than at York the previous year). Expenditue, on the other hand, also reached a record high of £1709 8s 9d (£220 more than at York).[48] Impressive as was Harrogate's performance for a non-industrial, relatively small town, Sheffield's performance for the 1874 show was dazzling. Again, it was the most financially successful to date, with 64,000 members of the public paying for admission and total receipts soaring to £4498 15s 1d (£1246 18s 1d more than at Harrogate). Expenses were also up, at £3798 16s 3d (£547 more than Harrogate), but there was still a most handsome profit to be made.[49]

Apparently in the belief that the show was inherently successful and that greater expenditure on the show would bring an even greater profit, the Council became ever more ambitious in its financial commitments. It allocated a record £1485 to the premiums for the 1875 Show at Driffield; £600 was donated by the Driffield local commitee, and £15 by the butchers of Hull, bringing the total value of premiums to the unprecedented height of £2100. On this occasion, however, the Council's calculations were misguided. For whilst plenty of exhibitors came, far fewer members of the public attended, so the gate money taken was a hefty £1585 less than at Sheffield. And since expenditure was up yet again, £378 5s 8d above Sheffield's expenses, the show incurred a loss of £1264 1s 8d.[50] Hardly a mortal blow, but it did mark the end of a period of almost untarnished optimism for the show. By late 1877 the Society would actually be running an overdraft to keep its show afloat.

There remain two topics to discuss before closing this chapter of the YAS's history. First, its key policy-makers and managers. Second, the revival of its chemical programme.

As H.S. Thompson became more deeply involved in the RASE, less of his time could be spent as a manager of the YAS. Nonetheless, he retained virtually all his sub-committee seats until the mid-'60s and frequently attended meetings of the Council, even chairing some of its most difficult sessions, such as the special meeting called to consider the final report on the financial irregularities of 1863–

4.[51] He was in harness again as a member of the local committee for the 1866 show at York; he attended a few Council meetings in 1867 and 1868, and chaired the AGM in December '68, before disappearing from view for a couple of years as he wound up his activities in the RASE, returning to active participation in the YAS Council in 1871. Then he was at last content to let others manage without his guiding hand.

Perhaps because of the diversion of Thompson's attention towards the RASE in the 1850s and '60s, the YAS's chemical concern lapsed to a considerable extent. Spence, then Spence and Holden, and then Holden alone (after Spence's death) continued to function as the Society's analytical chemists until the mid-'60s, when the need for them seems to have petered out. At the same time, the scientific content of the *Transactions* declined, as did the journal itself. (See Appendix C.) Thompson clearly, and rightly, believed that the cause of English agricultural chemistry and the battle against Leibig could be forwarded most effectively through the *JRASE*, and as that journal's committee chairman he pursued a determined course alongside Lawes and Gilbert. (See Appendix D for a selection of Thompson's correspondence with Lawes and Gilbert, from the Rothamsted Archives.)

The YAS's interest in agricultural chemistry was resuscitated in 1871, precisely the year when Thompson again began to attend meetings of the YAS Council on a regular basis, as well as to sit on various sub-committees. It is tempting to suggest that Thompson was behind this resurgence. Whilst this is likely, the figure who put this policy to the Council, and showed the most concern for its outcome, was Thomspon's close friend and colleague, in the RASE as well as in the YAS, John Dent Dent. In April 1871, on the advice of Professor Voelcker, then the consulting chemist for both the RASE and the BWES, the YAS Council resolved to pay a retainer of ten guineas per annum to an analytical chemist in Leeds, Mr Alfred Sibson, 'provided he will furnish analyses of manures etc., to members of the Society, in the same manner and on the same terms as the RAS now pay to Professor Voelcker'.[52] In December of that year, however, feeling that a mere retainer would not be adequate, Dent persuaded Council to advertize for 'a duly qualified Consulting Chemist for the members of the Society'[53] and a Chemical Committee was set up to effect this move.

In January 1872 this committee selected Thomas Fairley of Leeds, on a salary of 100 guineas per annum, to conduct analyses for YAS members, to provide a quarterly report on his work, to attend the meetings of the Chemical Committee, and 'to attend at the Secretary's office in York every Cattle Fair Thursday'. The Council immediately appointed him.[54] His work so steadily impressed them that from October 1873 onwards he regularly presented his quarterly report in person at Council meetings, becoming virtually a *de facto* Council member. His first report to the Council amply confirmed the need for his services, for he presented evidence of the danger of adulterating feedstuffs. Linseed cake that had been analysed was 'very inferior, containing much starchy matter, seeds, chaff, and probably other refuse materials', while cotton cake contained '50% of husk and cotton wool' which 'would be likely to cause serious mechanical obstruction in the digestion of any animal using it as food'.[55]

For a period of 47 years, until his death in 1919, Fairley provided YAS members with analyses of a wide variety of feedstuffs, manures and waters, the reports on which would regularly be printed in the *Transactions*. He showed that many manures were being sold at prices far above their real value[56]; that many river-waters were unfit for drinking[57]; that farmers should insist on having the contents of feeds and manures specified on their receipts; and so on.

As the revitalized scientific programme got underway, as the show expanded, and as the Society's assets (debentures, rolling stock, cash account and various paraphenalia) grew, the YAS needed a more spacious and permanent office. Parrington's own house in York, which since April 1869 had served for Council meetings and all other business, now proved inadequate. So, in March 1873 a contract was signed with a Mr Manby in York to rent his rooms at £45 per annum (of which Parrington had to pay £15 and Fairley £5). While this provided better working facilities, it did not, of course, reduce the work-load, of Parrington in particular. By October 1875, that load had become so heavy that Parrington tendered his resignation. He agreed to stay, however, when, on the initiative of the Finance Committee and Dent, a Mr Marshall Stephenson was appointed as Assistant Secretary (at £100 per annum). It was fortunate that the Council managed to retain Parrington, for the next few years were going to be a rough passage for the Society as British agriculture entered its most prolonged period of depression since the eighteenth century.

We cannot leave this phase of the development of the YAS without trying to recapture some of the atmosphere of its Show. We might take a relatively unexceptional example, the 1860 event at Pontefract, and see what the *Yorkshire Gazette* made of it:

Wednesday, August 1
The First Great Show Day

The attendance of visitors at the implement yard yesterday was limited, but this morning the trains from various parts, and omnibuses, cabs and numerous other vehicles brought large numbers of persons to Pontefract. The town from an early hour presented a scene of gaiety and rejoicing, the streets generally being festooned right across with garlands of flowers and evergreens, and from the windows of the houses were suspended flags and banners of all descriptions. . . .

In the first place we will speak of the implement yard, which was of course open to the public, and great interest was manifestly felt by the visitors who inspected the vast array of agricultural mechanism which invited their attention on every hand. There was a continual noise kept up in this department throughout the day. The steam engines were at work puffing and blowing away, and the thrashing machines were in full operation displaying their useful capacities, their monotonous buz and hum falling not very pleasantly upon the ear without a moment's cessation. The turnip and straw cutters *ad infinitum* were worked from time to time . . . and other implements had their use practically tested by being put in motion.

But the most attractive object in the implement field was the gigantic and powerful brick moulding and pressing machine of Messrs Bradley and Craven, of Wakefield, which was at work today and attracted crowds of spectators. . . .

The display of short-horned cattle next claims our attention. . . . The bulls of any age, seven in number, were a fine lot and when they were brought into the ring to undergo the ordeal of the judges, their symmetrical proportions were seen to advantage by the visitors who stood around the circle. . . . In the class for yearling-bulls there was a spirited competition, entries numbering thirteen. They were a magnificent group of young beasts, and all, as far as we can judge, seemed worthy of receiving the prizes offered by the society. . . . It is worthy of remark that the yearling bull which obtained a prize at the Royal Society's meeting at Canterbury did not succeed in gaining a premium at this Show; and the animal which carried off the third premium at the Royal Show came in first on the present occasion. The ten bull calves exhibited were of good breed and in fine condition. . . . The cow and heifer classes were of a superior description, and fully sustained the reputation of Yorkshire for cattle breeding.

In sheep, the traits of fine blood and quality were discernible in every class. The shearling rams numbered twenty-four, certainly a large entry, and the competition for the prizes was most severe indeed. The successful exhibitors in this class were Mr S. Wiley, of Brandsby, near York; and Mr J. Borton, of Malton. . . .

We next come to the pigs, which were in the primest condition possible, the boars and sows of the large breed fully justifying the truth of the name applied to them,* for they were really of gigantic growth; and with respect to the porcine tribe as a whole brought together on the show ground they could not be excelled.

A most important feature of the exhibition was the horses. The stallions, roadsters, coaches, hunters, and also agricultural horses were of the first class description, and . . . suffice it to say that the exhibition of the equine species was of the first class description. There was a large amount of competition in many of the classes, there being 15 entries for stallion for hunters, 16 for stallion for roadsters, 16 for stallion for farming purposes, and other classes were contested with the same degree of severity.

The special prizes offered by the Earl of Harewood and Lord Wenlock for hunters, were competed for by a numerous lot of horses in each case. . . .

The poultry pens were not occupied by birds equal in quality to 1859. The Hull show in this respect excelled the Pontefract. Nevertheless, there were in many of the classes good specimens of several kinds of the feathered tribe.

The show of fox-hounds was by no means an unimportant section of the exhibition. . . . Finer fox-hounds could not be produced for they constituted the cream, so to speak, of all the celebrated packs of hounds in Yorkshire and other parts of the country.[58]

As for the business and other social meetings held during this show, there was the Council Meeting at 11.00 a.m. on the Wednesday in the Sessions House,

---

* The pigs were divided into three classes: 'large breed', 'small breed', and 'any breed'.

followed immediately by the AGM. At 5.00 p.m. the Great Dinner began, attended by members of the YAS, several of the more eminent visitors to the show, and 'the leading inhabitants of Pontefract'. This was held in the commodious New Market Hall which was decorated with flowers and evergreens and sported a large banner inscribed 'Success to the Yorkshire Agricultural Society'. Adding to the colour, and perhaps *only* to add to it, we are told that 'a large number of ladies were admitted to the gallery which runs around the hall, to witness the dinner and to hear the speeches delivered afterwards'. Between 200 and 300 gentlemen were 'assembled at the festive board, which was plenteously provided with the choicest viands in season supplied by Mr Dunhill, of the Red Lion Hotel'. The Saltaire Brass Band played from the gallery. The usual loyal toast of 'The Queen' and 'The Prince Consort and the rest of the Royal Family' were drunk 'with enthusiasm'; the President proposed the health of 'The Army and the Navy' and then of the YAS, to which H.S. Thompson responded 'on behalf of the committee of management' with a punchy speech defending the working trial and premiums for implements. (It might be remembered that this was the year when some of the country's leading implement manufacturers had protested by not exhibiting their implements at the RASE show.) There were further speeches and applauses, and hugely popular jokes about politics, as well as further toasts, among which were 'The labouring classes' and 'The ladies'. Of course, since ladies were not fomally part of the company, a gallant gentleman had to respond on their behalf!

As if all this bustle and festivity on the first day of the show were not enough, the second day was actually 'the day for the million' when 'crowds of people presented themselves at the entrance to the show-field, from the hour of opening, eight o'clock, up to between two and three in the afternoon, when a vast concourse of persons was assembled'. On this occasion the rain kept off, so 'the company were enabled to promenade' to their hearts' content through the showground, stopping perhaps to marvel at the implement field, which was alive with pulsing, chattering machines of all sorts, or to admire the white and green rosetted prize beasts, or to watch the horse-judging, which was apparently a great attraction. And if one tired of all this, there were choice specimens of the human species for the public to look out for: the noblemen, clergy and gentlemen of the county – the Earls Cathcart and Harewood, the Lords Galway, Herries, Middleton and Wenlock, most members of the Council, and Reverends galore. An attendance of nearly 20,000 persons on the two public days of the show was certainly an adequate reason for satisfaction.

Finally, we might examine the YAS's relationships with other agricultural societies during this third quarter of the nineteenth centry. With the RASE, the YAS continued to enjoy an intimate relationship, largely because there was still a very substantial overlap between their Councils and sub-committees. Men like Thompson, Cathcart, Dent and George Lane Fox were key policy-makers within both, and we may be sure that behind the scenes there continued to be a free interchange of ideas and information between the two societies. Whilst the RASE had easily outstripped the YAS in size of membership and scale of impact, the YAS's early contributions to the RASE's development, and the continuing quality of its own efforts, were not forgotten. As the reporter of the YAS Show at York, 1871, put it:

> These societies are the two great generals that command the agricultural army of this country, the vast number of district and local societies being the colonels and other officers, who take a prominent part in such an army in its constant and perservering warfare against sterility and unproductiveness, and against anti-quated and exploded systems of husbandry.[59]

With its 'colonels and other officers' (i.e. the other agricultural societies of Yorkshire) the YAS also seems to have developed excellent relationships, as is evidenced by those societies' frequent donations to the premiums at The Great Yorkshire. We also know that several Council members in the YAS were prominent in some of those societies – Thompson in the Cleveland Agricultural Society, and Denison, the Legards and R.F. Shawe in the East Riding Agricultural Association.[60]

Surprisingly, there was one society with which the YAS actually acquired a hostile relationship during this period, namely the Highland. The two societies first clashed over the date of the YAS show, which by the 1850s seems to have drawn potential exhibitors away from the HASS's own event. In December 1853 the HASS wrote to the YAS Council asking them to hold their forthcoming show (at Ripon) on a date other than the first week in August, since the HASS Show had been fixed for the same week (at Berwick). The YAS Council refused to budge, arguing that the first week in August was stipulated immutably in its 'Rules and Regulations'.[61]

In December 1856, the HASS complained more strongly about the YAS's event falling in the same week as their's. Once again, the Council adamantly refused to change the date since it was immutably 'a fundamental Rule of the Society which declares that such Show shall be held in each year on the first Wednesday in August'.[62] Then, in August 1859 the YAS took the offensive, sending a memorandum to the HASS urging them to change the date of their show, and so to put an end to the annoyance.[63] The HASS was not amused. Eight years later, however, they seemed willing to compromise, since in December 1867 their Secretary informed the YAS that his society had changed the date of its show to the last week in July, in order to avoid clashing with the YAS event that year at Howden.[64]

This was not the end of the matter, however, for in 1873 a letter was received from the HASS informing the YAS Council that its show at Stirling would be on the same days as the YAS's at Harrogate. The Council coolly decided 'not to notice the communication', and it appears that the two societies were scarcely on speaking terms for a number of years thereafter. One wonders whether the clash of dates was the actual reason for this animosity or whether there was a deeper cause, for it was somewhat specious of the YAS to say that its date was unchangable. It was not. For example, in late June 1866 when it was suddenly learned that the Prince and Princess of Wales were due in York during the second week of August, Council (or rather, the six members present – probably not even the quorum) unhesitatingly altered the dates of the show accordingly, thus unflinchingly violating their 'immutable' rules.[65]

It is not unlikely that a general cause of this unease between the YAS and the HASS was the challenge that a highly successful Great Yorkshire Show posed to the HASS, which, undoubtedly, saw itself as *the* agricultural society of the North. Inevitably, if only unspokenly, there was some rivalry. And more particularly, at the very period when the YAS show was going from strength to strength, the Highland Show was returning losses, and its directors were wondering whether it would be better not to hold their event annually, but rather triennially. In fact, between 1848 and 1856 it was held biannually.[66] The Highland's anxiety about the proximity and success of The Great Yorkshire is therefore understandable. The Yorkshire Agricultural Society had matured most powerfully.

4 THE CHALLENGES OF DEPRESSION, 1870–1914

The great depression which hit British agriculture for twenty or more years after the mid-1870s has been variously attributed to a worldwide upheaval in prices, mainly brought about by changes in the supply of gold in relation to monetary demand, to the eventual repercussion of the repeal of the Corn Laws in the 1840s, and to a culmination of all those technical changes in manufacture and transport called The Industrial Revolution.[1] There were also causal factors arising out of the geography and climate of the British Isles.[2]

Whatever the precise timing and character of this depression, and it is open to a variety of interpretations, there is little doubt about its basic features and causes. To take the weather, the autumn of 1875 was unusually damp, and was followed by abnormally heavy rainfall in the winter of 1876–7; this led into a stretch of two and a half years of exceptionally wet weather and below average temperatures. The winter of 1878–9 was disastrously cold, the following winter scarcely better, with the result that there were heavy losses of hill sheep. In turn, this caused maximal inconvenience elsewhere, for the run of wet seasons from 1878 to 1882 brought a nationwide epidemic of sheep rot on almost all arable and grassland farms in low-lying areas. Livestock was further depleted by the ravages of foot-and-mouth in 1881–3.[3]

When better seasons began in 1883 most farmers, and even the arable heavy-land farmers, would ordinarily have been able to recover. But not so in this case, for by the early '80s grain prices had fallen so drastically that radical transformations were required. Before 1860, wheat prices had fluctuated widely, largely because of the highly variable home production, but during the '60s and '70s these fluctuations diminished as the rising tide of imports reduced the variability of total grain supplies. Wheat prices fell and, perhaps more importantly for the overall distribution of grain production, wheat prices rose less in years of low yields after 1866. In the late '70s, though, wheat prices stabilized generally (with one abrupt rise in 1877) whilst the prices of barley and oats fell, so that wheat was still the most profitable grain crop and seemed to remain so as the run of wet seasons came to an end in 1882.

In that year wheat prices averaged 45s per quarter. But then they fell – to 30s per quarter in 1889 and 24s in 1894. At this last level, wheat was actually below the price of barley, and only 6s per quarter higher than oats, instead of being higher than barley and more than 20s above oats, as was usual.

In short, between 1875 and 1882 a combination of appalling weather and falling prices curtailed the profits of the farmer; from 1882, the fall in the price of wheat prevented many farmers from staging a recovery. The difficulty of this second period was exacerbated by a fall in the prices of meat, livestock and dairy produce, which began in 1883 and lasted into the mid-'90s. Again, this fall was largely caused by the rising tide of imports from Russia, the Danubian belt, India, Denmark, North and South America, Australia and New Zealand. British farming was in a state of siege. British farmers were beginning to realize, by the mid-'80s, that the depression was not a transitory phenomenon but a structural one, and agricultural bankruptcy rapidly increased.[4]

The larger agricultural societies, as well as associations impinging only indirectly upon the agricultural industry, took heed of a number of the difficulties facing ordinary farmers and undertook significant collaboration with the government as it became increasingly apparent that nothing short of nationally concerted action could be effective. Additionally, the government itself shed the early- to mid-Victorian ideology of *laissez-faire* and actively sought to direct the fortunes of agriculture. This it did through provision of agricultural training and education, most notably at tertiary level; though the establishment, in 1889, of the second Board of Agriculture (the first Board having been disbanded in 1815); and through consultation with the agricultural societies in an attempt to discern grass-root needs within the farming community.

Many of the developments within the YAS during this period can be understood only within this context. For example, the enormous financial losses incurred by some of the shows (those of 1876, '78, '87, '92, and '94 in particular) have to be attributed very largely to the generally depressed agricultural economy. Equally, the overtures that were made to the YAS Council for financial support of agricultural training and education (to which Council responded remarkably parsimoniously) have to be seen within the context of national educational efforts.

Of course, there were also many features of the YAS's development which were more or less autonomous, depending upon the personal dedication and managerial competence of its Presidents, its inner Council members, its Secretaries, its show stewards and others. At times, these men also made mistakes, and occasionally even jeopardized the existence of the show, bringing the Society to the verge of bankruptcy. This is not to blame them for incompetence, as the times were extremely difficult. But, as we shall see, the dynamics of a great agricultural show had changed significantly since the first half of the nineteenth century, and thus a new mechanism, both fiscal and physical, was needed for the show.

The analysis in this chapter falls into two chronological portions: 1876–1900, and 1900 to the outbreak of the First World War. The break at 1900 is not simply due to the change of century. Indeed, as the next chapter will suggest, there are solid reasons for saying that the twentieth century did not really mark its own character, for Britain at least, until 1919, and that the nineteenth century ended only in the embers of the war. Rather, 1900 is the punctuation mark of this chapter because it was the end of a stage in the development of the Society and the Show, for reasons which were internal to the YAS itself. Around 1900 there were deep financial, structural and personnel changes within the YAS, which did not so much alter its character as enable it to weather the further difficulties up until the war years.

At the beginning of 1876 the Society suffered its worst financial blow since its foundation, finishing some £1000 poorer than it had been at the beginning of 1875. This drop was entirely due to the low gate-money taken at the 1875 show, its higher than usual costs, the large amount that the Society itself had paid in premiums (£1485, compared with £1276 at the 1874 show and £1195 in 1873), and the purchase of more permanent rolling stock (such as turnstiles). Nonetheless, the YAS Council, guided by the powerful Finance Committee and encouraged by the local committee, planned ambitiously for the next show, at Skipton. £1400 came out of the Society's own coffers towards premiums, and for the first time in the show's history, an extra allocation was made for music in the showground, with £100 being paid to engage a military band.[5]

Unfortunately, it rained on all three days of the Skipton show, rendering it a financial disaster. The total income from it reached only £2616 (compared with £2911 at Driffield and £4419 at Sheffield), and the Society was obliged to take out an overdraft at the end of the year to make ends meet, preferring not to realize any of its railway investments. Drastic as this step was, Council showed no excessive anxiety, and the Finance Committee retained its confidence and freedom.[6]

The show would be planned as usual, particularly as the next one was to be at York where, barring the whim of God or Gladstone, a profit was sure. So indeed it was, despite some anxiety over rinderpest, for at the Knavesmire site at York the Society could count on a number of permanent facilities, reducing the cost of setting up the show, and a large paying public. Indeed this ninth YAS show at York could have returned a handsome profit, with income up at £3586 and expenditure on the site itself down to £2030.[7] On the other hand, other expenses were still high, chief of these being the Society's own payment of £1476 towards the premiums. Consequently, the year 1877 registered a profit to the Society of only £58 3s 2d, insufficient to reduce its overdraft.

On this slightly sombre note, Parrington again announced his wish to resign in order to have more time for his own business interests. With great regret, Council this time had to accept his resignation. Although there is no doubt that Parrington had contributed enormously to the development of the Society and the show since taking office thirteen years previously, the change in personnel seems to have provided the YAS Council with an opportunity to embark on a new course.

To begin with, Parrington's successor, Stephenson (who had been Assistant-Secretary), quickly followed Parrington's precedent by taking a series of initiatives: to recruit more members, to have arrears better paid, etc.. Secondly, presumably to fill the gap in the management of the show caused by Parrington's departure, it was now proposed, by the long-serving member of

Council, Mr T.C. Booth, that an 'Honorary Director of the YAS's Shows' should be appointed. This proposal, incidentally, was seconded by H.S. Thompson's relative and successor on the Council, Captain Childers Thompson. A committee was then set up, to work on the idea and to review all other features of the show.[8] Within a fortnight this committee was making what could have turned out to be a most fruitful recommendation for the fortunes of the Society: that the post of Honorary Show Director should be created, and that it should first be offered to the Earl of Cathcart and, in the event of his declining it, to Admiral Duncombe.[9] The Council immediately accepted the recommendation, and there was now a clear opportunity to bring the show under closer management. This was not to happen, however, for Cathcart declined and so it seems did Duncombe. Cathcart's reasons probably related to his heavy commitments in the RASE, but Duncombe's cannot be discerned, and it is rather puzzling that he did not take on this extra duty since he did continue to play a central role in the Society's management until the later '80s.

Since neither nominee would serve as Honorary Show Director, the ultimate responsibility for the finances and preparation of the show remained with the Council and the Finance Committee, whilst the immediate task of ensuring each Show's smooth running lay with the local committees and the stewards, who were now eight in number – two for cattle, two for sheep and pigs, and two for horses and implements.[10] Undoubtedly, this system was perfect for the actual running of the show, and the 1878 event at Northallerton (the third to be held there) turned out to be 'one of the most successful Exhibitions of Stock and Implements ever held by the Society', as Stephenson reported. But things were still far from happy with regard to its overall financial strategy, for to meet the loss on Northallerton the Society had to increase its overdraft.[11] Two committees were now set up to review the problem; one to see what might be done in the implements section to reduce its cost, and the other to review the cost of showyard construction.

In October of that year Stephenson submitted a detailed report on the show, and the second of the two committees recommended that 'the Society take the fitting up of the Show Yard into their own hands, and that Mr Thos Kilvington, the yard foreman, be appointed as Clerk of Works at a salary of £100 a year from Jan. 1, 1879'.[12] This was undoubtedly a wise decision, keenly endorsed at the Annual Meeting of the Council in December. Besides, Kilvington's promotion was simply a recognition of his sterling service during the past thirteen years. Even without these changes, however, the next show would probably have been a financial success, for it was held at Leeds where a strong display of implements and a large public attendance could be guaranteed. So, with ample optimism, the Leeds show was planned on a grand scale. The Society offered £1340 towards the premiums (the Leeds Local Committee offering £750); three military bands were engaged to provide music throughout all three days – the 4th Royal Irish Dragoons, the 21st Hussars, and the 1st West Yorkshire Artillery; extra facilities for refreshments were also arranged. One minor hiccup, the failure of the Society's bankers, Messrs Swann, Clough and

Co., did not deflect the Council from its planning, and at the end of the day all turned out well with a record public attendance of 53,000, the largest profit in the show's history till then, and the temporary curbing of the cost of setting up the showyard. (See Table 4.1.)

Table 4.1: Show income and expenditure (excluding costs of premiums) 1875–80.

	Driffield 1875	Skipton 1876	York 1877	Northallerton 1878	Leeds 1879	Barnsley 1880
Income	£2911	2616	3586	3069	5049	3324
Expenditure	£2593	2108	2030	2414	2013	1742

This was all in spite of 'the widespread depression which had alike effected [*sic*] in a greater or less degree every interest in the country', and the boisterous weather.[13] This Leeds show put the Society back in the black by about £200 at the end of the year. It would not be the last time when Leeds would come to the Society's rescue.

The next shows, from 1880 to 1884, were at Barnsley, Hull, Halifax and Ripon, although there was no Great Yorkshire Show in 1883 because of the RASE Show at York that summer. These were financially as well as agriculturally successful, testifying to the wisdom of taking in hand the task of setting up the showyard and establishing a new committee in October 1879 – the Showyard Sites Committee. This came into existence when it was realized that the site offered by Rotherham for the show in 1880 was not at all suitable. The location had to be switched to Barnsley, and the new committee was created to inspect all sites offered for future shows before the Council would sign any contracts with potential host-towns.

The new committee turned out to be hard-working and invaluable, and by 1882 its composition accurately revealed the inner core of management within the Society: Lord Auckland, Admiral Duncombe, the Rt Hon. G.E. Lascelles, and Messrs John Dent, Basil Woodd and Charles Clay. Already, in 1880, this committee was actually determining where to hold the show; Council no longer selected the location merely on the criteria of who was offering the most in prize-monies and hospitality.[14]

The excellent preparation for the show, coupled with the remarkable assiduity and dedication of the Society's management core and the tremendous competence of Kilvington and Stephenson, prepared the Great Yorkshire to prosper greatly during the remainder of the century. Premium-monies rose by about 13 percent between the average for the 1880s and that for the 1890s, although these figures do not include a remarkable burst of extravagance in 1890–92 when the values of the premiums were £2940, £3190 and £3065 (at Harrogate, Bradford and Middlesborough shows).

Even more significant than the actual monies was the expansion in the number of classes for exhibition and awards. At the Ripon show (1884) dairy-produce premiums were introduced. Slightly later, bee-keeping was brought into the system, and suddenly, at the Hull show (1889), the livestock classes mushroomed. Since the first show, the only cattle class was usually for Shorthorns, with only two (or occasionally three) sheep classes. Now, at Hull, there were three classes for cattle: Shorthorns, Jerseys, and 'Polled Aberdeen or Angus'; four for sheep: Leicester, Lincoln, Shropshire Downs, and Mountain; the usual number for horses – Thoroughbreds and Hunters, Hackneys and Harness, Agricultural, and Coaching; one class for pigs; as well as classes for butter and cheese and bee appliances. Henceforth, there would always be a larger number of classes for livestock than in the show's first 50 years, reflecting livestock developments outside the county and the loss of the region's hegemony in Shorthorns. This brought in top breeders who might not otherwise have exhibited at The Great Yorkshire – particularly those of Aberdeen Angus from across the border.

Qualitatively, in terms of the exhibitors of implements and livestock, and in terms of social atmosphere, the show continued to be unfailingly successful. Again, we might turn to the *Yorkshire Gazette* to catch the flavour of it, in the rhetoric of the day. This time, we might take a new and risky location for the show – Middlesborough, in 1872. The *Gazette*'s reporter writes:

The iron town of mushroom growth has this week given a hearty welcome to the Yorkshire Agricultural Society, whose annual show was held on Wednesday, Thursday and Friday. The site of the show was within the mile from the station along Marton road . . . and the ground occupied measured 35 acres. The ground was easy of approach from the town by several spacious thoroughfares. The principal route was gaily decorated with bunting so that one might have supposed that Royalty was being honoured. Middlesborough, which is handsomely built, presented a festive appearance during the show days, its wide streets and roads being thronged with people. . . .

On entering the show ground you soon realised the plan which had been adopted in arranging the departments. . . . The machinery in motion, the implements, carriages and miscellaneous exhibits were brought under notice from the principal avenue, following the course of which to the right the horses in stalls, the rings for judging horses, the cattle, sheep, and pigs were reached. It was soon apparent that the secretary to the society, Mr Marshall Stephenson, had made the completest arrangements in every direction which the site would admit of. . . . There were 1138 entries of live stock, the largest total, with the exception of the record number at Harrogate, 1238 in 1890, since the first show in 1838, when a humble display of 301 was regarded as a good start. . . . Of the £3065 contributed in prizes, £2022 was given by the Society, £928 by the Middlesborough and District Local Committee, £60 by the Cleveland Agricultural Society, £45 by the Aberdeen Angus Breeders, and £10 by the Leyburn Market Club. Two gold medals were also offered by the Polled Cattle Society. . . .

The amount offered in prizes for cattle was £48 less than last year, when £668 was given. Short horns got £385 as before, and they made an average show; the champion awards for Jerseys were withdrawn, and there was a falling off in the quality, but this was counterbalanced by an improvement in Aberdeen-Angus cattle, which constituted the finest collection ever seen in Yorkshire. Two champion prizes, five firsts, four seconds, and three thirds are kept in the county. Of these, Yorkshire shorthorn men retain one champion, one first, two seconds, and three thirds. The champion bull is the Earl of Feversham's 'New Year's Gift', which his lordship purchased from the Queen at the Windsor sale in March last year for a thousand guineas. . . . The Aberdeen-Angus cattle were an exceptionally fine lot. . . The Scotch breeders made a special effort to distinguish themselves. Many of the winners at the Highland and Aberdeen exhibitions were present, and the bulk of the prize money goes across the border. . . . There was a marvellous exhibition of horses. Hunters, hacks, coaching, and heavy horses were all in great force, and nearly all the great winners of the present and past few seasons were present. A large proportion of the principal prizes are retained in Yorkshire or are awarded to horses bred in the county. . . . Here [in yearlings particularly] the Prince of Wales, Burdett-Coutts, the Earl of Londesborough, and numerous other skilled breeders were to the fore. . . . There was a magnificent show of Cleveland coaching stallions, three year old and upwards. Mr. Burdett-Coutts once more brought out his famous coaching horse, Sultan, and the first prize Cleveland brood mare with foal was Mr. George Barker's Beauty . . . who took Lord Feversham's prize a week previously at the Cleveland Society's show at Gainsborough. . . . The Wensleydale Long-wools were the best section of the sheep exhibits. They ran up to 51 entries, and there were no two opinions about it being the best collection ever brought together.[15]

The country-wide composition of the exhibitors, and the general reputation of the show, were also evinced by the provenance of the judges, who came from all over Britain except the southern counties of England: from Cambridgeshire, Dumbartonshire, Leicestershire, Monmouth, Nottinghamshire, Shropshire, Staffordshire, Surrey, and, of course, Yorkshire. The implements section was likewise diverse, with the large stand of Messrs Henry Bushell and Sons providing, as usual, 'a large and interesting display of agricultural implements', both of their own and others' manufacture. This year, they were displaying the 'McCormack light steel self-binding harvester', their own Farmers' Stone Mill which was in use throughout Britain for grinding all sorts of grain, a Hornsby two-horse self-binder, and a variety of other new designs in reapers, horse rakes, churns, cream separators, ploughs, weighing machines, chaff cutters, and pulpers. One notable ommission from this report of the implements section, however, is W. Crosskill and Sons of Beverley. Indeed, it was evident that as the large, heavy-engineering towns in the county were developing, a number of the long-established agricultural manufacturing centres (like Beverley and Malton) were becoming less competitive and were therefore losing out.

Finally, on the subject of this show at Middlesborough, it may be noted that the top Shorthorn premium went to the Earl of Feversham, of Duncombe Park, Helmsley, who was already one of the mainstays of the YAS and later became a central figure in its management.

There are two general comments to be made about the YAS's shows during the period from 1884 to the 1890s. First, their general excellence in terms of quality of implements and of livestock seems to have been the main cause of the general increase in the Society's membership. This was felt especially after the more conspicuously successful shows, such as those at Harrogate (1890) and at Bradford (1891) when membership rose by 11 percent on each occasion, just topping 1000 after the latter, for the first time since 1839.

Second, there again was no correlation between a show's quality and its financial success, with some of the most excellent shows being the most disappointing financially. For instance, the show at Sheffield (1886) was felt to be one of the most interesting in the Society's history, yet its income was unexpectedly low, due, it was felt by the Council, to the general agricultural depression.[16] Again, the show at York (1887), which was the celebration of the YAS's 50th anniversary and 'would always be remembered for bringing the finest Exhibition ever held by the County Society' held on 'one of the finest sites in England and favoured with the most brilliant weather', turned out to be one of the most disastrous financially. The reasons are easy to identify in hindsight: heavy contribution (£2010) from the Society's own coffers to the premiums; and a meagre financial contribution from the local fund, coupled with low turnstile receipts – both attributable again to the depression; and the high cost of setting up the showyard.[17]

Then, starting in 1890, a new factor entered into the financial formula of the show, which was to plague it for the next fourteen years: the sale of the showyard timber. Until that time, the Society's strategy of seeing to the construction of the showyard under the skilful hand of Kilvington proved to be generally successful. Indeed, at the end of 1889, Kilvington was awarded a 25 percent rise in salary, plus a £25 bonus, for his work on the Hull show that year.[18] After the Harrogate show in 1890, when it came to selling off the vast amount of timber that had been purchased to erect the showyard, the Society found itself in unexpected trouble. Due to the general depression in trade, timber prices had slumped. Instead of losing about 15 percent on the purchase price, which had been the average loss during the 1880s, it now lost over 30 percent, entailing an unexpected drop in profitability of over £500. And so one of the most excellent shows, with a public attendance of some 60,000, showed a profit of a mere £150![19]

Throughout the 1890s and into the 1900s this situation simply had to be endured. The Bradford show (1891) repeated the over 30 percent loss on timber, its profit thus being reduced from about £1500 to £800. The Middlesborough show (1892) suffered a 38 percent loss on its timber, or about £1000. The next two suffered on the same percentage level, and the 1895 show at Halifax endured a massive 44 percent loss, of over £1200. The impact of such losses upon the Society can be gauged from the fact that the total annual income during this period was averaging £6000–7000, and in 1894 it was obliged to dispose of some of its debentures in the North Eastern Railways Company to meet its expenses.[20]

Making matters worse, several of the shows suffered from poor weather.

Moreover, the North Eastern Railway (the Council felt) was not providing an adequate service; Kilvington retired at the end of 1898; membership was not rising uniformly, and sometimes subscriptions were seriously in arrears, both attributable to the agricultural depression; and a number of key management figures died. By 1896, the YAS Council again decided to review the whole strategy of the show, and two of its key members, Colonel Gunter and Mr Charles Clay, moved resolutions:

> That the whole question of the Timber and Fittings of the Showyard be considered by the Council, with a view of seeing whether it would not be more to the interest of the Society to retain the Timber and Fittings than to sell it after the Show.

And

> That the Council take into consideration the advisability of either discontinuing the Show on the 3rd day, or providing some attractions of interest to the members of the Public.[21]

Both these resolutions were passed onto the Showyard Sites Committee for consideration. The committee reported that neither was advisable, the first because of the huge storage and transport costs it would entail – by the time of the 1890 Harrogate show the permanent rolling stock for the event amounted to 120 tons. The latter was inadvisable because no one wished either to emasculate or to cheapen The Great Yorkshire.

Some changes were made however. The date of the show was moved to the Wednesday, Thursday and Friday immediately after the middle of July, because this period had just been tried for the 1896 show at York (to coincide with the visit of the Duke of York) and had been found surprisingly convenient.[22] Then, at the 1897 show, again in Harrogate, show jumping took place for the first time, proving immediately popular, with the takings at the grand stand for the single show jumping day equalling the usual grand stand takings for all three show days.

The Council, the Finance Committee and the Showyard Sites Committee seemed determined not to allow these various difficulties to hamper the event's expansion, let alone force any retrenchment. And expansion there was, with input from various individuals and organizations. As far back as 1884, at the show at Ripon, two other societies obtained permission to hold their AGMs on the Great Yorkshire Showground: the Cleveland Bay Horse Society and the Hackney Stud Book Society. Moreover, some of the smaller agricultural societies were giving up their own shows whenever The Great Yorkshire was hosted in their areas: In 1895, for example, the Halifax and Calder Vale Agricultural Association gave up its annual show and its annual subscriptions to the YAS in return for its own members being granted full YAS privileges at the Great Yorkshire Halifax Show.[23] These and other societies were also frequently contributing premium monies, a most conspicuous event in this respect being the 1896 show at York for which the break-down of contributions was as follows:

	£
Total premium money	2380
From the YAS	1275
From the Local Committee	1000
From the President	25
From the Earl of Harewood	10
From the Shorthorn Society	10
From the Guernsey Cattle Society	20
From the Cleveland Bay Horse Society	20[24]

It is noteworthy too that this show at York saw a further expansion of livestock classes; there were now five classes for cattle (Shorthorn, Dairy Cattle, Jersey, Guernsey, and Aberdeen-Angus), five for sheep (Leicester, Lincoln, Oxford Down, Wensleydale, and Scotch Mountain), eight for horses (Hunters, Hackneys, Coaching, Cleveland Bays, Harness, Shire, Clydesdale and Agricultural), one for pigs, and premiums for butter, bee appliances and honey, as well as shoeing smiths. There was no regular award of premiums for poultry, although several members of Council were in favour of them.[25]

The 1896 (York), 1897 (Harrogate), 1898 (Leeds) and 1899 (Hull) shows all made a profit, although these were so seriously curtailed by timber losses that at the end of 1898, yet again, the YAS Council ordered a review of matters. This time, the committee comprised the Finance Committee plus the Showyard Sites Committee, their brief being 'to study the Society's expenditure with a view of its reduction'.[26] In the following April, this Committee recommended that the Society should 'look more to an increasing income from an increase of membership, than to any material decrease in expenditure', and this caused the Council to embark upon another membership drive, by means of a resolution 'That a committee consisting of members of the Council be appointed in each of the Ridings to endeavour by personal canvas to augment the role of membership'.[27] There was good reason to believe in this strategy, for the general rise in membership during the '80s and '90s had now brought the figure to its highest ever: 1186 (as of February 1899).[28]

Other developments were in the pipe-line, which seemed to augur well. Stephenson retired at the end of 1899, much to the Council's regret, 'seeing the valuable services he has rendered for the past 22 years to the YAS', and recognizing 'that it is very much owing to his energy and ability that the Society has risen to the very high position it now occupies'.[29] Stephenson was not really departing, however, for he was promptly appointed 'Honorary Director of the Society's Showground', as well as being elected an Honorary Life Member and given a seat on Council. The society at last had an executive, albeit an honorary one, whose sole responsibility was the show. At the same time, a new and promising Secretary was appointed out of a field of 132 applicants: Mr John Maughan, at £200 per annum.

Yet there were some very anxious minds on the Council at this turn of the century. It was known that in 1900 the RASE would be holding its show in York, and since it had been the custom not to mount the Great Yorkshire Show whenever the RASE was in the county, it seemed to some members of the YAS Council that such should be the practice again this time. On the other hand, powerful enticements were being offered to hold the show that year by a deputation from Doncaster, representing the Doncaster Corporation, the Doncaster Agricultural Society plus the Doncaster Race Committee. Their advocacy at the annual Council Meeting on the Hull showground inclined Council towards the idea of going ahead with the event. The next month (August) the whole Council went to Doncaster to gauge the local enthusiasm and to negotiate in detail. They decided there should be a show. Yet a minority led by Earl Feversham argued anxiously against the plan, fearing a disaster.[30] They argued, however, to no avail.

The Great Yorkshire Show at Doncaster (1900) may be inscribed in the Society's annals as the Great Yorkshire Disaster. As Feversham had predicted, the economic condition of the farming community and of its services would not allow two major shows to be supported in the county within a month of each other. The Great Yorkshire lost around £3000, and suddenly the future of the Society and its show seemed perilous. The Vice-Presidents had to sign a bond on behalf of the Council for a hefty overdraft at 5 percent interest, placing the whole of the YAS's investments as partial security against that.[31] On 18 December 1900 the Council decided upon a rescue plan – to launch a county appeal – and on a proposal by two of the key managers, the Rt Hon. George Lascelles and Colonel Gunter, it was resolved:

> That this Council does not feel justified in holding another Show until the funds of the Society are placed on a sounder basis. . . .[32]

On the same day, the AGM was apprised of the seriousness of the situation, although there does not appear to have been any discussion of Council's decision to suspend the show itself. In fact, since the county appeal quickly raised several thousand pounds, the show did in fact go ahead in 1901, although on a less grand scale in terms of premiums, and with higher showground charges for rentals of boxes, stalls and pens in particular. The Council also seems to have been nervous about any potential competition; for instance, it now resolved that the show be held on the last Wednesday, Thursday and Friday of July, and that the Secretary should write to Lord Hawke 'to ensure that the County Cricket Matches in future do not interfere with the Show's dates'.[33] The Council must have been desperate to suggest displacing the county cricket schedule!

As everyone realized, the financial disaster of this show was attributable in part to general weaknesses in the whole organization of a peripatetic event. The YAS's excellent secretary, Marshall Stephenson, had been acutely aware of these weaknesses and, apparently alone on the Council, he had long been advocating a permanent showground for the Great Yorkshire. Indeed, by the close of the century the idea of the permanent show had been under consideration not only within the YAS but also in the RASE, which had set up a special committee to look into the causes of its own show's losses, and to weigh up the prospects of a permanent Royal Show. The RASE committee finally recommended that the Royal Show should be held on a permanent site – deciding, in short, that the people would have to be brought to the show, rather than the show to the people.

Precisely how much support Stephenson had within the YAS for his own belief in a permanent site for The Great Yorkshire is difficult to tell. The printing of a paper on this issue in the *Transactions* of 1899 suggests that he was not alone, and that several people had already been calculating the costs and benefits of the scheme.[34] On reflection, the costs did not seem horrendous. It was reckoned that the Great Yorkshire would need 40 acres, which would have to be in or close to a large urban area. Such a piece of land, at £100 per acre, would cost £4000, which could be borrowed at three percent interest. The annual interest repayment would thus be a mere £120 (considerably less than the amount then being spent just on music for the show). Permanent buildings, it was calculated, might cost another £4000, bringing the total annual cost to some £250, which, even with hidden extra costs, would compare most favourably with what was then being spent on showyard fittings, and lost on timber.

As for a site for the Great Yorkshire, it seemed obvious that York would be preeminently suitable, 'with its attractive traditions, its central position, its railway accommodation, and the likelihood of a good site being found'.[35] Yet, for reasons which will become clear, the permanent showyard was not to be founded for another 50 years. It would seem that an excellent idea, which would have saved the YAS and the RASE and other major societies, a vast amount of time, money and almost crippling anxiety was passed over.

At this stage, with the Society and show apparently on the brink of ruin and most uncertain of the future, we should examine what had been happening to its central personnel and its ideology during the period from 1876 to 1900. There had in fact been a complete change in the Society's management and something of a revitalization of its science policy. On the other hand, there had also been a weakening of its founding ideology.

With Thompson's departure from the scene at the end of 1872, and his much-lamented death in 1874, the central direction of the Society came into the hands of non-founding members. Of course, some newer members had already been co-opted onto the influential sub-committees of the Council – Earl Cathcart, John Dent, George Lascelles, and Sir George Wombwell in particular. Alongside them, and even after Thompson's departure, one or two of the now elderly founders continued to play active management roles, in particular George Legard, whose services had been recognized by election to the Presidency in 1869. Becoming a Vice-President in 1870, Legard was chairing Council meetings until the late 1870s and should clearly be regarded as one of the crucial managers of the Society's first forty years.

However, after the late 1870s, non-founders were exclusively in charge of the Society, and the question must be asked: how closely did they sustain their founders' philosophy? The answer is clear: very closely indeed. Several of them, Cathcart and Dent in particular, had worked closely alongside Thompson,

Legard and Johnstone in both the RASE and the YAS and intimately knew their *modus operandi* and shared their vision.

The most incisive way to identify the men who steered the Society through this troubled period (1875–1900) is to observe the compositions of the most entrusted sub-committees: the Finance Committee (for the whole of this period), the several temporary committees set up to handle sudden matters of importance (such as the resignation of the Secretary), the Showyard Sites Committee (from October 1879), the Experiments Committee (from July 1885 to March 1886) and the Journal and Experiments Committee (as it was styled in 1886).

The figures who emerge most forcefully from a survey of these committees are listed in Table 4.2, which identifies the central policy-makers, officers and Council members for the entire period of this chapter, 1875–1914. Their dedication to the Society was crucial to its survival during this time and the longest serving of them, the Earl of Feversham and the Rt Hon. George Lascelles in particular, must surely have provided an invaluable sense of continuity as agriculture, society and the YAS itself underwent substantial changes. Other figures, however, are equally noteworthy, though for different reasons. Admiral Duncombe (who had been President in 1866) was nothing less than a chief executive, and immensely effective too by virtue of his chairmanship of the Finance Committee, his frequent chairing of Council meetings and his high standing among members of the Society. His crucial role was taken over by Lascelles (President in 1879) who shouldered the main burdens of management until the early years of the next century. Then G.A. Duncombe, Lord Middleton and Lt Col J.W. Dent in particular took over the reins of the Society.

At this point, we might focus on one group of these central management figures, those responsible for the revitalization of the science policy: John Dent, George Legard, Earl Cathcart, Charles Clay, George Lascelles and John Coleman. We have seen that from 1872 onwards the new analytical chemist, Thomas Fairley, was presenting a regular chemical report to the Council. Now, from the mid-'70s, the principal issue that he was dealing with – the adulteration of manures and feedstuffs – became a matter of nationwide concern.[36] At the end of 1874 it was learned that the Peruvian Government, under pressure from the governments of those countries which were the main consumers of Peruvian guano, was seriously considering introducing chemical analyses and controls of its most valuable export commodity. Several of the agricultural societies in England immediately recognized the value of this move, and the YAS was among the first to add its voice. In January 1875 John Dent proposed sending a memorandum to the Earl of Derby (HM Secretary of State for Foreign Affairs), worded as follows:

> The Council of the Yorkshire Agricultural Society, having heard that the Peruvian Government have under their consideration the future sale of Peruvian Guano according to standard analysis, beg to express to the Rt. Hon. the Foreign Secretary their gratification at this proposition: being of opinion that such

Table 4.2: Central policy-makers and implementers in the YAS, 1875–1914

PERIODS OF ACTIVE INVOLVEMENT

	1875	1880	1890	1900	1910	1914
Lord Auckland	————————————					
W.C. Booth	———————————————————1898					
Earl of Cathcart	————————1887					
J.D. Dent	————————1885					
Adm. Duncombe	————————1888					
Ayscough Fawkes	————————————————1897					
Earl of Feversham	———————————————————————————————1916					
George Legard	——1879					
Basil Woodd	——————————————1895					
Rt Hon. George Lascelles	1877——————————————————————————1910					
Col Gunter	1879———————————————————1904					
Charles Clay	1883————————1896					
Lord Wenlock	1887———————————————1911					
George Lane Fox	1884————————1896					
Earl of Harewood	1888————————————————————1914					
G.B. Peirson	1892——————————1908					
G.A. Duncombe	1892————————————————1914					
Lord Middleton	1899———————————1914					
Henry Hawking	1900——————————1914					
Lt Col J.W. Dent	1911——1916					

regulation will give to the English Agriculturist renewed confidence in this manure, and will considerably increase its use.

At the same time the Council trust that the Peruvian Government will not place any restriction or increased duty upon the export of Nitrate of Soda, the value of which as a manure is now so fully appreciated in this County.[37]

The memorandum was signed by Admiral Duncombe and duly sent. From Fairley's reports it is clear that guano adulteration was a considerable problem for farmers in Yorkshire – as well as nationwide.

Dent's concern for the YAS's promotion of science was evident in a number of other proposals that he put to the Council during the 1870s and '80s, first as a senior Council member and later as a representative of outside bodies. In 1876 he moved

> That a grant of £100 be made out of the funds of this Society in aid of the investigation into the nature and treatment of Pleuro Pneumonia and Foot and Mouth Disease, now being carried out by Dr. Burdon Sanderson for the RASE.

This motion was seconded by the Earl Cathcart, and carried.[38] Again as a Council member, in 1879, Dent keenly supported the idea of establishing a Chair in Agriculture at the Yorkshire College of Science. In October of the previous year overtures had been made to the Society with this aim in mind, and the Council had set up a small committee to look into the matter, consisting of Dent, Lascelles and Woodd. In March 1879, when a deputation from the College waited upon the Council, a lengthy deliberation occured, in which Dent, Coleman, Lascelles and Woodd tried to persuade the Council to give some financial support to the proposed chair – to no avail.

For the next six years there was no other sign of extra efforts being made to promote the cause of science within the Society. Fairley's useful analyses for YAS members were the Society's only scientific pursuit. Then, in 1885, by which time Dent had left Council, an Experiment Committee was set up, testifying to the continuing chemical interest among some members of Council and to a national movement in agricultural experimentation. Charles Clay proposed the motion

> That a committee be appointed to consider the best means of carrying out investigations in the county of York into subjects of practical utility to agriculture, either in conjunction with other societies, or otherwise.[39]

As Clay pointed out, the RASE had recently embarked on a similar scheme; the Durham Agricultural Society, the Cheshire Agricultural Society, the Northumberland Agricultural Society and others were all moving in the same direction, and the Bath and West had already set up its own Experiments Committee. In seconding the motion, Earl Cathcart pointed out that the RASE was willing to cooperate (as indeed it did) and that its Council had passed a resolution in favour of forging links with any local agricultural societies with a similar interest. Cathcart's comments, of course, bear witness to his central role in the RASE at the time.

The YAS's Experiments Committee was thus created as part of an informal national network (the RASE resolution had called it a 'free association') of scientific experimentation, with the following membership: Earl Cathcart as chairman, Admiral Duncombe, Messrs Clay, Booth, Coleman, Pearson, and Edward Riley, with the President, Secretary and analytical chemist as *ex officio* members. By January of the following year it was made clear exactly what type of research this committee should be planning, for the 'Report of the Special Experiments Committee' of the RASE had been received and studied. Council wrote to the RASE requesting them to 'suggest experiments for adoption in cooperation with such of the county societies as may be willing and competent to join in the so suggested common undertaking'.[40]

In March of the same year, the YAS's Experiments Committee was renamed the Journal and Experiments Committee, reflecting the considerable overlap already existing between the two bodies (Cathcart and Duncombe were now in charge of the *Transactions*). In July the Committee presented its own Report to the Council, outlining a series of experiments with artificial and farmyard manures on mangolds and turnips. Three YAS members undertook to make the trials: Mr G. Wright (of Sigglesthorne, near Hull), Mr J. Watson (of Gardham, Cherry Burton) and Mr J. Wightman (of Hampole, near Doncaster). In the autumn the Committee visited all three and found the experiments sufficiently well advanced to suggest to Council that their report be printed in the *Transactions*. By the end of 1886 another key figure, Lascelles, had joined the Committee.

It may be said that from now on the three committees which were most influential in determining the Society's policy, and in steering a course through the turbulence of the late '80s, '90s and 1900s, were the Finance Committee, the Showyard Sites Committee and the newly-formed Journal and Experiments Committee. Central figures such as Cathcart, Duncombe, Lascelles, Clay and Coleman were members of at least two, and sometimes all three, of these.

Changes in the management of the whole Society, however, were imminent. At the end of 1887, Earl Cathcart retired. In March 1888 Coleman died, and Admiral Duncombe, who worked harder now than ever before, frequently chairing the Council as well as serving on all three committees, was struck down in February 1889. He had been a member of the YAS Council for thirty years, during which time 'his attention to the interests of the Society has been indefatigable, and his opinions on all subjects connected with the Society always commanded entire approbation'.[41] From now until the end of the century, Lascelles, Basil Woodd, and the Earls of Feversham and Harewood would steer the Society.

This new coterie, whilst maintaining the interest in science that was already existent, seemed unwilling, however, to promote it further. Indeed, this management seemed generally reluctant to participate in the national expansion of agricultural and scientific education which was a feature of this period.[42] Between 1888 and 1896 it received several deputations from well-respected agricultural bodies requesting the YAS's support for educational and scientific proposals. Yet it responded negatively to all of these.

The first deputation was from the York Chamber of Agriculture, headed by ex-President and ex-Council member, John Dent Dent. The deputation asked the YAS to help establish an itinerant dairy school in the county, to educate the community in the scientific principles and practice of making butter. As they pointed out, the Bath and West had set up such a school and there was a good chance of getting government aid for the project. The YAS Council declined to help, however, declaiming that 'they are not prepared to approach the Government with the view of obtaining any grant', adding that 'the Council is already devoting a considerable sum this year to the Dairy Exhibitions and Competitions at the Hull Show.'[43] Indeed, it was true that the dairy section at the Hull show was to be the biggest and most successful to date.

A second deputation, from the Farmers' Club, represented 'a very strong feeling . . . by all the leading farmers in the district that it was desirable that an experimenting station should be started in the North of England'. They conceded that 'farmers quite recognized the useful work done by the society in offering prizes', but pointed out that 'a more permanent benefit to agriculture would be derived from the establishment of an experimenting station on a practical and scientific basis'.[44] Despite this request being very much in keeping with the modest research already in hand under the aegis of the Journal and Experiments Committee, and despite the support of Lord Wenlock within the Council, who proposed that at least £200 per annum be set aside for the project and that the YAS approach the government for a grant of the same size, the Council voted 'No', saying that they had 'no sufficient funds nor the requisite staff at their disposal to deal with the large question of the establishment of Experimental Stations in the County'.[45]

The Council's reluctance is understandable in the light of the heavy losses recently incurred by the show at York (1887), which had obliged the Society to sell a large chunk of its North Eastern Railway 4 percent Preference stock. Moreover, there had been anxieties over an occasional decline in membership, although the general trend was upward, and the problem of arrears was rearing its ugly head again. It was clear that the Council was happy to spend extra monies, nonetheless, on causes of its own choosing. Thus, Stephenson's salary was readily raised by £100 in October 1887; the Society decided to pay a massive £1710 out of its own funds to the premiums list for the 1888 Huddersfield show (the first time it had ever been held at Huddersfield, and therefore something of a risk); moreover, the financial ambitiousness of the 1889 show was hardly less. Clearly, funds *could* have been made available for an experimental station, or for agricultural education in the form of a dairy school.

Calls upon the YAS to support agricultural education in the county were again made in 1890 and 1895. In the first of these instances, it was again Lord Wenlock who urged Council to help finance a chair in Agriculture at the Yorkshire College of Science in Leeds.[46] In the second instance, an ordinary member of the Society was urging the Council to take more interest in the recent developments in technical instruction in agriculture that were being promoted by the County Council and the Yorkshire College.[47] Again, the Council refused to commit any of the Society's funds or to offer even tacit support to such plans. Again, there is evidence that the Council was willing to spend money on matters of its own choosing. This now seems to have meant the show. Thus, the Society was paying for two veterinary inspectors to attend the show instead of just one: Mr Alexander Cope (from the Board of Agriculture) and a Mr Stephenson (from Newcastle-on-Tyne.) The curious nature of Council's conduct in these instances is all the more apparent if one realizes that these requests were being made at the very time when central and local government authorities were taking unprecedented steps to help the agricultural community educate itself.

First, on the national scale, in 1887 and 1888 the Departmental Commission on Agriculture and Dairy Schools, comprising some of the most respected authorities from all over Britain, issued a set of scientific and practical reports and made a number of strategic recommendations for agricultural education and research. These recommendations, approved by the Central Chamber of Agriculture and the national Farmers' Club, were:

1. That there should be established and maintained, at the cost of the State, a Central Normal School of Agriculture.

2. That State aid should be liberally given to certain Endowed and County Schools on condition of their establishing an Agricultural side for the proper teaching of the Theory and Practice of Agriculture – practical instruction being carried out on a Farm. . . . Arrangements should be made for the delivery of Courses of Lectures by the Teaching Staff or other Lecturers, open to Farmers of the District.

3. That Grants should continue to be given by the State in aid of local effort to provide Technical Instruction in Dairy or other branches of farm work.

4. That aid should similarly be given to Local Agricultural Associations or Chambers of Agriculture engaged in Scientific Research.

5. That in all cases where State aid is afforded, it should be of a permanent character, subject only to certain definite conditions laid down by the Board of Agriculture, and to the admission of Annual Inspection by an officer of the Board.[48]

Accepting these recommendations, Parliament voted £5000 per annum for their implementation, and by 1890 this had been augmented with a further £6000 per annum from the Science and Art Department's allocation for agricultural education. Therefore, at the time of the deputations from the York Chamber of Agriculture and the local branches of the Farmers' Club, in December 1888, the YAS Council should have been acutely aware of the central government's willingness to help meet precisely these types of request. Moreover, it should have been realized that the county of Yorkshire had an excellent chance of receiving enough governmental funding, for the original commission had recommended the setting up of only seven district dairy schools – five in England and Wales, and two in Scotland, which would surely have entailed starting one in the North of England. Adequate finance, approximately one-seventh of £5000, would be provided.

By December 1890, when Lord Wenlock made his next request for the YAS to support agricultural education by contributing towards the chair in Agriculture at Leeds, more money had become available from central government for local initiatives in agricultural instruction. This had happened by one of those curious accidents that have not infrequently led to important developments in British agriculture. It had long been felt that public houses were too prolific in the towns, and the Government decided to reduce their number. In fairness, however, it was argued that there would have to be compensation for the surrender of licences; so, in the budget of 1890, a special tax was levied on liquor with the purpose of providing the necessary funds. However, public outcry at the idea of paying back the publicans was so strong that the government backed down, and so found itself in possession of an income of several hundred thousand pounds per annum for no specific purpose. Thus, wrote H.E. Dent, 'in a lethargic and half-empty House [of Commons], Arthur H.D. Acland suggested that the money should be allocated to technical education, and it was so agreed.'[49] This money – commonly called 'the whiskey money' – was made available to County Councils to be spent on technical education, or relief of rates. Many of them devoted it to agricultural technical education.

The West Riding County Council received almost £30,000 of this 'whiskey money' in 1890, and it immediately established a Department of Agriculture at the Yorkshire College of Science in Leeds, with James Muir (formerly of the Royal Agricultural College at Cirencester) as its head. It should also be noted that the whole agricultural community of the county was involved in the move, with an initial conference held at Harrogate, and later conferences all over Yorkshire.[50] Prominent agriculturists in the county also subscribed to the project, guaranteeing £400 per annum initially for five years. The Board of Agriculture itself was so impressed by the speed and thoroughness with which the department was set up that it too offered financial support.

In this light, and despite its efforts in other directions, the YAS's coolness towards the several requests for its support of agricultural education during the late '80s and '90s seems decidedly at odds with enthusiasm both nationally and locally, in societies such as the Bath and West.[51] The YAS seemed to have temporarily lost its grand, founding, educational vision.

But this is not to say that it had lapsed into lethargy. Even leaving aside the massive effort that went into the show, other concerns were also being promoted by the Society's Council. For instance, the YAS increasingly supported the type of work that Fairley already had been doing. By the end of 1891, they were sufficiently persuaded of the extent and the iniquity of adulterating feedstuffs and manures that they decided on firm action, printing in the *Transactions* the names of those manufacturers and suppliers whose merchandise did not comply with their guaranteed analyses.[52] But, characteristically by now, the initiative for this action originated with the RASE, who, two and a half years earlier, had asked the YAS to help them combat this menace.

Finally, in this section dealing with the period 1875–1900, mention needs be made of several key members who died or retired just before the century ended. At the end of 1896, the long-serving Council member and 1868 President, George Lane Fox, died; in July 1897, Charles Clay; in late 1898, W.C. Booth and Edward Riley; in the summer of 1899, Ayscough Fawkes. All had been diligent members of the YAS Council and various committees, as well as being regular figures at the showground. Then, at the end of 1899, Stephenson retired as Secretary, and although there were high hopes that he would continue to render valuable service as an honorary director of the showground, his unexpected death in July 1902 prevented him from making any substantial impact in that capacity.

The turn of the century was thus very much the end of an era for the Society's management and, as we have seen, an anxious period in the history of the Great Yorkshire Show.

The disaster of the 1900 show was overcome in remarkably good time thanks to the generosity of the Yorkshire community. By July 1901, the County Appeal had reached some £2200 which, with the Society's securities (minus its bank debit), brought its resources up to a level at which another show could be held. The show that year (at Bradford) did incur a loss, but only of a mere £270, which was easily covered by the receipts from a new life membership scheme. Anyone donating £15 or more to the Bradford local committee was automatically accorded life membership, and many Bradford residents had taken advantage of this offer.[53]

The Council also set about re-establishing its capital, deciding in future to place all life subscriptions together with the balance of the County fund (after the clearing of all debts) in a general capital account. In October 1902, moreover, it usefully resolved that at future shows anyone who subscribed £20 or more to the local fund should be elected a life member of the Society, provided that the net amount so donated for each show reached £1250 or above.[54] This series of measures quickly took effect, with the capital account standing at just over £4000 by the end of 1902, and £5564 by the close of the following year. By 1905, the Society's auditor was able to announce a clean bill of health. Financially and otherwise, the YAS was on the way up again.

Undoubtedly, the most valuable aid to recovery came, again, from the borough and burghers of Leeds, where the 1902 show had been held at the Council's request. This show at Leeds, which had been planned on a large scale despite certain economies, turned in a handsome profit of £1758, helping to put the Society so firmly back in the black that £1000 was promptly re-invested in North Eastern Railway debentures. Indeed, 1902 was a year of remarkable optimism, with innovations ranging from the adoption of an official badge for the Society (submitted for approval to King Edward VII, the Society's patron since 1886) to the appointment of a new honorary director of the showyard, Council member Henry Hawking. This spirit seems to have been maintained for the remainder of the pre-war period, thanks largely to the excellence of the

Society's central body and to the generally strong finances of the show.

To begin with the show, the 1903 event at Sheffield was almost as successful as the Leeds venture, allowing a further £1500 to be invested in debentures. The 1904 show at Huddersfield was less spectacular, but was nonetheless successful in every way, signalling a development that would quickly become a permanent feature of the show – the attendance of representatives from the Board of Agriculture.[55] The 1905 show, at Hull, was similarly successful, and was memorable for an exhibition of cheap labourer's cottages, based upon the scheme launched in the late 1850s. Indeed, the enduring suitability of the prize-winning cottages designed in 1858 and 1861 was shown by the Council's decision to reprint those plans. (See Plate 4.)

From now until the outbreak of war, every show was a financial success, with the exception of Middlesborough (1906), Beverley (1909), and Rotherham (1911). The show and the Society were confidently back in business and, ironically, seemed more able than ever to expand on the eve of the Great War, thanks to the stupendous success of that year's show at Bradford which recorded the largest attendance in its history, of 82,461. (See Table 4.3 for data on the show, 1901–14)

Table 4.3: Basic show data in the period of recovery, 1901–14

Year	Place	Financial result (approx., in £s)	Public attendance
1901	Bradford	− 270	54,439
1902	Leeds	+ 1760	48,206
1903	Sheffield	+ 1500	54,913
1904	Huddersfield	+ 510	53,407
1905	Hull	+ 590	49,951
1906	Middlesborough	− 720	42,952
1907	Barnsley	+ 200	46,386
1908	Halifax	+ 300	57,976
1909	Beverley	− 300	38,217
1910	Leeds	+ 700	59,321
1911	Rotherham	− 1750	37,435
1912	Royal Show	—	—
1913	York	+ 120	53,628
1914	Bradford	+ 1829	82,461

The overall optimism of this period can be detected through particular developments in the organisation and composition of the show, especially in the reintroduction of several abandoned features from the early years. To everyone's surprise, these proved profitable and worthy of a serious agricultural show. They included a poultry section, introduced at the Halifax show (1908), and a horticultural section, tried at Leeds in 1910. The first of these features actually entailed a loss in its first year, but it immediately proved such a crowd-puller that the Council decided it should continue, justifying itself on the grounds that 'poultry farming is now so important an adjunct to agriculture.'[56] As for the horticultural section, that was but one of several new features tried at the Leeds show to cater more widely to what the Society now had more cause than ever to be grateful for: the tastes of the paying urban public. This section contributed handsomely to the profitability of the show, which returned a sizeable £700 profit overall, despite heavy losses on timber sales.[57] By now, it should be noted, the Society was sending its own deputation to Leeds whenever it felt in need of holding a show there Leeds was therefore unique among the towns of the county in not having to wait upon the Society nor having to submit a bid for the privilege of hosting the Great Yorkshire.

Mention of timber sales, however, reminds us that several flaws in the show system had not yet been eradicated, and that the show and the Society were still financially vulnerable. On one or two occasions the timber sale losses were so heavy that they wiped out the show's profit completely. For example, the show at Rotherham (1911) should have made a profit, thanks to the very generous contribution towards premiums by the local committee of £1250. However, a massive 40 percent loss on timber, coupled with a low attendance, caused a £1750 deficit, which inevitably put the Society's annual account unpleasantly in the red. Indeed, there were still a few years when total income to the Society could not cover its expenditure. That this could be attributed primarily to the uncertainties of the show is suggested by the fact that in 1912, when there was no Great Yorkshire because of the Royal Show at York, the Society made a slight profit of about £200.[58]

Mention has already been made of the Board of Agriculture's attendance at the Great Yorkshire in 1904. The first decade and a half of the twentieth century saw a substantial nationwide effort, led often by the RASE, at coordinating the efforts of the agricultural show societies. In early 1907 the RASE hosted a conference on the management of agricultural shows, which was also intended as an opportunity to assess the general well-being of agricultural societies as a whole.[59] The YAS Council sent a high-powered delegation led by the Marquess of Zetland, including three key Council members, Lord Middleton, Henry Hawking, and Robert Fisher, as well as the Secretary of the Society. Towards the close of 1907 the RASE was again soliciting cooperation over possible avenues of legislation to deal with cattle tuberculosis, and to further this cause Hawking, Fisher and the Secretary were sent down to London.[60] This bore fruit in the form of a successful delegation from the agricultural societies visiting the Local Government Board and the Board of Agriculture and Fisheries, as it was called then, on which Lord Middleton was the YAS's delegate.

By 1910, the central government was seeking to consult with the agricultural societies, using their own initiative rather than that of the RASE to get things going. This rapidly became a feature of the YAS's life. In 1911, for example, there was a large agricultural conference in York, organized entirely by the Central Chamber of Agriculture. By this time, the Board of Agriculture and

Fisheries was also assiduous in its attendance at the YAS's, and others', shows. For the Great Yorkshire Show at Bradford (1914), the Board went as far as to help stage a 'forestry exhibit' – a seed which germinated in the inter-war period and finally bore fruit in the form of the 'forestry and permanent woodland exhibit' at the Great Yorkshire Show of today.

Aside from the central government's involvement, the local societies were also seeking each others' company. Thus, in 1911 the Herefordshire and Worcester-shire Agricultural Society called a conference of show secretaries; and although no formal conference was actually held, there were valuable informal meetings for the exchange of information and mutual advice on handling problems. The YAS itself had already decided to open its arms to certain types of societies, for in 1906 the Council resolved 'That this Society becomes affiliated with such of the different Breed Societies as may from time to time be considered desirable.'[61]

This formalized interest in breed societies soon manifested itself in an expansion of the Show's livestock classes, which had come a very long way since the founding period. Thus, for the 1913 show, at York, the classes were planned as follows:

Horses: Thoroughbreds and Hunters: Breeding classes.
Hunters: Riding classes.
Hackneys, Cobs and Ponies.
Polo Ponies.
Cleveland Bays and Yorkshire Coach Horses.
Shires.
Harness Horses.

Cattle: Shorthorns.
Dairy Cows.
Jersey.
Aberdeen-Angus

Sheep: Leicester
Lincoln.
Wensleydale.
Scotch Mountain.

Pigs: Large Whites.
Middle Whites.
Tamworth.
Lincolnshire Curly-Coated
Berkshire.
Large Black.[62]

Finally, we must see what was happening with the management-core of the Society. Several of the key figures from the 1880s and '90s who had steered the YAS through its crisis of 1900–01, and engineered its reconstruction, departed. Colonel (and now Sir) Robert Gunter died in late 1905, Lord Herries in 1908, Lascelles and Bacon Frank in 1911, and Lord Wenlock in 1912. Lascelles in particular had given tremendous service to the Society, having been a Council member since 1864; initiated into the Socety's ideology and management during the days of Thompson and Legard; a show steward in 1867, 1871 and 1879–97; President in 1878 and Vice-President thereafter. The Council's tribute to him conveys the extent of his contribution, and to the far-seeing historian neatly encapsulates a 'type' ranging from Spencer and H.S. Thompson in the founding years, to Sir John Dunnington Jefferson (in the modern period) which the YAS has been most fortunate to have at its heart. This Council, in its grief, declared:

> It is no mere tribute to the memory of Mr Lascelles to describe him not only as taking a leading position in County affairs and in agricultural matters in particular, but one whose sound business and practical knowledge combined with ready sympathy endeared him to all classes.[63]

As before, the central policy-makers during this period can be identified from the composition of the various specialist committees within the Society and from those most frequently participating in the Council and in the management of the show. In 1907–8 the Earl of Feversham, Lord Middleton, Lascelles, Major J.W. Dent, and Messrs Fisher, Hawking, Stanyforth, Peirson and Winn were the central figures. By the end of 1911, the management profile was similar. The most influential figures can be gauged from the chairmanships of the six sub-committees: Lord Middleton, chairman of the Finance and Showyard Sites Committees; Earl Feversham, chairman of the Selection Committee, which had been set up to nominate new members for Council; Major Dent, chairman of the Journal and Chemical Committee; Hawking, chairman of the Prizes and Judges Committee, and Show Director; and Sir Matthew Wilson, chairing a recently established Horticultural Committee. Alongside them were Colonel G.A. Duncombe (who not infrequently presented the report on the show, or on finance) and Messrs Peirson and Winn, whose loyalty and usually unobtrusive devotion to the Society were impressive.

During this period, too, the deaths of a number of past Presidents were recorded with great sadness by the Council and remind us that whilst the President of a society might often be a figurehead, a dedicated President can be one of its most precious assets. Two such men whom the Society lost were Lord Wenlock and Sir George Wombwell. Lord Wenlock had become a member of the YAS in 1881 and was elected a member of Council in 1885 and '86; he became President in 1886–7 for the Jubilee show, and Vice-President in 1888. His seat on the Council was interrupted by his absence during a period in India as Governor of Madras (1890–96), but as soon as he returned to England he resumed his active interest in the Society, which again showed its appreciation by electing him President for 1912. Lord Wenlock had already accepted his second presidency before his death in February 1912, and the list of Presidents in Appendix A therefore names two for this year – both Lord Wenlock and his successor, the Rt Hon. H.W. Fitzwilliam.

Equally dedicated was Sir George Wombwell, a colourful character who was one of those utterly invaluable figures providing continuity within the YAS. He had become a member in 1855 during the period of management of the founding fathers, President in 1867, Vice-President in 1903, and Council member for some years. On his death in 1913, Council proudly recorded him as 'a distinguished Yorkshireman and one of the survivors of those who rode in the Charge of the Light Brigade'.[64]

If these were the leading lights of the Society's life, no less important were its paid, and less conspicuous, staff. John Maughan worked solidly throughout this period, and without doubt the Society owed him a great debt, which it happily acknowledged. In 1910 he was given a generous salary rise plus an allowance for travel and lodging, which reflected the task he now had of representing the YAS in London and liaising with other societies. In 1914, Mr Frederick Walker, whom he had been employing as his Clerk (out of a £50 allowance for clerical assistance that the Society had been paying him), was taken onto the Society's payroll at £110 per annum so that Walker could have more substantial assistance with his ever-growing workload.[65] In implementing the Society's policies, Maughan also had the unpleasant experience of handling two libel cases brought by a Hull-based manufacturer: the same manufacturer, Messrs Brooke and Walker, brought one case against Maughan personally, and the other against the YAS. The plaintive lost, but the society had to meet its own legal expenses of £524.[66]

Thomas Fairley was also serving the Society with great reliance, regularly submitting lengthy chemical reports to the Council which continued to be printed in the *Transactions*. By 1911, his workload had also increased and his own personal assistant was taken onto the Society's staff as an assistant analyst. Fairley continued to serve the Society until his death in 1919, having been the YAS's consultant analyst for a record period of 47 years.

Mention should also be made of the veterinary inspector for the show, Professor Cope of the Agricultural Department of the Privy Council, who had been in regular attendance at the Great Yorkshire for some years. He had to handle a wide variety of problems, including complaints against other exhibitors, a type of problem which had become quite serious during the last quarter of the nineteenth century. When he died in 1906, he was replaced by Professor J.R.U. Dewar, of the Royal Veterinary College, Edinburgh, as the official veterinary inspector.[67] Even more intimately connected with the running of the show was the Clerk of Works who, since the retirement of the first and most excellent holder of that post, Thomas Kilvington, was Mr James Lawrie. Undoubtedly, Lawrie continued to enjoy Council's confidence, as had Kilvington, but by 1902 he was ailing and in December 1904 an assistant Clerk of Works, Mr Frederick Pottage, was appointed. By December 1905 it was evident that Lawrie would not recover his vigour, and so he was gently persuaded to tender his resignation. The Society offered him a pension of £25 per annum for the next four years, and installed Pottage in his stead at £100 per annum. At this time, the Society did not operate a pension scheme for its staff, and until it did so in the late 1930s it displayed considerable sensitivity and compassion towards those of its employees who had to retire, and to the relatives of those who died in harness. Without doubt, those who genuinely served the Society enjoyed its consideration.

Finally, in an account of this period, one might mention various miscellaneous points which illustrate the matters of detail which successive Councils and committees had to juggle with in attempting to sustain and improve the show. As ever, railway cooperation was crucial. Despite several severe shortcomings, particularly for the 1890 show at Harrogate when the North Eastern Railway, whose chairman was then John Dent, caused grave dissatisfaction, there was a general feeling of mutual trust between the YAS and the companies. The multiplicity of railway companies, of course, made negotiations for special passenger services and discounts especially intricate and the Secretary had to build up a good relationship with each and every one. Maughan seems to have been adept in this respect. For instance, for the 1905 show at Hull he managed to obtain a $37\frac{1}{2}$ percent discount on return tickets for all the Society's members travelling by the Great Central, the Great Northern, the Hull and Barnsley, the Lancashire and Yorkshire, the London and North Western, the Midland, and the North Eastern Railways.[68] Cheap railway services were necessary to attract a large paying public.

At around this time, it also became necessary to define more clearly the legal status of the YAS and of the Great Yorkshire Show. During the early 1900s, the Society had been paying tax on its investment-income, and it was only in April 1905 that the Inland Revenue Office could be persuaded to recognize the YAS as a charitable institution.[69] The Inland Revenue were still not entirely clear about the legal nature of the show, however, for in the same year they threatened to take court proceedings against one of the vending exhibitors at the Hull event for not having taken out a hawker's licence. Maughan was obliged then to liaise with the other major agricultural societies in order to have the show registered as a 'fair or market' under the Hawkers' Act.[70] This episode, indeed, exemplified the increasing legislative and institutional complexity of British society. Any major enterprise now had to be managed within a legal and fiscal calculus very much more intricate than in the period when the YAS was born.

But even the most careful of calculations could not entirely guide the YAS's managers in their planning and policy-making. The show in particular was as open as ever to trial and error, and, it was hoped, success. Saturday was tried as the third show-day at Rotherham in 1911, but it did not pass off well enough to be repeated. However, another experiment worked brilliantly: a display of primitive breeds of sheep at the 1914 Bradford show, by a Mr H.J. Elwes, who presciently reckoned that there was more to rare breeds than met the commercial eye.[71] Indeed there is, and today the exhibition by the Rare Breeds Survival Trust at the Great Yorkshire Show ranks as one of the most interesting features of the YAS's enterprise.

But, ironically, just as the show was proving again to be a viable enterprise, with scope for innovation within a long-term strategy (as indicated by the Council's instruction to the Showyard Sites Committee in 1913 to select the show's locations three years in advance), war broke out. How the Society continued to be useful during the war years, despite the absence of its show, and how it survived the massive social and economic upheaval of the war's aftermath, are the subjects of the next chapter.

14   Third Earl Spencer, first President of the Society, by Charles Turner (National Portrait Gallery, London)

15   Visit of HM The Queen to the 1977 Great Yorkshire Show

16   The Great Yorkshire Show in the 1980s: the Cattle Parade

17   Machinery   lines

18   Charolais cattle

19 Sheep on show

20 The Flower Show

21 Major General Geoffrey Collin, Honorary Show Director, presenting the winner's trophy in the 1986 Farms Project for Schools to members of Clint, Burnt Yates Primary School

5 THE GREAT WAR AND AFTER, 1914–39

In broad terms, the impact of the First World War on British farming was financially beneficial and conducive to greater efficiency in terms both of calories made available to the human population and of labour-intensity. It is widely accepted, on reliable evidence, that British farming made quite handsome profits during the war itself and that this was not a period of anxiety for the farmer, as farmer at least.[1] But equally significant, both for the general history of the war and its aftermath, and for the history of agricultural societies such as the YAS, was the change in the relationship between government and agriculture.

Until the installation of the second coalition government, under Lloyd George, in December 1916, farming had functioned largely within a *laissez faire* ideology, although, as we have seen in the previous chapter, the context within which agricultural institutions had to operate was becoming more intricate after 1900, with quasi-official networks beginning to permeate the agricultural community. Until then, government had shown minimal interest in farming affairs, leaving farmers free to produce as they felt and the landed interest (which was still considerable, even politically) largely unfettered. During the first two years of the war, as food imports diminished and the domestic demand for farm produce rose due to the expansion of the armed forces and the existence of full employment, there was every encouragement for farmers to farm as they wished, with profit. Admittedly, unit costs rose; but product costs rose much faster.

At the end of 1916, however, ideas inherited from the latter half of the nineteeth century were swept away when, to meet the exigencies of war, agriculture became a *controlled* industry. Lloyd George's government introduced legislation based on two fundamental policies – one of food production, and the other of food control. Overall, the intention of this legislation was to encourage crop production (wheat, oats and potatoes) in preference to livestock production. This, in turn, was based upon a lesson from science: that the energy in crops is utilized far more efficiently by humans if consumed directly, rather than indirectly (in the form of meat and milk).

Without going into the intricacies of the food production policy, it may be said that it somewhat curtailed the farmers' profits. They were being persuaded to expand areas of production that they would not have developed voluntarily, and had to meet higher costs in the process. The other policy, that of food control, which was the responsibility of the newly formed Ministry of Food, had three consequences worth noting here: a slowing-down of the rate of inflation in food prices, a raising of the nutritional standard of the national diet, and a more equal distribuition of the food supply. Two of the means employed to achieve these ends, namely price controls and the production of breadstuffs, had a direct and negative impact upon farming profits.

The significance of these wartime developments for the agricultural context within which the YAS's wartime and post-war history must be set are as follows.

First, the government's new involvement in policy-making for the agricultural community, which directly affected the pattern and profitability of farming, meant that agricultural associations such as the YAS had to operate within what might be called a new social contract. For there was now another participant, and potential beneficiary, in the management of the land. This new social relationship was by no means an easy one. After the repeal of the 1920 Agriculture Act in 1921 ('The Great Betrayal', as it became known) there was little trust of the government by the agricultural community.[2] It thus became one of the tasks of associations such as the YAS to mediate between their farming constituents and the bureaucrats and legislators.

Second, the inflationary economics of agriculture during the war were part and parcel of a massive inflationary development at large, which few institutions and groups seemed particularly concerned about whilst the war lasted but which hit them as they tried to return to normality afterwards. (See Table 5.1.) An enormous difference between costs and prices was one of the basic determinants of the great social and functional change between pre-war and post-war Britain. This was alluded to in the previous chapter, when it was suggested that for British society 'The Twentieth Century' began essentially in 1918–19 and not in 1900. This emerged clearly in microcosm within the YAS whose managers found, much to their alarm, that the show could not return to its pre-war pattern and that the Society would have to actively re-launch itself with a wholly new set of policies and priorities in order to survive.

Table 5.2: Wartime price indices

	1900–13 (av.)	1914	1915	1916	1917	1918
Farm Product Prices	· 100	104	131	165	207	239
Cost of Living	—	100	123	146	176	203
Wholesale Prices	100	106	130	168	219	242

(From P.E. Dewey, 'British Farming Profits and Government Policy during the First World War', *Econ. Hist. Rev.*, 1984, *37*: 377)

Third, the wartime food policies, by not detailing a new strategy for peacetime agriculture, particularly *vis-à-vis* the international market, left British farming as vulnerable as ever before to overseas competitors. Heavy and cheap imports therefore built up in the 1920s, so that between 1927 and 1933 the prices of British farm products fell drastically, returning by June 1933 to their pre-war level. It became urgently clear that some form of protectionism had to be introduced, and with the Horticultural Products (Emergency Duties) Act in

November 1931 and the Import Duties Act in February 1932 the foundations of a new strategy for agriculture were laid. British farming then experienced modest growth once again, expanding between 1930–31 and 1936–37 by some 17 percent.[3]

Nonetheless, finding this strategy was not easy. The government was of course anxious to maintain low food prices for the nation's largely industrial, urban population, without adversely affecting industrial exports and economic relations with the Dominions, who were anxious now to enter into a genuine spirit of partnership with Britain. Indeed, it was only by late 1937 that the government arrived at its most substantial plan for British agriculture – the introduction of Exchequer-subsidies for farm produce.[4] Gratifying as this was for the agricultural community, farmers nonetheless still had genuine anxieties and particular grievances about their treatment by the government.

One fundamental cause of these anxieties was the farmers' general lack of social and political clout: by 1931, only 6.4 percent of those gainfully employed in Britain were working on the land. British farmers were much less politically powerful than their continental counterparts. To attempt to compensate for this, associations such as the YAS took a drastic step: they amended their constitutions in order to overturn their founding principle of non-engagement in politics. Henceforth, they would actually seek to contribute to the political debate whenever it concerned the fortune and future of the farming community.

This facet of the changing British society of the 1920s and '30s, together with other social and economic features, finds itself reflected in the YAS's history. Indeed, this whole background puts into context the development and excellence – and at times the urgency – of the Society's management policy during the period. It helps to explain why a new professionalism entered into the administration of the Society and the show in the early '30s, thus inaugurating the modern period in its history.

The large profit of the 1914 show at Bradford was made despite the decision to withhold much of the timber used to erect the showground, either to sell it off later or to use it at the next show, at Hull. In optimistic mood, the prize monies were set for the next show at a relatively high level (£2838), and a President was nominated for the year. All seemed set to proceed as usual but in December 1914, a few weeks after the outbreak of war, the Council suddenly found itself debating whether to mount a show at all in 1915. At least two of the most central policy-makers and managers, Major J.W. Dent and James Winn, were in favour of holding the show. At Hawking's suggestion, the decision was deferred for another two months, probably in the expectation that the war would turn out to be a rather temporary affair.

The decision not to hold a show was made at a Council meeting in February 1915, chaired by Colonel G.A. Duncombe who until recently had been chairman of the Finance Committee and was clearly a principal policy-maker of very sound vision. The most cogent reasons for holding a show were that it was at the very heart of the Society's *raison d'être*, and that a substantial proportion of the Society's staff and officers were engaged largely or wholly in the business of the show. Moreover, there was a county-wide desire for the show to continue. But the reasons *against* indicate that the difficulties might be astronomical. First, the railways had indicated that they were unable to guarantee adequate passenger and exhibition capacity since much of their rolling stock had been requisitioned for military purposes. Then, the Lord Mayor and the Property Committee of Hull strongly doubted that they would be able to raise a local subscription towards the event. They were also unsure whether the site that had been approved by the Showyard Sites Committee would be available; and they could not guarantee any alternative sites since all others were, or would be, occupied for the training of troops. Finally, the YAS Council itself felt that it could not estimate the cost of holding the show, whilst it could easily calculate the cost of not holding it. As the latter alternative entailed no risk, whilst the former would be enormously hazardous, it was therefore decided to cancel the show.[6]

This decision apparently rendered the presidency largely redundant, and Council therefore resolved at the February meeting not to elect the President designate after all. Instead, the post of Chairman of Council was created, to which Duncombe was elected unanimously. There was thus no President of the Society in 1915, and Duncombe's astuteness as Chairman of Council convinced the managers that this latter post should be part of the Society's constitution – as indeed it became in 1920. But without the show, what could the Society do to justify its existence? On the national level, it had been invited by the RASE to join in a General Committee for the Agricultural Relief of Allies. Messrs Winn and Maughan were appointed as the Society's representatives, Council voted not less than £100 to the Agricultural Relief of Allies Fund, and over the next few months a conspicuous amount of aid was sent from Britain, particularly to France and Serbia.

On the local level, the Yorkshire Council for Agricultural Education and the University of Leeds Department of Agriculture proposed to mount a series of demonstrations of direct relevance to wartime farming. At least one of these, a demonstration of labour-saving ploughs and cultivators, was taken up enthusiastically by the YAS Council. In late autumn 1915 a two day demonstration was held on a 52-acre site at the North Riding Asylum Farm which 'excited the greatest interest' and which 'agriculturists attended in large numbers.'[7] The main excitement there must have been the eight motor tractors on display, the use of which was greatly promoted during the war.

The Society made a small loss in 1915, a mere £409 18s 7d, which included deficits on the timber for the 1914 show and depreciation of its rolling stock. The war seemed set to last longer than anyone had envisaged, but with agriculture prospering and the members paying their subscriptions more promptly the Society's immediate horizon gave little cause for anxiety. It was, however, extremely difficult to live without the show, and not only for the Council and the staff. As the Council recorded:

The even temporary abolition of the large Agricultural Shows is a very serious matter for stock breeders and implement makers, and there never was a time when such exhibitions were of the greatest importance to both.[8]

So, at the end of 1915, the Council re-opened the debate on whether to hold a show in 1916, leaving the final recommendation to be made by the stewards. In February 1916, the stewards firmly recommended that no show be organised, and this finally persuaded Council to take appropriate steps to put the Society on a non-show footing for the remainder of the war, however long it would last. The Secretary, Clerk of Works and analytical chemist took reductions in their salaries or fees in February, with further cuts in the following year. Other cutbacks were made, such as the suspension of the *Transactions*, with the result that the Society actually made a tiny profit on the year in 1916. At the annual Council meeting in December 1916 it was also resolved to re-elect all officers and Council members *en bloc*, and not to fill up any vacancies until after the war.

1916 saw a second demonstration of labour-saving devices. The third full year of war, 1917, apparently saw virtually no activity of this sort, but in 1918 a successful foal show and sale was held. In both these years, the Society managed to balance its books and show a profit of about £200.

Immediately after the war was over, however, the Society sprang back to life. In December 1918 the sub-committees were re-appointed, with much the same personnel as they had in 1914. The Earl of Harewood was re-elected President, a post he had held since 1916, (1915 being the only year in which there had technically been no President); a show was also being planned. In January 1919 the staff salaries were restored: the Secretary reverted to his £250 per annum plus £25 travelling expenses; the Clerk of Work got a rise to £200, as did the Chief Clerk to £160. The Secretary was also allowed to engage an office boy, at no more than £1 per week. The Society again moved into top gear. The Showyard Sites Committee and the stewards recommended York as the venue for the show, and a deputation was received from the city.[9]

Before discussing this post-war phase of the Society's history, we should look briefly at the losses which the Society sustained during the war. Inevitably, the Society did lose members in action, but apparently none of these were Council members or members closely associated with the show. However, some of its most valuable managers died of natural causes during this period: the fifth Earl of Feversham (1915), Lt Col H.F. Dent (late 1916) and Jacob Smith (December 1917). Parrington also died, but his death had little actual impact upon the Society's fortunes since he had not been active on Council since 1878. The greatest of these losses was undoubtedly the death of Feversham. He had joined the YAS as an annual subsciber in the 1850s, was first elected to Council in 1858, became a Vice-President in 1871, and occupied the Presidency three times – in 1872 for the show at Malton, in 1883 when there was the RASE show at York, and in 1902 when the event was held at Leeds. He was also a Trustee of the Society, taking charge over its investments, and a regular attender of the show and of Council meetings. Moreover, being the largest landowner in the county and very active in its affairs (at one time he was a leading Shorthorn breeder too) his influence was felt far and wide. His long and valuable participation in the YAS had undoubtedly supplied an avenue of communication between the Society's management and the landed interest at large. And to the Society's administration he had further contributed: two of the YAS's most excellent Secretaries, Thomas Parrington and Marshall Stephenson, had both been his estate-agents![10]

The death of Jacob Smith (of Humburton) was also noteworthy, for like Feversham he had been initiated into the Society during its Thompsonian heyday. He had joined in 1849 as an annual subscriber, had compounded as a life member in 1884, had served on Council from 1875-95 and as a show steward from 1882-95, and at the time of his death in December 1916 was the Society's oldest member. Jacob Smith may indeed be regarded as representative of a 'type' without whom the YAS could not have survived: committed, long-serving and, bearing in mind the very difficult times Council had to weather whilst he had been a member, long-suffering, unobtrusive in the public records, but immensely popular and hard-working behind the scenes. There have been many others like him in the Society's history, too many to name individually, but to valuable to be passed over. Let this recollection of Jacob Smith be their rememberance too.

Now let us take up the Society as it paused on its starting-blocks in early 1919, ready to race away with a great, jubilant show at York. There is no doubt that, like almost everyone else, the Council presumed it could pick up the threads of the pre-war era and forge ahead, helping to build 'a land fit for heroes'. In February, however, alarm bells began to ring. A preliminary estimate of the cost of a show at York looked so formidable that Maughan was instructed to prepare a more detailed estimate. When this was presented to the YAS Council a few days later, the horror of the problem became plain. Costs of labour and materials had risen so greatly during the war that it would cost some £6000 more to erect a showyard now than it had in 1913, when the Great Yorkshire Show had been at York. For example, timber which had cost £11-14-3 per standard in 1913 would now cost £42. So, knowing that some 300 standards of timber would be required and estimating a timber-sale loss of 33 percent, a show would lose some £4200 on its timber alone! With the enormous initial expenditure that the event required, the Council suddenly saw that the society could be crippled, and all would be lost. There could be no show again that year.[11]

At the same despondent meeting, it was again decided to promote demonstrations of labour-saving devices and machinery throughout the county, especially 'of an educational character'. A couple of months later, the Council decided that it would still contribute to the show scene by making grants and premiums available to smaller show societies, a number of which had applied to the YAS for support. A new sub-committee was set up to handle the matter, comprising Messrs Hawking, Kendrew and (another) Jacob Smith, with £400 at its disposal. This scheme, although temporary, did prove of real use to the county's smaller societies, helping them to get their own operations going again. The recipients of the YAS's grants included the local shows of Northallerton, Malton, Wharfedale, Selby, York (horse show), Ryedale and Pickering, and Penistone.[12]

By June 1919, however, there was again the bright prospect of a show in the form of a joint event held with the RASE, at Durham in 1920. Hawking was in earnest negotiation with the RASE, and by the time of the AGM at the end of the year the matter was clinched, very much to the YAS Council's satisfaction and to the YAS's financial benefit, as it turned out. The YAS would help substantially to organize the joint show, and would donate £1000 towards the premiums. The RASE would reap the actual profits – or bear the losses. In January 1920 Council also decided to go ahead with its own show for 1921 at Leeds, rather to the annoyance of York whose earlier offer to host the first post-war Great Yorkshire Show had been accepted. Thus, by early 1920 the YAS seemed set to return to business as a show society.

In the realization that things had changed radically and irrevocably, not only for the show but also for the entire Society, a special committee was wisely set up, in April 1920, to examine every aspect of the YAS's administration and organization. This body comprised Lord Middleton, Lt Col Stanyforth, Major J.W. Dent, Captains Greenwood and Wickham-Boynton, and Messrs Hawking, Day, Paget, Jacob Smith, and Thorp. The only absentees from the core of the Society's policy-makers and managers were Colonel Sir G.A. Duncombe (who had been created Baronet in the New Year Honours List of 1919), and Lord Deramore. This committee did an exhaustive job, clearly realizing that the Society had to be put on a new footing to face the new times. Their report was ready in June, and their recommendations adopted by the Society at an emergency general meeting, called in October.

The main feature of the report and the EGM were the new 'Objects and Rules of the Society' which signalled a fundamental shift in the YAS's structure and ideology. The YAS was now to become a more expansive organization, with scope to engage in matters that had formerly been forbidden and with a different sense of where its executive powers lay. As the special committee told the Council, 'We deem it wise to place "The Objects of the Society" on a wider and more comprehensive basis' and 'The Rules have been very carefully revised in order to adapt them to present-day requirements'. The committee was also convinced that the administrative and executive duties within the Society would become heavier and that steps should therefore be taken to consolidate, or even to create, the appropriate infrastructure. In particular, they recommended the appointment of a 'whole-time Secretary' who would not now be expected or allowed to engage in outside business of his own. They also advised the creation of a new post, under the new rules, of Chairman of Council, to relieve the Presidnt of his often heavy burden, and whose duty it would be to conduct the meetings of Council and to keep in close touch with the show director and Secretary.

The new 'Objects of the Society' (which are worth comparing with the very cursory original objects, quoted in chapter 2) went as follows:

> For holding an Annual Show for the Exhibition of Live Stock, Poultry, Farm Produce, Horticultural Produce, also of Machinery, Implements, Tools, Appliances, Utensils, etc., connected with or appertaining thereto; such Annual Show to be held successively in different parts of the County.
>
> For the improvement of Live Stock, Poultry, Implements, Machinery, and Appliances in connection with Agriculture.
>
> For Demonstration of methods and processes connected with, and for the furtherance of, the interests of Agriculture, Horticulture, Arboriculture, Apiculture and Allied Industries.
>
> For Agricultural Education.
>
> For scientific research and experimental work.
>
> For watching and advising on Legislation affecting the Agricultural Industry and for improving, assisting and promoting Agriculture generally.[13]

As for the new 'Rules of the Society', these followed the pattern of the original rules, with amendments of personnel and numbers as was now appropriate. Of the twenty rules, two in particular merit quotation: rules 3 and 5. Rule 3 stipulated that

> The Council shall consist of the Patrons, the President, the Hon. Vice-Presidents, the Vice-Presidents, the Hon. Treasurer, the Hon. Director, together with 27 Ordinary Members to be elected by the Members of the Society by ballot through the post. Nine members of the Council shall be elected from the North Riding, nine Members of the Council from the East Riding and nine Members of the Council from the West Riding. The Council shall have power to co-opt not exceeding six Annual Members of the Council.
>
> Of the 27 Elected Members of the Council, one-third from each Riding shall retire annually but shall be eligible for re-election. Any vacancies on the Council which may occur between one Annual Meeting of the Society and another shall be filled by the Council. . . .

Rule 5 set out the duties and powers of Council, beginning with the provision that 'The Council shall from their own number annually appoint a chairman of Council'.[14]

Lord Middleton, who was already a Trustee and Chairman of the Showyard Sites and Selection Committees, was promptly elected Chairman of Council, this becoming the first official holder of this post, although Colonel Duncombe was the first incumbent when the post was created *ad hoc* in 1915. Lord Middleton also happened to be the President at the time. The new structure and the tighter delineation of functions were timely, for almost at once the Council was faced with fresh anxieties over the show. The joint RASE-YAS event had incurred a hefty loss. Fortunately for the YAS, the RASE had had to bear the weight of this, but the Council realized that next time the burden would be all their's. A whole new strategy had to be found for the Great Yorkshire.

To begin with, as Sir William Worsley warned the Council, it could not be presumed that the sources of income for the show would be the same as before. There had been a radical redistribution of wealth in the country as a result of the war, and the Society would have to take account of this. Moreover, the escalation in costs and prices had to be allowed for. As Council went ahead with the tenders for its first post-war show, the horrendous magnitude of these costs struck home again and again. Thus, the tender that was accepted for printing the *Transactions*, the prize schedules and the show catalogues came to £176 10s 0d, compared with £82 10s 0d in 1914.[15] Overall, the 1921 Leeds show, it was estimated, would cost some 250 percent more than the last event held there, in 1910. The Council therefore had no choice but to raise the entrance fee and other charges for the show, the largest rises being in turnstile admissions: for the first day, up from 2s 6d to 5s, for the second day from 1s to 3s, and for the third day from 1s to 2s.

Yet, notably, the YAS Council was not at all faint-hearted. They were determined to make the Leeds show worthy both of both the Society and the city which had always so welcomed and sustained them. A substantial prize schedule was settled upon, at a maximum level of £3000. It was agreed to amalgamate with the Roundhay Horticultural Society (of Leeds) to organize the flower section. The Clerk of Works was awarded another salary rise in anticipation of his extra work and responsibility, and Council even considered making the show a four-day event.[16] The Prince of Wales was invited to become the Vice-Patron of the Society, to which he agreed, and all seemed set for success – or financial disaster. The risk was enormous.

In the event, the determination and courage of everyone involved paid off magnificently. Astoundingly, the Council and the several sub-committees got their estimates exactly right and, more crucially, hit upon an excellent means of planning for the show and hugely expending the Society's membership. Consequently, the profit of the Leeds Show (about £2000) was but a prelude to a prosperous decade in the Twenties.

Despite the success of this show, and perhaps as a result of the extra duties that were to be imposed upon certain personnel as a result of the new rules, two key figures resigned soon afterwards. The Secretary, John Maughan, resigned expressly because his YAS duties were now hampering his own professional work outside the Society. His 22 years of service were of course warmly appreciated. Henry Hawking, Honorary Showyard Director since 1903, also retired most probably due to ill-health which had prevented him from even attending the show. The Council greatly regretted his departure too, conferring upon him the Society's greatest recognition by making him an Honorary Vice-President.[17] It is, indeed, probable that Hawking's decision to retire preceded and prompted Maughan's, for Maughan's own letter of resignation suggests that Hawking had been his pillar of strength.

> My thanks [declared Maughan] are especially due to Mr Hawking, with whom I have been so long associated; the great progress which the Society has made during

the past 22 years is, to a very great extent, due to his personality and invaluable assistance.[18]

Council lost no time in advertising for a new, full-time Secretary and appointing a new Honorary Show Director. For the post of Secretary, they received a flood of 410 applicants, doubtless drawn by the generous salary of £500. In November, their choice was made and they were clearly happy with it. They had selected Mr Alfred Cavers, who had been Assistant Secretary in the HASS since 1910. He was given one permanent clerk plus three temporary assistants for the show. At the same time, a long-serving member of Council, Leopold Paget, was appointed Honorary Showyard Director.[19]

Planning for the next show, at Hull, could now proceed, driven by the energy generated from the success at Leeds, where profits, it should be noted, had been achieved despite a loss on timber re-sale of 47 percent, or £4390. This event too turned out to be enormously successful, with such a large public attendance that its profit was a staggering £5000 or so (approximately 25 percent of the total cost of the event). By the time of the following show, at Sheffield, the Council was confident enough to expand both the classes and the range of activities. So, the Sheffield show would feature an extensive poultry section and, for the first time, a carcass competition (for bacon only). Council now also agreed to join with Leeds University and the Yorkshire Council of Agricultural Education in organizing a countywide Clean Milk Competition, whose objects were:

> To demonstrate to producers and employers that without expensive plant and specially constructed buildings, it is possible to produce milk of higher hygienic and better keeping qualitites than at present.[20]

Sheffield produced the largest attendance in the show's history hitherto, and garnered a respectable profit, partly due, one might guess, to the visit by His Royal Highness, Prince Henry, as the Society's Vice-Patron. It would appear that three magnificent successes in a row simply bred further success. Certainly, from now onwards there is evidence of greater interest shown in the Great Yorkshire Show by outside organizations and individuals. For instance, the 1924 Show at York saw a resumption of conspicuous donations of premiums by other agricultural societies and by individuals. These donors included the British Friesian Cattle Society, the English Blackface Sheep Society, the British Dairy Farmers' Association, and the 'Genuine Homer Club' (presumably for pigeons, not ancient Greek poetry), amongst others.

Also conspicuous during this period was the increasing attendance of agriculturists from the Dominions, anxious to visit agricultural shows in Britain to build up their own techniques in breeding and management. At the same time, they could offer their own experiences, and, indirectly, tempt British farmers to emigrate. The testimonies of these overseas visitors bear eloquent witness to the excellence which the Great Yorkshire Show had again achieved by the mid-1920s, indicating that the six year hiatus and the rough shock of the war's aftermath had not lowered its standard. Thus, one of the sixty South

African farmers to visit the 1925 show at Bradford declared to the press:

> Having seen the Royal Show twice and the Highland Show once, I must say that
> the contention that the Yorkshire Show is one of the biggest in the country is
> justified. Though not as large as the Royal, and numerically inferior in Live Stock
> exhibits, the quality of the stock is certainly equal to anything I have seen.[21]

A Canadian visitor to the 1926 show at Harrogate, a Mr Ogilvie from the
University of Wisconsin College of Agriculture, Madison, USA, paid glowing
tribute to the Society when he wrote to the Council:

> I invariably refer to the Yorkshire Show in my reports of my trip as the second
> largest and, to my mind, the best of the English Agricultural Shows.[22]

There is no reason to doubt Ogilvies's objectivity, although his praise did
come straight after attending the Harrogate show, which happened to be the
jewel in the Yorkshire's crown. The event was so spectacular, and so profitable,
that it consolidated the basis of the YAS's plan to set up its permanent
showground there. No trouble had been too much for the Harrogate
Agricultural Society and the local committee in preparing the site (on The
Stray) and other facilities. A remarkably full programme was prepared for all
three days, essentially similar to today's, although less varied and less orientated
towards pure entertainment. Her Royal Highness Princess Mary attended, for
her husband, Viscount Lascelles, was that year's President. And, most
important of all, there was the livestock, with 1650 more entries than at any
previous show! In their annual report, the YAS Council declared that

> The Harrogate Show which left a surplus of £3840 10s 7d was unquestionably the
> most successful in the history of the Society.[23]

After Harrogate, this spell of triumph and optimism in the show's history was
occasionally fractured, as British agriculture entered a six year period of heavy
competition with overseas markets, while the British economy slumped. The
first of the show's financial failures in this period was at Darlington in 1927,
where the coal stoppage of 1926, which led to the General Strike, created its own
particular difficulties. The population of the West Riding suffered financially as
a result of the strike, and there was simply less money in their pockets to spend on
attending the shows.[24] Yet, as so often in the YAS's history, a poor financial
performance and low public attendance in no way vitiated the show's success
from an agricultural point of view. In this respect, the Darlington show was
excellent, with record livestock and implement entries (7077 in total) and a
magnificent educational exhibition.

The fortunes of the show were restored temporarily in Halifax in 1928, where
a huge profit of some £6000 was made. Again, the show depended heavily on its
appeal to an urban public, for this year was especially difficult for the farming
community. Indeed, as the depression bit deeper over the next four years, even
this could scarcely enable the show's books to balance, with losses sustained on
the Hull (1930) and Bradford (1933) shows. The former of these events appears

PROGRAMME
WEDNESDAY, JULY 21st.

Admission 5/- each person. Children under 12 years of age 2/-.
Members and Exhibitors Free.

SHOW YARD OPEN FROM 9 A.M. TO 8 P.M.

9 0 a.m. Judging in Main Ring—Hunter Classes 13 to 21.
Judging in Main Ring—Shires.
Judging in Main Ring—Clydesdales.
Judging in Cattle Ring No. 1—Shorthorns.
Judging in Cattle Ring No. 2—British Friesians, followed by Welsh Blacks.
Judging in Cattle Ring No. 3—Ayrshires, followed by Aberdeen Angus.
Judging in Cattle Ring No. 4—Jersey Cattle, followed by Blue Albions.
Judging of Sheep, Pigs and Goats.
Judging of Poultry.

9 30 a.m. Horse Shoeing Competition, Class A.
10 0 a.m. Judging of Wool, Cheese, Hives and Honey.
10 30 a.m. Judging of Horticultural Exhibits and Allotment Holders' Produce.
Judging in Main Ring—Yorkshire Coach Horses.
Judging in Main Ring—Cleveland Bays.
11 45 a.m. Judging in Main Ring—Hackneys.
12 0 noon Meeting of Council.
2 0 p.m. Judging in Main Ring—Hunter Classes 22 and 24.
Judging in Cattle Ring No. 2—Pedigree Dairy Shorthorns.
Judging in Cattle Ring No. 3—Non-Pedigree Dairy Cows.
Butter-making Competition, Class A.
3 0 p.m. Lecture and Demonstration, by Mr. James Cameron, on Heavy Horses, adjoining Heavy Horse Section.
Lecture on " The Hen from Within," and Demonstration by Mr. W. Powell Owen.
3 30 p.m. Judging in Main Ring—Harness Class 35.
3 45 p.m. Judging in Main Ring—Hunter Classes 25 and 26.
4 0 p.m. Demonstration by Mr. F. W. Parton, " Trussing and Boning Poultry."
5 0 p.m. Judging in Main Ring—Harness Class 36.
5 15 p.m. Jumping Competition, Class A.
8 0 p.m. Show Yard Cleared.

Demonstrations and Lectures on Clean Milk, Wool, Bee-keeping, Bottling Fruit, and Poultry, at intervals during the day.

Reserved Seats (numbered) in Grand Stand 7/6 and 5/-. Unreserved Seats 3/-. Unreserved Covered Stand (end of Ring) 4/-.

ADMISSION OF MEMBERS.

MEMBERS OF THE SOCIETY will be admitted into the Show Yard, to the unreserved portion of the Grand Stand at the Horse Ring and General Enclosure (opposite Stand) provided there is room, to the Fox Hound Show, Dog Show, and to the Horticultural Exhibition by non-transferable Badges which must be signed. The like privileges are accorded to donors of £3 and upwards to the Harrogate Fund.

THE MEMBERS' DINING ROOM is provided for the use of Members and their friends. Admission by Badge only (admitting one Lady also) provided there is room.

THE MEMBERS' READING AND WRITING ROOM, AND LADY MEMBERS' ROOM ADJOINING, WITH LAVATORY ACCOMMODATION, ETC., in the centre of the Show Yard. Admission by Badge only.

Members who desire to receive their telegrams and letters without the trouble of calling for them at the Post Office in the Show Yard, are requested to have them specifically addressed to the " MEMBERS' ROOM, SHOW YARD, HARROGATE." All Telegrams and Letters addressed simply " Show Yard," will be retained at the Post Office until claimed.

The programme for the 1926 show at Harrogate. This was the first of the modern three-day events.

THURSDAY, JULY 22nd.

Admission 3/- each person. Children under 12 years of age 1/-.
SHOW YARD OPEN FROM 8 A.M. TO 8 P.M.

9 30 a.m.	Horse Shoeing Competition, Class B.
	Judging Hunter Classes 27, 23, 28 and Championship.
10 0 a.m.	Judging of Pigeons and Rabbits.
11 0 a.m.	Fox Hound Show—Judging.
	Butter-making Competition, Class B.
11 30 a.m.	Lecture and Demonstration, by Mr. James Cameron, on Sheep, adjoining Sheep Section.
12 0 noon	Parade of Cattle.
12 45 p.m.	Meeting of Members in Council Room.
1 30 p.m.	Judging of Polo Ponies.
2 0 p.m.	Band of the 8th King's Royal Irish Hussars, by kind permission of Lt.-Col. A. Currel.
2 30 p.m.	Judging of Harness Horses, Class 37.
	Butter-making Competition, Class C.
2 45 p.m.	Judging of Hacks and Riding Ponies.
3 0 p.m.	Lecture and Demonstration, by Mr. James Cameron, on Cattle, adjoining Cattle Section.
	Lecture and Demonstration on Poultry by Mr. F. W. Parton.
3 25 p.m.	Judging of Harness Horses, Class 40.
3 40 p.m.	Jumping Competition—Class B.
4 20 p.m.	Judging of Harness Horses, Class 41.
4 35 p.m.	Parade of Heavy Horses and Light Horses in Hand.
5 0 p.m.	Jumping Competition, Class C.
8 0 p.m.	Show Yard Cleared.
	Stock Attendants' Concert.

Demonstrations and Lectures on Clean Milk, Wool, Bee-keeping, Bottling Fruit, and Poultry, at intervals during the day.

Reserved Seats (numbered) in Grand Stand 7/6 and 5/-. Unreserved Seats 3/-. Unreserved Covered Stand (end of Ring) 3/-.

FRIDAY, JULY 23rd.

Admission 2/- each person. Children under 12 years of age 1/-.
SHOW YARD OPEN FROM 8 A.M. TO 8 P.M.

10 0 a.m.	Judging in Cattle Ring No. 1—Premium Bulls located in Yorkshire under Ministry of Agriculture's Scheme.
11 0 a.m.	Parade of Heavy Horses.
	Judging of Dogs.
11 30 a.m.	Judging of Harness Classes 38 and 39.
	Lecture and Demonstration, by Mr. Jas. Cameron, on Cattle, adjoining Cattle Section.
12 0 noon	Parade of Hunters and Light Horses.
12 30 p.m.	Butter-making Competition, Championship Class.
1 30 p.m.	Horse Shoeing Competition, Class C.
2 0 p.m.	Band of the 8th King's Royal Irish Hussars, by kind permission of Lt.-Col. A. Currel.
	Parade of Cattle.
	Lecture and Demonstration, by Mr. James Cameron, on Sheep, adjoining Sheep Section.
2 45 p.m.	Jumping Competition, Class D.
3 30 p.m.	Judging of Harness Horses—Championship.
	Lecture and Demonstration, by Mr. Jas. Cameron, on Heavy Horses, adjoining Heavy Horse Section.
	Horse Shoeing Competition, Class D.
3 45 p.m.	Parade of Hacks and Children's Ponies.
4 15 p.m.	Jumping Competition, Class E Championship.
5 0 p.m.	Military Demonstration, by kind permission of Lt.-Col. A. Currel, Commanding 8th King's Royal Irish Hussars.
8 0 p.m.	Show Yard Cleared.

Demonstrations and Lectures on Clean Milk, Wool, Bee-keeping, Bottling Fruit, and Poultry, at intervals during the day.

Reserved Seats in Grand Stand 3/-. Unreserved Covered Grand Stand (end of Ring) 2/-. Unreserved Seats 2/-.

to have caused the first twinge of general anxiety in the Council since 1921, for it now set up a sub-committee to examine the costs of the showground. One of its members was eventually to become a principal architect of today's Great Yorkshire Show: Lt Col John Dunnington-Jefferson.

With a heavy loss on the Bradford show, 1933 marked the slough in the Society's development during the interwar period. The Society as a whole actually registered a loss in this year, admittedly of only £238, but enough to be a distinct obstacle to the show's progress. The rapid climb thereafter might be attributed to three factors: a general strengthening of the national economy, the effectiveness of the protectionist legislation of late 1931 and 1932, and key changes in the YAS's management.

This last comment is not intended to suggest that sound management had been lacking within the Society. Yet it is conspicuous that in 1934 there was a remarkable reorganization in the power profile within the Council. Leopold Paget, who had been an excellent Showyard Director and Chairman of the Prizes and Judges Committee for the past twelve years, died suddenly. He was immediately replaced as Honorary Showyard Director, initially for only one year, by Dunnington-Jefferson, who was also elected Chairman of Finance.[25] Dunnington-Jefferson was already a zealous member of Council besides being a senior Vice-President, and his succession is not at all surprising. But what does surprise, and perhaps bears testimony to his enormous ability, is that by October of that year he was in virtual control of the Society and of its show. With the success of the recent show much to his credit he was re-appointed Showyard Director for 1935 and elected Chairman of the Prizes and Judges Committee. He also sat on the General Purposes and Journal and Education Committees.

Due in part to his all-pervasive influence from then onwards, but also to one or two other key figures such as Lord Middleton and Lt Col Stanyforth, the subsequent shows resumed their usual character. The 1935 show, at Sheffield, which was attended by the Prince of Wales on the second day, was gratifying in every way and showed a healthy profit. The event at Beverley in the following year featured a number of new or revived events, such as a large and popular hound show. And, as had always happened when the Great Yorkshire had visited Beverley, the Mayor and Local Committee pulled out all the stops to give the event as auspicious a launch as was humanly possible. As on previous occasions, this Beverley show had the extra cachet of being held at the race course on the Hurn pastures, and the calibre of the horse entries can therefore be imagined. There was also a record collection of agricultural machinery, and the whole affair netted a profit of nearly £3000.[26]

Dunnington-Jefferson's greatest challenge as new Showyard Director came with the planning of the next event to be held, at York, in celebration of the Society's centenary. He was fortunate in having ample funds at his disposal, for with the exception of the single year, 1933, the Society had been growing increasingly affluent since its first post-war show. The Council were determined to make the show a spectacular one, apparently oblivious, however, of the fact that the extravagance of the last great celebratory show at York, in 1887, had caused severe financial problems for the Society. His Majesty King George V was invited to accept the Presidency for that year and thus to preside at the show, but he declined, agreeing, however, to become the YAS's Patron.[27] In haste, Her Royal Highness The Princess Royal was offered the Presidency. She accepted and turned out to be not only gracious but also remarkably active in that role, chairing the General Meeting and personally delivering the annual address on the showground.[28] The site itself, the classic Knavesmire which had been the Great Yorkshire's location at York ever since its second visit to the city in 1842, was of course superb: covering some 50 acres, with free supplies of gas, electricity and water, it was then one of the very best show sites in Britian. The occasion was also blessed with perfect weather on all three days (13–15 July) for the first time in 16 years, so the paying public poured in, enabling the city to win the Attendance Gold Cup from the previous record-holder, Bradford.

As we have done earlier in this *History*, we might turn to the coverage of this centennial Great Yorkshire Show in the *Yorkshire Gazette* to catch its flavour. The showyard, we are told, 'was virtually a town of wood and canvas'. And it was more than just an exhibition of stock and implements, for

> It covered every department of rural life, and did much to provide the bridge over the gulf between the interests of town and country, which is agriculture's crying need today.

As for the livestock, that included not only the cream of Yorkshire but also some of Britain's which had been exhibited in the previous week at the Royal Show. The total of livestock entries, at 1402, had been exceeded only twice before in the show's history (at Harrogate in 1926 and Darlington in 1927), and the number of classes was now beyond compare. The cattle represented were now: Shorthorns, Pedigree Dairy Shorthorns, Non-Pedigree Dairy Cows, Aberdeen-Angus, British Friesian, Ayrshire, Jersey, Guernsey, and Red Poll. Breeds of sheep included: Leicester, Lincoln, Wensleydale, Oxford Down, Suffolk, Lank, Swaledale, and Masham; of horses: Hunters, Shires, Percherons, Suffolks, Clydesdales, Yorkshire Coach Horses, and riding classes (noteworthy is the disappearance by now of agricultural horses as a class); of pigs: Large White, Middle White, Large Black, Berkshire, Wessex Saddleback, Essex, Cumberland and commercial classes. There were classes and premiums for hives and honey, cheese and butter, foxhounds, pigeons and poultry, dairying and horse shoeing. But notably absent, in view of its success when mounted on previous occasions, was the flower show. The implements and machinery section was perhaps the most impressive ever, with a record of 337 implement stands, perhaps reflecting the fact that for some years there had been a strong representative of this section on the Council, in the person of Mr Henry Bushell.

By now the YAS had a vigorous Publicity Committee (to be discussed) whose activities were evident in the relationship cultivated with the press at this show. For instance, there was a fine press luncheon, and the talk given there by Lord Middleton bears quoting for an indication both of how some things had changed, and also how others had not:

Just think of the changes that have come in a century – in machinery, in cattle food, and transport. If our grandfathers and great-grandfathers were here next week their comments would be worth listening to. They would, no doubt, find much to admire in modern agricultural methods and perhaps something to criticise.

Perhaps they would tell us that in spite of all that science has achieved, muck and lime are still the best foods for the land. They would probably be right there.

They would possibly criticise us for not paying more attention to land drainage. If my grandfather were to touch on that, I would respectfully enlighten him about death duties, taxation, rates, and modern costs of production, all of which things press so hardly on those who would like to improve their land but cannot. I think that he would stare at me incredulously, but when it had sunk in perhaps he would pat me on the shoulder and say, 'Well, well, rural England has paid a pretty stiff price for progress'.

What would our forebears of 1837 say of our stock? I think that they would be pleased with our cattle, sheep and pigs, but they might question our wisdom in producing much of our breeding stock at the show in disgustingly fat condition. I think that the minds of many of their descendents today are exercised about this, but no one has yet solved the problem in a practical way, and produced workable rules and standards to guide the judges so that they may operate fairly.*

They would criticise our cart horses for being too big and coarse, and say that our hunters are too much like racehorses.

One just wonders what the future holds. Whether the changes from 1937 to 2037 will be as sharp as the changes from 1837 to 1937. I suppose that all the machinery of today will be museum pieces in 50 years' time. Will horses on the land survive for another century, or will they disappear?[29]

The centennial show was fortunately a substantial financial as well as social and agricultural success, and all of its profit (some £4000) was placed in the hands of Lord Middleton and Lt Col Dunnington-Jefferson to invest.[30] The administrative staff received a 10 percent bonus on their annual salary as a reward for their extra efforts, and a gold medal was struck and sent to the Princess for her very real service as President.

The following show, at Doncaster, was again successful and indicated that the Great Yorkshire was all set to expand and to incorporate features of direct interest to the Society's now swelling numbers of ordinary members. One such feature was the award of long service medals and certificates to farm-workers with at least 40 years' service (including war service), a revival of the long-service premiums that had been given at the shows in the 1830s. This revival began at the Halifax show in 1939.

By 1939, Council was again planning the show three years in advance. Wakefield was selected for 1940, Malton for 1941. Coincidentally, the same spirit of expansionism and optimism pervaded the Council as in 1918, just before war broke out. This time, however, the Council was in no doubt about whether

---

* Precisely the problem debated within the YAS in the 1840s, prinipally between H.S. Thompson and Hawkesworth Fawkes. See Chapter 2.

to hold any shows during the war. At its first meeting after the outbreak of war, the Council cancelled all show plans and put itself firmly on a wartime footing. The President at the time, Brigadier General Sir Edward Whitley, agreed to continue as President and Chairman of Council for the duration of the war.

We must now retrace our steps to examine the policy-makers and officers and the workers on the showground and within the secretariat who were responsible for the Society's impressive development during this interwar period.

After the death of the Earl of Feversham at the end of 1916, the Council and the more important committees were dominated by Lord Middleton, Lt Col E.W. Stanyforth, and Major J.W. Dent. They were closely and very ably assisted by a half-dozen or so others: Captain Greenwood, Col Sir George Duncombe, and Messrs Davy, Hawking, Jacob Smith, Paget and Winn. Generally, the President (when he was an active one, like the Earl of Harewood in 1919, Lord Middleton in 1920 or Major Dent in 1921) or otherwise the Chairman of Finance would preside at Council meetings, and would often put his personal stamp upon the proceedings. This continued to be the case even after the creation of the official post of Chairman of Council. Indeed, the post as such carried little independent weight for its first six years, when the President would usually chair Council meetings and appeared still to be the *de facto* executive. Indeed, the President of the Society and the Chairman of Council were one and the same persons in 1920, '21, '27, '30, '33, '35, '38, '39 and for the duration of the war, thus obviating the principal reason for creating the latter post, namely to lighten the President's burden. So far as the actual functioning and success of the YAS was concerned, it is doubtful whether a sharper separation between the two offices would have made much difference. But for a social historian, it is instructive to see how power tends to be concentrated, even in so benign a fashion.

Among other developments in this period were the appointment in 1923 of two new trustees, Lord Bolton and most significantly, Lt Col Dunnington-Jefferson, and the creation of a powerful new committee in November of the same year – the General Purposes Committee.[31] The latter was almost certainly the first significant step to be taken by a Chairman of Council, at this time Lord Deramore, acting independently of the President (Lt Col Stanyforth). The committee was created by amalgamating the Selection and the Showyard Sites Committees, and it comprised the President, the Chairman of Council, the Chairmen of all the standing committees, and nine others. Its setting up reflected the increasing complexity of the Society's functioning and needs and the requirement for tighter management. In this respect, it quickly became very effective, and by 1925 it obviously dominated the inner thinking and working of the society.

This committee also shaped the composition of the Council. In January 1925 it nominated nine new members to be co-opted onto Council, one of whom was Dunnington-Jefferson.[32] By then, its principal figures, the management-core of the Society, included Stanyforth, Captain Greenwood, Major Dent, Lord Deramore and Messrs Hawking and Jacob Smith. Most of these men continued to play a directive role throughout the remainder of the Twenties and Thirties, Stanyforth, Greenwood, Dent and Jacob Smith in particular. It may therefore be said that there was a very powerful element of continuity in management and ideology during these two decades. And this, combined with the remarkable business acuity and efficiency of several of these individuals, surely accounts for the Society's prosperity and steady development, despite the agricultural and general depressions.

Whilst this continuity lasted right up to the outbreak of the Second World War, the mid 1930s saw some change in the central management, with the deaths of four key figures, Sir George Duncombe and Leopold Paget in 1934, and Lord Deramore and Major Fawkes in spring 1936 (at the same time as the Society's Patron, His Majesty King George V). Deramore and Fawkes, like so many other central figures in the YAS's history, had been both active in the Society and deeply influential in their own areas of the county: Deramore in the East Riding, and Fawkes in the West. Fawkes had also been long serving as a show steward and must have been missed by many. Within this period, Dunnington-Jefferson took up his duties as Show Director and Chairman of Finance.

There appears to have been something of a debate, perhaps even an altercation, over the roles and powers of the central personnel at about this time. In particular, there is an indication of some tension between the new Showyard Director and the Society's Secretary, for in January 1935 Council felt obliged to specify the duties – and the cooperation – they expected from the holders of the two positions. They began laying down a 'general principle':

> The Secretary is the Society's Executive Officer, taking his instructions either direct from the Council, or, in so far as the Show arrangements are concerned, from the Honorary Director.
>
> The Honorary Director is the link between the Council and the Secretary, so far as Show arrangments are concerned, with authority from the Council to direct the Secretary as and when he considers it necessary to do so.

Revealingly, the Council went on to say:

> The satisfactory interpretation of this general principle can only depend upon mutual good-will and co-operation between the Secretary and the Honorary Show Director.[33]

Councils' detailed specification of how the Show Director should go about his business, and of how the Secretary should go about his with regard to the show, suggests that Dunnington-Jefferson was attempting to bring very much more of the show's management under his authority, with the Council's backing. In this respect, it appears that the task of Honorary Showyard Director now entered a new phase with much more control placed formally in his hands. The Director was no longer essentially a Council member who would coordinate the efforts for the Show, but rather a largely independent figure whose authority derived from his post. It might be added that members of the Society today who remember

Dunnington-Jefferson would say that he was also anxious to acquire greater personal authority, for the *modus operandi* of his very strong personality required a full excercise of power. The great fruits of that exercise were to be the financial development of the Society and the achievement of the Great Yorkshire's permanent showyard.

Another figure of authority during this period was Lt Col Stanyforth who was among the significant number of YAS Presidents also acting as Presidents of the RASE, thus continuing that interchange of ideology and information between the two societies. His duel presidency in 1923, when he was understandably more occupied with the RASE, signalled the start of the independent development of the Chairman of Council. But Stanyforth himself was Chairman of Council for the next two years, and again in 1937, thus contributing to several key features of the YAS's character. One other figure must here be mentioned – Captain Greenwood, whose chairmanship of Finance from the 1920s to 1934 ensured that the Society's investments were handled on a more extensive basis than ever before, and that its capital grew steadily. When he had taken up his post, the YAS's funds were mainly in railway stocks, and were worth about £4000; when he retired as Chairman of Finance (but not from the Council) in 1934, the YAS possessed a whole new portfolio of investments, worth some £40,000 (exclusive of rolling stock).[34]

Indeed, it is worth looking in some detail at the evolution of the YAS's investments' portfolio after the First World War, as this reinforces the main thesis of this chapter: that it was then that the YAS shed its nineteenth-century character and, with notable success, acquired the essentials for its modern, corporate existence. In January 1923, after two successful post-war shows, and several years into a highly successful post-war recruitment drive (discussed in detail below), the YAS's investments stood as follows:

£
2066 in London and North Eastern Railway 3% debentures.
2000 in New South Wales $3\frac{1}{2}$% debentures.
1000 in Australia stocks, at 5%.
1500 India stocks, at $4\frac{1}{2}$%.
1500 as local loans, at 3%.
1300 Conversion $3\frac{1}{2}$% stocks.

Total: £9366.

As this breakdown suggests, the Society was now moving away from its traditional financial affiliation with the railways. It rapidly continued this process, so that when the 1925 show at Bradford turned in a handsome profit, the Finance Committee invested all of that and more besides in gilt edged securities. In the hands of Greenwood and the Society's trustees, principally Lord Middleton and Dunnington-Jefferson, this diversification into Dominion and Empire stocks and gilts continued. Then, in 1947, on the advice of its new trustee, the Westminster Bank, the Society's capital was re-invested in bank accounts, insurance and domestic shares.[35]

This evolving strategy was stimulated in part by the steady generation of income from membership. Immediately after the war, a new recruitment strategy took effect whereby each member of the Council was charged with the task of actively canvassing his own area of the county. In 1920, felt Council, this strategy was already working well, with nearly fifty new members joining in that year. Messrs Ben Day (of Leeds) and Jacob Smith (of Knaresborough) had recruited 13 and ten new members respectively.[36] In the next four months, however, recruitment rose rapidly, with 245 annual subscribers and seven life members being added within this period.[37] By June of the same year, a total of 414 annual subscribers and 15 life members had been added. This *annus mirabilis* for the YAS's membership growth, which, we may recall, had languished below 1000, and often below 800, between 1840 and 1891, was to be repeated in 1924 (when 562 new members were entered), 1926, 1929 (600 new members), and 1933. In 1934 membership rose above the 4000 mark. And with the start of the junior membership scheme, in January 1938, younger blood than ever before was entering the Society.

Some half-dozen factors seem to have underlain this rise in membership: the excellence of the show; the Society's contact with the county's farming community through its other activities, such as the Clean Milk Competition and its cooperation on educational ventures with the Agriculture Department at Leeds University and the Yorkshire Council for Agricultural Education; the work of the Propaganda and Publicity Committee, set up in June 1930; the renewed excellence of the *Transactions*, which was resumed under Major Dent in 1921 and soon become a semblance of its founding self; and the personal dedication of a handful of Council members. The first of these factors has already been discussed. The second (educational) factor needs closer examination. On the subject of two others, a brief comment is due, and on the remaining factor some discussion is desirable since it brought the Society firmly back to that ideology of the founding years: 'Progress with Science'.

One Council member stands out in the Twenties for his recruitment of annual subscribers – Jacob Smith, of Knaresborough. In some years, he was securing two new members per week, and in performing that service as well as being a frequent attender at Council and working on several committees, he may be taken as representative of the behind the scenes stalwarts of the Society's management. Never elected President, never Chairman of Council, he was ever present on the showground and widely popular as a farmer among farmers. His name is among a conspicuous proportion of names on the Society's roll today which were also there in Thompson's time.

The Propaganda and Publicity Committee merits mention for it too symbolized, and helped engineer, the Society's changing character. By 1931, this committee had an annual budget of some £600–700, roughly the size of the Secretary's salary, and there was ample confidence within the Council that this money was well spent. Certainly, the newspaper advertising for the Society, the bill posting, the press conferences and the public presentation of the extra show activities which were suddenly conspicuous in the Thirties should have been effective in attracting new members, and very probably were. This committee was also charged with the task of bridging the gap between town and country, an aim that Earl Spencer and his colleagues had hoped the show *per se* would fulfill, and a task still regarded as important today.

Next, we must consider the journal and the resuscitation of its science policy. We have seen that before the First World War the Society was promoting science, particularly chemistry, in the form of a chemical consultancy for its members. On the death of the long-serving chemist, Thomas Fairley, in 1919, a Mr Burrell (of Leeds) was appointed, initially on a trial basis of one year on a £20 retainer, but then on a more remunerative, permanent basis. At the same time, a new veterinary inspector, Professor Seton (head of the Agriculture Department at Leeds) was appointed as successor to Professor Dewar. With both men, Major Dent, then Chairman of the Journal and Education Committee (as the former Journal and Chemical Committee was re-named in December 1921) apparently established a personal rapport.

In January 1921 Dent submitted a recommendation on behalf of the Journal and Chemical Committee that the *Transactions* be resumed and that contributions should be solicited from the staff at Leeds University.[38] This was done, and by the 1930s agricultural scientists at Leeds were contributing highly scientific papers to the journal. Dent was also anxious to get science contributors nationwide, and by 1924 he was succeeding. In that year's issue there were articles, commissioned by the Journal and Education Committee, from Professor James Mackintosh of the National Institute for Research in Dairying at Reading, and from Professor James Watson at Edinburgh. Dent also asked Burrell, the Society's analyst, to write detailed chemical reports more often, to be printed in the *Transactions* as before.[39] By 1924, Burrell was obliging, submitting a massive report to the Council, which its members were apparently expected to digest cheerfully at a single sitting.

This promotion of chemistry continued when Burrell died in 1927 and was replaced by H.T. Lea, a consulting chemist from Leeds. In January 1929 a further step was taken with the creation of a new Research and Investigation Committee, whose initial task was to organize experiments on sub-soils in conjunction with the Agriculture Department at Leeds.[40] This pursuit of research continued into the next decade, even though Dent retired from all of his posts within the Society at the end of 1929 (for reasons which are obscure), and indeed the *Transactions* became more science-oriented than ever. For instance, the 1931 issue carried a thoroughly *à la mode* chemical paper on 'Colloids and Agriculture' from the Seale-Hayne Agricultural College, Newton Abbot, a botanical paper on grasses, as well as articles on technical aspects of farming.

One of the consequences of this policy that ordinary farmers may have taken a direct interest in was the continuing debate about the extent and nature of manure and feedstuff adulteration. By 1935, mainly as a result of the Fertilizers and Feeding Stuffs Act (1935), the Society's consulting chemist was able to report that in general there was relatively little adulteration, although he did warn of a continuation of the practice of tampering with cereal-feeds. The latter was not serious enough to injure animals physically, as had been the case in the late nineteenth century, but, nonetheless, it reduced the feedstuffs' nutritive value, and hence hit the dairy farmer's pocket.[41] As the Act took effect, the Society's chemist became increasingly alarmed at another problem – the contamination of drinking water. By 1938, he reckoned that most drinking waters sent to him for chemical analysis were unfit for domestic use.[42]

Leas's excellent work as consulting chemist, which was much appreciated by the Society's managers, ended with his death at the very outbreak of World War Two. His replacement, Mr John Evans, based at the Public Analyst's Laboratory, Sheffield, continued to provide an analytical service to members, and to report regularly to the YAS Council. The suspension of the *Transactions* from 1941 until 1946, however, coupled with wartime exigencies, meant that the science policy once again took a low profile. Moreover, the chemical consultancy was officially terminated in October 1945, having perhaps outlived its usefulness to the Society's members.

Mention has been made of the Society's involvement with agricultural education, which developed markedly in this interwar period, particularly in collaboration with the University of Leeds and the Yorkshire Council for Agricultural Education. We should retrace our steps to examine this development in greater depth.

The Yorkshire College of Science was established in Leeds in 1874 to develop and teach the sciences pertaining to Yorkshire industries. Within a couple of years, its brief was widened, as was indicated by the change of its name to The Yorkshire College in 1877, when it became a component of The Victoria University (which also included colleges at Liverpool and Manchester). It became autonomous, as the University of Leeds, in 1904. Mention has been made in the previous chapter of the creation of its Department of Agriculture in 1890. The county committee responsible for this achievement was headed by Lord Herries, who was a landowner in the county and a member of the YAS's Council. In the latter capacity, and as President in 1894, he initiated the YAS's close connection with those institutions for agricultural education that were developed both then and subsequently.

The scheme for financing the Department of Agriculture which Herries's county committee arrived at consisted of an annual private subscription grant of about £450 plus about £1000 from each of the three County Councils of the Yorkshire Ridings, with a supplementary grant from the Board of Agriculture. This resulted in Yorkshire's agricultural education being quite unique, entailing a fusion of college and county interests under one roof. This itself was reinforced by the continued management of the Leeds Department of Agriculture by members of the YAS's Council.

When that department was created, the constitution of The Yorkshire College required that it have a committee of management. Lord Herries was the natural choice for its chairman, and he remained in control until 1897 when the committee was replaced by another body, the Joint Agricultural Council. This came into existence as the management body of the experimental working farm,

Manor Farm, just outside Garforth Village, near Leeds, which was then leased by the East and West Riding County Councils, where the department's staff could conduct research and give practical instruction. The Joint Agricultural Council, made up of representatives of the two County Councils, suggested to The Yorkshire College that the farm and the department should together come under the auspices of the same management body. This was promptly effected in the form of a new Joint Agricultural Council, chaired by Lord Herries, comprising representatives of the two County Councils and the College, with the Principal and Secretary of the College also allowed to attend meetings.

In 1902 the North Riding County Council entered the scheme, and the Joint Agricultural Council was succeeded by the Yorkshire Council for Agricultural Education, an annually appointed body. Over this much more comprehensive committee, Herries also presided, until 1908. He was then succeeded by Major J.W. Dent, who gave himself unsparingly to this work in the course of the next twenty years, at the same time functioning as a key manager of the YAS and its main promoter of science. Dent was succeeded by another central figure in the YAS, Major F.H. Fawkes, who had to relinquish the post, however, after only five years, for reasons of health. He was succeeded by Sir Percy Jackson.

We thus glimpse how intimate was the connection between the YAS's management and the evolution of agricultural education in Yorkshire. Under Dent, this connection was furthered by the purchase of two farms at Askham Bryan, near York, in 1927, in anticipation of having to leave Manor Farm. At Askham Bryan, the Agricultural Council, first under Dent but mainly under Fawkes and then Jackson, planned a substantial Farm Institute to provide three-term courses in agriculture, horticulture, dairy, poultry husbandry and other aspects of food production. The subsequent developement of Askham Bryan College of Agriculture is beyond the scope of this chapter, but it must be said that the YAS continued to maintain personal contacts with the college, as well as cementing a more formal connection in the 1950s. Today, this connection is symbolized by the fact that the present Chairman of the YAS's Executive Committee (Mr Lance Gilling) is a former Principal of Askham Bryan College, and the current Principal is a co-opted member of the Council. The YAS's network spreads and spreads.[43]

Two further features of the society must be mentioned. With the way cleared, by the new 'Rules and Objects', for the Society to take up political or legislative issues of agricultural relevance, successive Councils showed themselves eager to do so. In 1922–3, the Council debated possible legislation on means for checking the importation of livestock diseases, and in April 1923 it sent a memorandum on the matter to the Ministry of Agriculture and Fisheries, other agricultural societies and various committees.[44] In the following year, the Council collaborated with other societies on the vexed question of the income tax status of agricultural shows.[45] In 1927 the importation of Canadian cattle elicited Council's advice for proposed legislation.[46] In 1928 the income tax battle seemed finally to bear fruit, with a clear recognition that the Society's charitable status entailed the same for its show.

Finally, we must return to the salaried staff. We have seen that Cavers was installed as Secretary in late 1921. He quickly proved his worth and, as usual, Council generously expressed its appreciation. In 1924 £200 was set aside to purchase a car for his exclusive use and to cover all his motoring expenses for the first year.[47] Two years later, he was awarded a 30 percent salary rise, and there were further rewards for his professionalism. The most substantial of these, for the entire staff, was the comprehensive superannuation scheme introduced in 1938.[48] Cavers' massively increased workload (compared with those of previous Secretaries) also demanded extra staff, who have been appointed without parsimony by successive Councils: there were at least two full-time clerks by 1926 as well as ample seasonal staff for the show. The excellent Clerk of Works, J.E. Pottage, was also given due recognition financially and in the appointment of ancillary staff. The size of the salaried staff was, of course, one of the features which made the Society in 1939 so markedly different from in 1919. With the coming of war, however, three-quarters of them departed for national service.

How the YAS was maintained during the Second World War and sprang back into action in 1946, to be transformed once again as it had been in the Twenties and Thirties, is the subject of the next chapter.

6 THE SECOND WORLD WAR AND AFTER, 1939–63

By any standards, British farmers weathered the war well. When fighting broke out, the national agricultural strategy was very similar to that of 1916 and simple in conception: it aimed to raise the production of those foods which were most efficient, while production of livestock (with the exception of cattle) was to be depleted.

The pattern, productivity and profitability of British agriculture responded quickly to this national objective. In just three years, the gross output of British agriculture rose by two-thirds, and during the war as a whole farming net income rose more than three-fold.[1] Perhaps the greater part of this rise in income came about because of price-rises rather than as a result of great increases in gross output, but the Ministry of Agriculture also provided unprecedented facilities to encourage the latter, by subsidising the cost of lime and other manures, and establishing a pool of agricultural machinery specifically to help farmers convert from grassland to arable and to enable them to plough deeper and cultivate more intensively. By the end of the war, the British countryside looked far better than it had beforehand. The national diet was well-balanced, and farmers were in a strong position to prepare for the negotiation of a post-war agricultural policy.

In formulating this policy, the government fully accepted the strategic importance of a confident and prosperous agricultural sector, and everyone seemed agreed upon the futility of reverting to what many called the 'dog and stick' farming of the depression. This was enshrined in the Agricultural Act of 1947, whose general objectives were:

> Promoting and maintaining . . . a stable and efficient agricultural industry capable of producing such part of the nation's food and other agricultural produce as in the national interest it is desirable to produce in the United Kingdom, and of producing it at minimum prices consistently with proper remuneration and living conditions for farmers and workers in agriculture and an adequate return on capital invested in the industry.[2]

These objectives were to be quoted time and again during the implementation of the post-war policy and whenever departures from it were being considered. For the main agricultural products, at that time constituting some 80 percent of gross output, achieving these objectives was encouraged through price guarantees, at first paid directly by the Exchequer and later, as wartime controls were lifted, by 'deficiency payments' representing the difference between the guaranteed price and an average market price for each product. Guaranteed prices were settled for eleven products: cattle, sheep, milk, eggs, barley, wheat, oats, rye, potatoes, sugar beet and wool. The prices were fixed annually, following an annual agricultural review involving close consultation between Ministers and the various farmers' unions. The latter were thus in a unique position among British industries in having a statutory right to consultation about the prices which their produce would fetch. This system was acceptable because, until the 1960s, the prices fixed were at the expense of the general taxpayer and not at the cost of the consumer.

The early years of the implementation of this Act were dominated by the manifold task of post-war reconstruction and the role that agriculture could play in that task. The Government thus envisaged the steady growth of the agricultural industry, a vision that persisted almost unbrokenly until the mid 1970s. Initially, as spelled out in the 1952 Annual Review, net output was to be raised by 1956 to 60 percent above pre-war levels. Priority was to be given to the development of livestock enterprises, aiming 'above all, to raise to the utmost the production of beef and veal, mutton and lamb'.[3] In a similar manner, the government sought to improve the productivity of grassland in order to grow more oats and barley, which would, in turn, alleviate the shortage of feed grains. All in all, greater efficiency had to be achieved.

The target was in fact met, and this testifies to the professionalism of the British farmer as well as to the excellence of the relationship between the farming community and the government. Greater efficiency was successfuly encouraged in a number of ways. First, the additions to the guaranteed prices after 1951 were less than the increases in costs, with the declared intention that increases in net farming income could come about only through higher efficiency. However, a strategic document released in 1956, *Long-term Assurances for Agriculture*, limited the Government's ability to adjust the guarantee downwards: for any product, the guaranteed price in any year could be no less than 96 percent of the previous year's level, and for livestock products the reduction could be no greater than 9 percent in any three-year period. Without these assurance, the guaranteed prices would certainly have fallen faster.

The second means of encouraging productivity was a change in emphasis and a movement from price-supports to subsidies on capital and chemical inputs and to structural changes within the industry.

By the late 1950s, concern began to be expressed over the cost of the agricultural policy and in particular over the price-support system. World prices of agricultural products were falling heavily, and Commonwealth producers complained that Britain's continued agricultural expansion was spoiling the market. Additionally, unless guaranteed prices could be brought down, the efficiency drive would make Britain's overall balance of payments more problematic. Thus in 1958, when there was actually a target of zero growth, various measures were taken to regulate the policy. Producer quotas, with penalties for over-production, were introduced in 1961 and 1963, and a two-part tariff for milk with lower and uncontrolled prices in the manufactured market was introduced.

Yet the relationship between the farming community and government remained constructive, with the government committed to its supportive role.(See Figures 6.1 and 6.2.) A White Paper published in 1960, following a

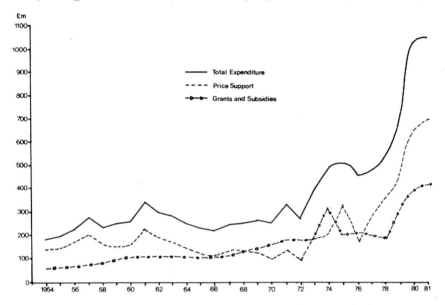

Figure 6.1 Public expenditure on agricultural support (current prices)

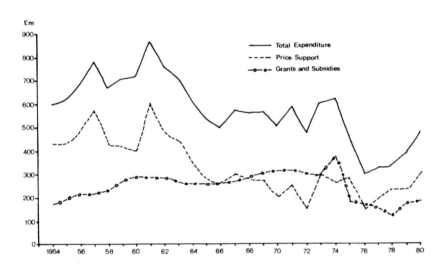

Figure 6.2 Public expenditure on agricultural support (constant prices)

meeting between the Prime Minister and the President of the National Farmers' Union, described agriculture as 'this great industry', emphasized its importance as a source of employment and as a valuable contributor to the balance of payments, and praised its increases in net output and productivity since the war.[4] The talks upon which this document was based bore fruit, for the White Papers of the early 1960s were fulsome in their recognition of farmers' achievements. There was an improvement in the relationship between guaranteed prices and costs and a shift in approach which eventually amounted to abandoning the original post-war policy – a shift that was initiated by the Annual Review in 1964, announcing the introduction of import controls for cereals and fatstock.

We thus see that the national agricultural policy was more or less a continuum from the years of the Second World War until about 1964. Thus, the general context of the YAS's development during this period may be handled more or less as of a piece. By a coincidence, 1963–4 also happened to be a turning point within the evolution of the YAS's own management and ideology. This accounts for the period to which this chapter is confined: 1939 to 1963.

At the outbreak of war, the YAS Council requested the President and Chairman of Council, Brigadier General Sir Edward Whitley, to remain in office for the duration of hostilities. The Council also promptly decided not to proceed with the two shows that were already in the pipeline – at Wakefield for 1940, and Malton for 1941. Indeed, little time seems to have been wasted before putting the YAS on a 'care and maintenance basis' for the foreseeable future, and this allowed the Society to balance its books each year.

In the first year of war, the journal was still printed and the new consulting chemist (appointed in January 1940) performed a few analyses for members. Little else was done, however, and the journal was then suspended. For the remainder of the war, the Society provided only a minimal chemical consultancy and made donations to several local agricultural organizations and clubs.[5] It also donated annually to the Red Cross Agricultural Fund.

Making due allowance for wartime exigencies and losses, membership held up as well as could be expected. It is likely that much of the credit for this must go to Dunnington-Jefferson, for not only were his wartime colleagues to recall how he had held the Society together[6] but it is evident that he more than anyone else was attempting to prepare the YAS for a resumption of normality. For instance, the AGM in January 1942 resolved that the Society's affairs during the remainder of the war should be managed by an Emergency Committee – and its Chairman was Dunnington-Jefferson. In that capacity, in the following year he made a recommendation that was to be immeasurably useful a number of years later: that there should no longer be individual trustees of the Society but that the Westminster Bank should become its sole trustee.[7] This was effected in January 1944 with the introduction of a new rule in the YAS's constitution, Rule 21:

That the Westminster Bank Ltd should be Trustees of all investments held by the Society and that further investments should be made by them on the instructions of the Finance Committee.[8]

At the end of the war Dunnington-Jefferson, knighted for his work as Chairman of the East Riding War Agricultural Committee (and henceforth in this *History* to be referred to as Sir John), undertook the task of getting the Society back into gear. For example, on the recommendations that he submitted to the Finance and General Purposes Committee a full salary scale was resumed in January 1946, some of which was backdated too. Thus, the Secretary was now to be paid £1250 per annum as from January 1945, a salary-level which indicates that this war had been about as inflationary as the first.[9]

As had happened at the end of the First World War, the Council now hoped that a show could soon be held, but central government thought otherwise. A memorandum from the Ministry of Agriculture and Fisheries insisted that 'it was not thought possible to hold a Show in 1946, owing to the serious shortage of constructional materials for priority uses, and the evident need in the national interest to concentrate the available building material upon such urgent tasks as housing'.[10] So, there was no Great Yorkshire Show, nor any other major agricultural event in 1946, and likewise in 1947. In October 1946, however, the YAS started to lobby for the RASE to hold its intended 1948 show in Yorkshire, and by January of the following year it learned that its lobbying had succeeded.[11] The RASE would visit York, and the YAS would have another year to prepare for its own first post-war show.

In this interval a number of developments took place within the Society. On the personnel side, Cavers suddenly announced his intention to retire at the end of 1947. He had been a most efficient and valued Secretary for 26 years and Council promptly expressed their appreciation for all that he had done by awarding him an annual gratuity of £250 to augment the pension that he would receive.[12] The announcement of his retirement must have come as a surprise. In fact, Cavers realized that he was critically ill and died shortly after leaving office. A small committee consisting of three of the key managers was set up to appoint his successor, comprising Sir Edward Whitley (then still President and Chairman of Council), Lord Middleton and Sir John. In November 1947 the choice was announced to Council by Sir John (which is indicative of his all-important role in the Society, since one would expect the Chairman of Council to announce the appointee). The new Secretary was Mr F.M. Baldwin. At the same time, the former Clerk of Works, J.E. Pottage (who had found himself lucrative employment elsewhere during the war) agreed to be re-appointed, much to everyone's delight.[13]

Another of the undoubted surprises at this time was Sir John's own announcement, in November 1947, that he intended to resign from the Honorary Show Directorship because of other commitments, and that he intended to leave before the Wakefield show of 1949 (to be the YAS's first post-war show).[14] Two reasons for Sir John's decision are apparent. First, Sir John had many interests in the East Riding, and doubtless felt that these were being neglected. Second, the preparation for the show at Wakefield was proving unusually difficult. Timber was still in very short supply, and although the immediate handling of that problem might be given over to a contractor, (as it eventually was) Sir John was doubtful that the job could be done by the second week in August. Sir John's intention to resign seems to have been accepted by the Council, but ten months later (September 1948) he allowed himself to be persuaded to stay on as Show Director until after the Wakefield show. Nonetheless, he was still adamant about resigning and nominated his successor, Major Humphrey Seed, who was now appointed to the new post of Assistant Honorary Show Director.[15]

Sir John continued in this interval to be the most active and influential member of the YAS Council, despite the presence of the very competent and greatly trusted Chairman of Council, Sir Edward, who was re-appointed as both President and Chairman for 1948. Thus, it was still Sir John who was making the nominations for the top offices. It was also he who, in January 1948, even as he expected not to be the director of any more Great Yorkshire Shows, proposed a radical restriction on cattle entries at the event, namely that

> entries of dairy and dual-purpose cattle should be restricted to those from Attested and Supervised Herds, and that entries of Beef cattle be restricted to those from Attested, Supervised or Licensed T.T. herds.[16]

Despite some opposition, particularly from Mr Frank Abbey, a newcomer to the Council and soon to be a most active and popular figure in the Society's management, Sir John's proposal was adopted.

Yet more radical was Sir John's proposal that the entire committee system be restructured and that the Society's rules be revised. Clearly, he felt that since the last reorganization, in the early 1920s, the tasks confronting the Society had evolved at a faster rate than its management structure could cope with. To the historian, this seems doubtful; the YAS of 1948 sems to have faced few new challenges that the YAS of the 1930s could not have handled. However, Council apparently agreed with Sir John, for in May 1948 a major re-organization of the standing committees and a revision of the 'Rules of the Society' were approved. Two of the previous committees, the Journal and Education and the Propaganda and Publicity Committees, were abolished; their business was henceforth to be handled by the General Purposes Committee. There were now to be seven standing committees (as shown in Table 6.1). One should also note the large size of the General Purposes Committee, and its Chairman, the 10th Baron Lord Middleton, whose father had been tremendously influential in the YAS during the period 1890–1920 and who himself would be a principal figure throughout the 1950s and '60s.

One other feature of this Council meeting, also revealing Sir John's ubiquitous influence in the Society, was his announcement, as Chairman of Finance, that the Society had purchased the property of 'Cliftonfield', Shipton

Road, York, 'for use by the Society as offices and a house for the Secretary'. The Society moved into Cliftonfield on the 18 June. Being the first piece of property to be owned by the Society, it must have been regarded as the YAS's permanent base for the future. The property cost £6250, for which a £7000 loan at 4 percent interest was obtained from the Westminster Bank.[17] A few months later, the loan was repaid by realizing £7000 of the Society's British Transport Stock.[18]

During these several months, the new Secretary had embarked on his task in the same spirit of freshness and innovation as had his predecessors. This had been especially notable with Parrington, Stephenson and Maughan, whose 'fresh brooms' had swept new enthusiasm into the Society's administration. In particular, the new Secretary had been contemplating the future of the show, and in the summer of 1948, in conversation with Mr G.R.H. Smith, a member of the Finance and the Prizes and Judges Committees, in the latter's garden at Oxton Hall, he mooted the idea of a permanent showground for the YAS.[19] In September of that year Mr Baldwin put his ideas on paper in the form of a substantial memorandum, which was placed before the Council and which Sir John introduced approvingly. Its possible import for the whole Society can be gauged from the composition of the committee now set up to study it: The President, the Chairman of Finance, the Chairman of General Purpose, Sir John, and two Council representatives from each Riding.[20]

Table 6.1: Standing Committee reorganization in 1948

Name of Committee	*Members of the four principal committees*
Finance	Lord Middleton. G.R.H. Smith. J. Digby Cooke. E. Alton. H. Beachell. G. Blair. D.H. Chapman.
Forestry	Lord Bolton. Capt. Nigel FitzRoy. Lt Col Vernon Holt. Col W. St Andrew Warde Aldam. Lord Hotham. Brig. R.C. Chichester-Constable
Prizes and Judges	J.E. Smith. Sir William Prince-Smith. G.R.H. Smith. C.W. Helm. Maj. Gordon Foster.
General Purposes	Lord Middleton. Frank Abbey. Brig. Chichester-Constable. J.W. Greensit. L.R. Burrell. Col A.E. Jacob Wilson. Air Comm. A.L. Godman. R. Fisher. Maj. Whatley Thompson. Sir William Prince-Smith. C.W. Helm. H.M. Beachell. Maj. R.S. Pearson. F. Barker. E.W. Putnam. Col W. St. Andrew Warde Aldam. J.A. Foxton. J.H. Rayner. Sir Alfred Ackroyd. F. Buttle. G. Kendrew.
Poultry	
Pigeon	
Hound	

N.B. The Show Director was an *ex officio* member of all these committees.

(From Council, 6 May 1948, YAS Minute Book No. 10)

The special committee and other members of the Council had ample time during that autumn and winter to consider Mr Baldwin's memorandum, for there was none of the usual tidying up after a show to be done (since 1948 was the year of the RASE's show at York) and many hands were already at work for the Great Yorkshire at Wakefield. It appears that Mr Baldwin's memorandum actually left the aegis of the special committee and became the property of the General Purposes Committee, for in February 1949 it was Lord Middleton, as Chairman of that committee, who opened the Emergency Council discussion of the matter and immediately gave his support to the idea which lay at the heart of Mr Baldwin's proposal – the acquisition of a permanent show site.[21] Middleton's comments were followed by Sir John, whose own comments reveal that he himself had not initiated the idea (contrary to later belief), and that he was against reaching too rapid a conclusion, 'which would affect seriously the whole future of the Society'.[22] Sir John appears to have been the most cautious of the discussants there!

A full discussion now took place. The possible disadvantages of acquiring a permanent show site included the possibility that it would be too far from certain regions of the county, and unfairly close to others. At least a peripatetic show came to virtually everyone's doorstep at some point. In fact, it was felt that the townsman in particular would lose out (thus reviving Earl Spencer's concern that the YAS should cater for town as well as country). No one seems to have entertained serious doubts as to whether the YAS could actually afford to acquire a site, for the good reason that its fixed and liquid assets were well in excess of £60,000. Sir John's own estimate was that to purchase and fully construct a site might cost as much as £50,000.

The advantages of having a permanent show site were numerous, and Council put on record the following eight:

1) That a static show could be developed to serve to the full the aims of the Society by providing the means properly to encourage Agriculture.

2) That a permanent site could be attractively laid out with permanent roads and buildings and that exhibitors, members and visitors could be better provided for.

3) That the annual costs of erection should ultimately be much reduced.

4) That a permanent site would be economical as regards labour and material.

5) That there is a good prospect of being able to run more than one show a year.

6) That there is a good prospect of being able to let the ground or buildings for other events.

7) That the membership is likely to increase as a result of the Society's enterprise.

8) That the problem of finding a suitable site each year, now becoming very difficult to solve, would no longer arise.[23]

A substantial majority on Council now agreed to recommend at the next AGM that a site for a permanent showground be sought and acquired. At the AGM, a couple of weeks later, approval was granted by 81 votes to three, and the task of selecting a suitable site entrusted to a committee comprising the

President (Sir Edward Whitley), the Honorary Show Director (Sir John), the Chairman of Finance and of General Purposes (Lord Middleton), Sir William Prince-Smith (representing the East Riding), F.W. Furness (representing the North), and F.K. Abbey (representing the East). They had some £10,600 in cash with which to open their bidding.[24]

In June, just three months after the committee began their task, a recommendation was available. Tellingly, however, it was not presented by the President or even the Chairman of Finance and General Purposes, but by the temporary, out-going Honorary Show Director, Sir John. Sir John's Midas touch was set to be more potent than ever. The selection committee had been offered sites in five towns: Pudsey, Leeds, Malton, York and Harrogate. Four of these were obvious choices: York was the show's birthplace and the political and social hub of the county; Leeds, with its large urban population, sustained a sizeable agricultural population around itself, and had several times snatched the Society from the verge of bankruptcy; Malton and Harrogate, located well within the agricultural community, had always extended a wonderful welcome to the show; Harrogate was conspicuous too because of its centrality within the county.

Two place-names, however, were conspicuously absent: Beverley and Hull. Hull had hosted some very successful shows and had always boasted an enterprising local committee. The efforts of Beverley's Mayors and local committees had always been second to none in terms of enthusiasm, courtesy and real financial assistance. Nonetheless, these two towns were presumably felt to be situated too far to the east for a permanent show site, which should serve the whole county. Besides, Beverley had lost much of the manufacturing and commercial greatness which it had in the early and mid-nineteenth century, although it was, and still is, a county administrative centre.

The Permanent Show Site Selection Committee actually visited five sites, one at York and the four offered by the ever-enterprising Harrogate Corporation. Sir John and Mr Baldwin visited all four and found one in particular admirable in every way. The committee therefore decided to open negotiations with Harrogate without delay. On 31 May, however, York sent a strong deputation with a counter-offer, which Sir John and Mr Baldwin inspected and found to be so impressive that they withdrew their recommendation for the Harrogate site. But Harrogate Corporation would not give up; they now intimated that they themselves could purchase the site and lease it to the Society in case finances were a limiting factor. York countered with a similar offer. The Committee was uncertain of which offer to accept. Besides, they felt it proper for the whole Council to make the choice, so an emergency general meeting of the Council was called to settle the matter.[25]

At the Extraordinary General Meeting of Council, 21 June 1949, Sir John presented the latest deliberation of the Permanent Show Site Committee and announced that, after all, the site offered at York was not very suitable, apparently reversing his original judgement. The site at Harrogate, however, was excellent, as he explained:

The Harrogate site is 1.3 miles from the station, is about 200 acres in one lot, is well wooded, has a South West aspect, has good road access, there is ample level land with room for expansion. In addition, the Harrogate Corporation is prepared to buy the land and lease it to the Society on a long lease.[26]

After a full discussion, the Council voted for the Harrogate site, charging the Committee to go to Harrogate 'with executive authority to proceed with negotiations in an endeavour to secure the ground for the 1951 Show.' The negotiations took almost 16 months to complete.[27] Yet even after handing over the full payment of £16,500, the Society still had a sizeable amount in available cash (some £11,000) with a further £1517 in its Life Membership Revenue Account, plus its investments. It had thus purchased its permanent show site, at Hookstone Oval in Harrogate, with ease.

Throughout the two years since Mr Baldwin's memorandum had been placed before Council, two Great Yorkshire Shows had been held. The success of the Wakefield show, which also enjoyed a visit by the exceedingly popular Princess Elizabeth, augured well for what must have been seen as an uncertain future. It was as though the Yorkshire community had been in need of a cathartic symbolization of their freedom from the anxieties of war and the constraints of post-war austerity. All three days of the show bubbled over with public enthusiasm and private pride, as visitors feasted their eyes on a spectacle even brighter in some ways than the Royal Show of the previous summer, when restrictions on building materials and food rationing had still been quite severe, where exhibitors showed the undiminished mettle of Yorkshire livestock. The profit of this show, a handsome £16,646, placed the YAS in its healthiest financial condition ever.[28] Council was thus in a mood to be generous: Mr Baldwin's salary was raised, a loan was made available to purchase a new car, and Mr Pottage was treated to a Land Rover. The Society seemed set on a course of post war expansion. Indeed, the recruitment drive that had been mooted in January 1947, which Mr Baldwin handled with vigour, was now netting huge increases, that of late 1949 due largely to Wakefield no doubt. The *Transactions* were recommencing. And thanks to Lord Middleton's sound chairmanship of the Finance Committee, the Society's assets stood at around £84,300.[29]

The Malton show (1950), though less spectacular in terms of public attendance, nonetheless reinforced the feeling that the management of the Society was in sound hands. Its profit (£6980) enabled the Council unhesitatingly to give Sir John and Mr Baldwin full authority 'to spend such money as might be necessary on roadways, drainage and boundary fences at Harrogate.' Every effort was to be made, and no cost spared, in mounting the next Great Yorkshire Show on its own permanent showground – the first in the whole country. (The Peterborough and the Shropshire and West Midlands Societies had acquired permanent grounds before the war but these were still undeveloped. In Ireland, the Dublin and Belfast were also working towards a fully developed site.)

Before examining the construction of the permanent showground and the many benefits and anxieties that it entailed, we might pause a moment and wonder how members of the Society felt at this turning-point. Previously dedicated to the migratory show suggested by Thompson at the original house-party in October 1837 as the best, single means of stimulating agricultural progress, the Society would now have to rethink its ends, for it had now chosen new means. And, as we shall see, its ideology was to be re-formulated as the permanent showground assumed its own voracious character.

The managers of the Society did not, however, turn their backs on the old, moveable show. Whether they genuinely thought that it would still be needed, or whether they were psychologically unable to let go of a glorious (yet often difficult) past, on the very day that negotiations were completed with Harrogate the entire Council unanimously adopted a report of the General Purposes Committee containing the following declaration:

> The Committee strongly supports the suggestion of the Honorary Show Director that although the enthusiasm for the permanent site had by no means lessened, it might be considered good policy and good practice to hold the Show at intervals and in rotation in the East and North Ridings and the Southern part of the West Riding.[30]

The resolution was carried unanimously, and unanimously sent into oblivion. The Great Yorkshire had settled for good.

Even before a permanent site had been chosen, the show was developing and new post-war features were being introduced. Thus, for the show jumping competitions at Wakefield, the British Show Jumping Association agreed to provide the equipment and organization. Needless to say, the event proved immensely popular. At the Malton show, the Young Farmers' Clubs attended in force; these proved to be a popular and long-lasting feature of the show when it moved to its permanent site. Since then, the Council and the Executive Committee have been keen to cooperate with the Young Farmers in a variety of ways, and today there is a warm relationship between them. It is, however, noteworthy that the Young Farmers were the ones to drive the bargain for their attendance at the Malton show, stipulating exactly how much space, what size of marquee, how many trophies, and what use of the pig-ring, the Society should provide.[31]

The acquisition of a permanent site for the show provided the greatest of opportunities for its development, both qualitatively and quantitatively. It was perhaps the prospect of this unique challenge that induced Sir John to withdraw his resignation as Honorary Show Director. Another factor was Major Seed's great reluctance to take over from him. Indeed, the Council was so relieved that it even ordered the rescindment of a resolution from as far back as September 1948 which dared to mention the possibility of his having a successor to him.[32] Major Seed continued as Assistant Director, and he did later become the natural successor to Sir John – in 1963.

The first Great Yorkshire Show on its own permanent showground must have looked rather similar to the previous events. The accommodation was of canvas and timber in the usual style for a migratory show, for in September 1948 a three-year contract had been signed with a major firm to build what was necessary each year, starting work in October and ending in the following June, on receipt of £750 monthly plus extra expenses. The 1951 show was the last specified in this contract. But if the style was much as before, the show nonetheless signalled something new. The Princess Royal was President again, and played her part richly. And now, after so many years, the decision was taken to make a formal arrangement to ensure that the Flower Show should be an integral and permanent part of the Great Yorkshire, for which Sir John enlisted the aid of the Northern Horticultural Society. So popular was this feature that in 1963 it was housed in its own exhibition hall which, today, is one of the first visits one must make. The 1951 event was also notable for a revival of a hound show, with fine displays of foxhounds, beagles, harriers and others. And, as the YAS Council had guessed when deliberating the pros and cons of a permanent site, the interest and publicity generated by the Society's conspicious enterprise fuelled the recruitment drive, so that its membership reached 10,000 by the day of the show.[34] Indeed, Council had already set 10,000 as an apparently arbitrary ceiling for membership, so there was now to be a waiting list.

Well before the first show on the permanent site, ambitious plans were being laid for the ground's permanent construction. In March 1951 a £20,000 contract was awarded to Messrs F. and H. Sutcliffe (of Hebden Bridge) to erect a set of semi-permanent buildings, of which a press block, a members room and bar, Council Room, Council Dining Room, Stewards' and Judges' Dining Room, stockmen's cubicles, and others were available in time for the 1952 show.[35] Contracts also had to be given for canvas and other temporary accommodation, for it would take some five or six years before most of the principal structures of the showground would be either semi-permanent or permanent. With all this in hand, and many more installations to make in time for the first permanent show, the decision was made in March 1951 to merge the Finance and the General Purposes Committees. This had the effect of coordinating and streamlining the many interlocking decisions that had to be taken. The membership of the new committee is noteworthy, of course, for it reveals those who were most involved in this crucial venture. They were: Lord Middleton, Sir William Prince-Smith, Sir Alfred Ayckroyd, Col Jacob Wilson, and Messrs F.K. Abbey, H.M. Beachell, D.H. Chapman and F.W. Furness, plus Sir John as *ex officio* member.

From the start, the show on the permanent site was a success from the points of view of exhibitors, spectators and the Society, and it will no longer be necessary in this *History* to mention each year's event. As a permanently sited show, the Great Yorkshire would not have such great differences from year to year as it had had whilst peripatetic. As the site construction developed, what the show had to offer inevitably expanded, and by 1959 the suggestion was being made again (as it had been, sporadically, in the nineteenth century) that it should be a four-day event.[36] We might look at this expansion alongside another developement connected with the showground, namely the alarming growth of the Society's indebtedness.

There is little doubt that those who gave the go-ahead for the acquisition of a permanent site for the show entertained few fears about the Society's financial condition; nor did they doubt that the Society would be wealthy enough to finance the site's development out of its own funds. But that development soon began to eat into the Society's finances. By March 1951, even before the first show on the site, the total expenditure had reached some £31,000, although at that stage the Finance Committee felt no qualms since it was estimating that once the showground was complete it would save some £7000 per annum in construction costs.[37] In December of the same year, a further £16,000 had to be set aside for the 1951–2 allocation, to go towards administrative buildings, roads, milking parlours and shedding. At the same time, a further £44,000 was budgeted to construct livestock accommodation and trade stands in time for the 1953 show.

The money required for this venture was borrowed from the Yorkshire Insurance Company, with whom the Society had placed some of its investments in the reformulation of its capital investment strategy in January 1947, whilst immediate expenditure had to be covered by a bank overdraft.[38] At this stage, the Finance and General Purposes Committee, though drawing Council's attention to the unexpected cost of the showground's development, seems not to have felt that economy measures might be due elsewhere. Indeed, staff salaries were raised[39], and the Council began to make an annual donation of £200 to the Leeds University appeal for the Department of Agriculture, admitting that 'the Society's contributions towards education and research are very slight'.[40]

Helping to offset this expenditure, it was especially gratifying to find that the trade stands were being fully booked[41] and that by 1952 the show could enjoy a bonanza in implement entry fees. In that year, implement entries alone brought £16,000 into the show's coffers – a massive, all-time record.[42] The Finance Committee estimated that, even setting aside a substantial amount for the site's development specifically in time for this show, it nonetheless returned a handsome profit.

By June 1954, with a substantial amount of construction completed and three successful shows to its credit, the Finance and General Purposes Committee set 1957 as their target-date for the showground's completion. Between mid-1954 and 1957, they now estimated, a further £139,000 would have to be spent on levelling the main ring, constructing the grandstand (to accommodate 6000 spectators), erecting cattle standings (to accommodate 602 cattle), extending the spectators' bank on the south side of the main ring, constructing the stockmen's dining and rest rooms and various small buildings and roads.[43] Virtually all of this was completed by spring 1958, with an enthusiasm and constant attention to detail that Sir John and Mr Baldwin were primarily responsible for. Additionally, a small farm of about 60 acres adjacent to the south side of the showground (Crimple Farm) was bought for £6600, most of it for use as a car park.[44] Sir John made this purchase, apparently in his relatively new capacity as Chairman of the Finance and General Purposes Committee.

For the show in 1955 the *pièce de resistance*, the main ring, was ready. From the very inception of the plan for a permanent showground there had, of course, been the intention of building a main show ring. However, with the YAS's long interest in horses and its more recent efforts at staging professionally managed show jumping, to which end it had joined the British Show Jumping Association (in 1949), a fine show ring was all the more imperative. By autumn 1954, 60,000 tons of soil had been removed, the ring site levelled and an attempt made at re-seeding. But there was appalling weather from autumn 1954 to spring 1955. April 1st, however, broke with fine weather and the whole task of re-seeding the $3\frac{1}{2}$ acres of the ring was accomplished in that one day. As Sir John and Mr Baldwin told Council, they were determined that the 1955 Great Yorkshire Show Ring would be the finest in the country.[45] It was. As it still is.

The showground's potential was recognized by other bodies gratifyingly early. In October 1951 the National Agricultural Advisory Service (NAAS) and the Agricultural Land Service (ALS) entered into an agreement with the Society to lease some five acres of the showground as a demonstration area to conduct experiments and demonstrations of a semi-permanent nature. This plot was to become a part of the show, but remain independent throughout the rest of the year. The lease ran initially for seven years, at the pepper-corn rental of £1 per annum.[46]

In 1954, the Provincial Director of the NAAS approached the Society to hold, in conjunction with the Ministry of Food, a demonstration of pigs and pig carcases on the showground. This fitted well with the development of the carcass competition in the show and the demonstration was held enthusiastically in May. In the same year the York and Ainsty (North) Pony Club held its annual camp on the showground, thus initiating a use of the ground for annual meetings by non-agricultural associations which now adds so much colour to the showground, even outside the Show itself. Conference usage also began. The Ministry of Agriculture, Fisheries and Food held a major conference at the showground in January 1957, whose success seems to have prompted Sir John to present a memorandum to Council on the systematic management of these extra-show events as regular sources of income to the Society. In October of that year, Council resolved to make this a revenue generating venture within the overall strategy and purpose of the Showground.[47] Applications were also being made by trade and other exhibitors to be allowed to construct semi-permanent offices on the showground. In 1960, two such requests came from the Yorkshire Pig Breeder's Association in conjunction with the National Pig Breeder's Associaion, and the Eaglescliff Chemical Company.[48] Industry was now regarding the Great Yorkshire Showground as an essential venue.

The major event outside the show itself during the period of this chapter was the 'Off the Grass' exhibition in 1962. Planned in conjunction with *The Farmers' Weekly*, with whom the YAS had long had a cordial relationship, even to the extent of holding occasional Council meetings at their premises in Harrogate, this was originally envisaged as a sheep-only exhibition, to be held in 1961. In March of that year, however, the decision was taken to make the most of the opportunities now afforded by the showground, and a sub-committee was set up to plan the event on a suitably grand scale. This body comprised the chief cattle steward, the chief sheep steward, Sir William Prince-Smith, Mr Lance Gilling (a co-opted member of the Council and Principal of Askham Bryan) and Sir John.

The sub-committee worked hard, formulating a clear set of objectives for the event, whose emphasis would be 'on commercial stock, together with demonstrations relating to grass and the various by-products of the cattle and sheep industries.'[49] These objectives, and indeed the very idea from the start, have to be seen within the general context of British post-war agricultural policy for their full rationale to become clear. There were press conferences in London as well as locally; a massive amount of organization and coordination was done, almost on the scale of a full show since it was a two-day event, and a sizeable budget drawn up.

Held in September 1962, the event was a huge success and may be regarded as the YAS's first major contribution to national agriculture in the era of the permanent showground. Yet financially the event ran at a loss, which came at a time when the Society's current deficit in overdraft and loans had soared to almost £200,000 and the inflationary trend of the '60s was beginning to bite into the profits of the annual show. 'Off the Grass' was a substantial achievement, but also a trial-run from which lessons had to be learned. Indeed, immediately afterwards Sir John set up a small sub-committee, consisting of Col Phillips, and Messrs Abbey, Gilling and McCann, 'to consider what plans the Society should make concerning future shows and demonstrations, with special regard to the experience gained from "Off the Grass".'[50] This became known as the Abbey Committee.

Development of the showground had slowed down during the latter half of the 1950s when the Council became alarmed at the unanticipated size of its overdraft and when it seemed that almost all the most necessary construction was complete. In 1961, however, the Finance and General Purposes Committee, still under Sir John's chairmanship, recommended that the policy of deceleration be reversed, 'and that work should proceed as rapidly as possible with the intention of trying to complete the building of the showground by 1964'. The estimated cost of this three-year effort was £138,000.[51] There were further financial constraints which, coupled with poor weather in the summer and autumn of 1961, frustrated Sir John's designs. Nonetheless, major projects were now initiated or resumed, the most difficult of which turned out to be the flower show building, which was intended to be ready in time for the 1962 event.[52] The difficulty of securing an appropriate design and the unexpectedly high cost of implementing it took the flower show project into an unsettled period as far as the Society's finances were concerned, and held back its completion until the end of 1967.

The showground's financial condition entered a difficult period in about 1961. By December of that year the Society had an overdraft of £184,000. Once the account for the very profitable 1961 show had been settled, and other income for 1961–2 started to come in, the debt dropped to £163,000 (by March 1962) only to rise again to £192,000 by October. At this stage, the Finance and General Purposes Committee recommended a severe curtailment of further capital expenditure.[53] Had it not been for this situation, the Society might have gone ahead with the purchase of a 128-acre farm adjacent to the car park, thus considerably augmenting the size of the showground.

Finally, with regard to the showground, in March 1963 Sir John announced his intention to retire from the Show Directorship after the 1963 event in order to make way for a younger man. He had held the post for nearly thirty years. The spontaneous expressions of regret and appreciation made by members of Council on hearing this announcement leave us in no doubt as to his central role for most of that period in the life of the Society. The President, the Marquis of Normanby declared that

> . . . his resignation would be a loss both to the Showground and to agriculture in general [and] that while Sir John had an iron hand he had a very warm heart, and the Society owed him a great debt.

Lord Middleton, who had been a major figure of influence alongside Sir John and whose own work on behalf of the Society cannot be underestimated, added his tribute, praising Sir John above all for his imagination and foresight. Colonel Phillips and Mr Abbey, on behalf of the stewards, said how much they had enjoyed and appreciated working under Sir John's direction, and Major Seed declared

> . . . that however much we might be looking to the future, we cannot fail to look back with appreciation over the last thirty years and recall the progress made during that period; and particularly remember how Sir John had held the Society together during the war.[54]

Even more fullsome was the tribute to Sir John in the annual report for 1963, which spoke of Sir John's period of service as one in which 'the Show had grown out of recognition. When Sir John took over, the annual surplus averaged about £1000; when he resigned, it exceeded £40,000.'

It would not be simplistic, then, to call the period covered in this chapter the 'Dunnington-Jefferson era'. In fact, whilst Sir John did step down as Honorary Show Director in May of this year (a few months earlier than he had intimated in March), he remained active on Council for several more years. Indeed, his voice became a strongly dissenting one, marking a change in the Society's ideology in the mid-1960s. That will be the topic of our final chapter.

But now we must review other features of the YAS's development during the 'Dunnington-Jefferson era', namely the development of the body of management (for Sir John was not the only maker and implementer of policy), the support of research and education, and the Society's more outgoing orientation.

While Sir John had been a key figure in maintaining the Society during the war, the President and Chairman of Council throughout that period and until

1948, Brigadier General Sir Edward Whitley, undoubtedly helped to provide a continuity of purpose and direction. He had chaired virtually every meeting of Council during the period October 1939 to February 1949, and although he did not sit on any of the committees after the reorganization in May 1948 he remained a behind-the-scenes figure, re-emerging in 1951–2 as Chairman of Council again. By 1955, the central figures of management were as follows:

Sir John Dunnington-Jefferson;

Lord Middleton;

Sir William Prince-Smith;

Brig. Gen. Sir Edward Whitley;

Major Seed;

Lord Bolton and Messrs F.W. Furness and J. Ramsden (elected as the representatives of the North Riding);

Messrs J.A. Foxton and H.M. Beachell (for the East Riding);

Sir Alfred Ayckroyd, Major Whateley Thompson and Messrs F.K. Abbey, T.S. Atkinson and C.W. Helm (for West Riding).

Most of these figures, in addition to serving as members of various committees, were also active on the showground during the event. Several also took their turn as Chairman of Council: Sir Alfred Ayckroyd in 1954, Lord Bolton in 1955, Sir William Prince-Smith in 1956, Lord Middleton in 1957. By 1962, two new figures appeared among the central management: Colonel F. Lane Fox and the Marquis of Normanby.

This period saw a number of excellent Presidents, a few of whom were also Chairman of Council during their Presidency. It would be invidious to single out any one for particular mention, except for The Princess Royal who was three-times President (1937, 1951 and 1957) and whose extraordinary interest in the Society and personal contribution to the occasion of the show, can be gauged from the following comment by Sir John on the 1951 event:

> . . . the Society owes a great debt to their President, The Princess Royal. Among the first to arrive and the last to leave on all three days, not to mention a pre-view on the afternoon preceding the Show, Her Royal Highness was quite indefatigable, and her active interest in all sections of the Show was a great encouragement in our first venture at Harrogate.[55]

Behind the scenes, the administrative staff expanded. In December 1951 the Finance and General Purposes Committee recommended a significant increase in the permanent personnel to cope more effectively with the growing amount and complexity of administration, brought about by the permanent showground and the rapid increase in membership. One appointment which resulted from that decision was that of Mr Alan Martindale as Office Junior in 1952, who has remained with the Society ever since and who now, as the Society's Deputy Secretary, is one of its most valued staff.

By January 1954, there were six central administrative staff, whose total in annual salaries amounted to £4025 per annum, of which the Secretary, Mr Baldwin, received £1700. The Society's continuing concern for the well-being of its staff was again evident in this period, particularly over the enforced retirement of a typist, Miss J.E. Pfluger. Miss Pfluger had been employed since 1922 and was due to retire in 1958. By June 1955, however, her general health was so poor that she was advised not to spend another winter in Harrogate. Council unhesitatingly allowed her to take early retirement and offered her an annual allowance until 1958 at the level of the pension she would then receive.[56] The Society was also anxious that its most essential administrative staff should not have to worry over housing. In 1955, at Sir John's suggestion, a house was built for the showground foreman. And in 1962, when the increase in the administration was squeezing Mr Baldwin out of Cliftonfield it was resolved to sell sufficient of the garden to him so that he could build a house for himself at his own expense.

Also on the payroll, although not as a permanent member of staff, was the Society's veterinary inspector. In October 1954 this post became vacant with the death of Mr J.W. Proctor, who had been in attendance at the show since 1935. He was succeeded by Mr G.N. Sutherland, MRCVS, of York.

It has been mentioned that in 1945 the post of consulting chemist was allowed to lapse. This does not indicate, however, that the Society intended to lessen its acknowledgement of the utility of science. Rather, it began to direct funding to agricultural education and research, at first on a small scale but by the early 1960s fairly considerably. In 1951, '52 and '53, an annual donation of £200 was made to the University of Leeds fund for its Department of Agriculture, and in 1954 it was resolved to raise this to £300. The £200 grants were used to finance a travelling scholarship, and the increase now allowed the department to send a post-graduate student overseas for a brief period of research in three years out of every four.[57]

Already in 1948, the Society had begun to donate two medals for agricultural education, to the best all-round students of agriculture at Leeds and at the Yorkshire Institute of Agriculture at Askham Bryan.[58] It is noteworthy that these initiatives were taken at the behest of the Finance Committee (1948) and the Finance and General Purposes Committee (1950s), and almost certainly at the instigation of Sir John, whose own interest in agricultural education was also being expressed in his capacity as Chairman of the Joint Committee which administered both the department at Leeds and the Institute. Sir John thus followed in the line of key YAS figures who were personally influential in the county's agricultural education programme. Ties between the YAS and Askham Bryan were furthered in October 1951 when its Principal, Mr J.A. Lindsay, was co-opted onto Council and appointed to the Prizes and Judges Committee.[59]

This increasing involvement in agricultural education might also be seen as a component in the YAS's more general involvement with other bodies. By the late fifties, it had seven more-or-less permanent Council representatives on the following:

> The Yorkshire branch of RABI (Royal Agricultural Benevolent Institution);

The Beekeepers' Association;
The East Riding Federation of Young Farmers Clubs;
The West Riding Federation of Young Farmers Clubs;
The North Riding Federation of Young Farmers Clubs;
The Board of Read Grammar School, Drax;
The Nuffield Foundation.

Sir John was the representative on the first and last of these. By 1963, the Society also had a representative on The Yorkshire Rural Community Council (Sir John) and The Yorkshire Council for Further Education (Mr Baldwin). By the early '60s, indeed, grants to education were also becoming more ambitious: a £450 research grant to Nottingham University for a project on Charolais and Hereford crosses with Friesian and Ayrshire cattle in December 1961, so long as funds were not available from the Agricultural Research Council, and in March 1962 a £100 grant towards the Leeds University Corsican Expedition (in which agricultural students were taking part).[60] Council was also urging, but not yet financing, research in ecology: in the summer of '66 they sent a resolution to the Ministry of Agriculture:

> That the Council of the Yorkshire Agricultural Society is concerned about the danger to wildlife in general, and bird life in particular, by the extensive and increasing use of chemical seed dressing. The Council also urges the Ministry to proceed as rapidly as possible with research into this question in order that some action may be taken.[61]

These outside interests were to broaden in the 1970s and '80s, and will be dealt with in the following chapter.

By way of leading us into that final period, mention should here be made of two events in 1963. The Abbey Committee set up in autumn 1962 in the wake of 'Off the Grass' now recommended that the YAS should become involved in setting up an organization for the collection of records on beef cattle and sheep. By March 1963, on the authority of Sir John and the Society's President, the Marquis of Normanby, Mr Baldwin had conducted a preliminary investigation and was proceeding to establish a venture along these lines. Council ratified this initiative.[62]

The second event was the issuing of a report by the President's Committee, in May 1963, recommending fundamental changes in the Society's management, the chief of which was the disbanding of the Finance and General Purposes Committee and its replacement by an Executive Committee. With the effecting of this move, which coincided with the appointment of Major Seed as Honorary Show Director, the Dunnington-Jefferson era ended. The locus of policy making and management was now to be essentially as it is today.

7 THE SOCIETY SINCE 1963

Following the increased respect and recognition accorded to British agriculture by central government in the early 1960s, which was a consequence of the meeting between the Prime Minister and the President of the NFU in 1960, a substantial change of approach commenced in the middle of that decade. This was announced in the Annual Review of Agriculture for 1964 which stipulated the introduction of import controls for cereals and fatstock. By 1969, further controls by way of quotas or 'voluntary arrangements' with overseas suppliers were either in force or in the pipeline for butter, poultry, cheddar-type cheese, and eggs.[1]

This redirection entailed the abandonment of any attempts at eliminating protection and support for agriculture or at forcing higher productivity by means of a reduction in the ratios between guaranteed and 'average-market' prices. Indeed, 1964 was the first year for a decade in which the value of the guarantees exceeded increased costs. Under this new policy of 'market management', protection for agriculture was effectively seen as permanent (for the first time, with the exception of wartimes, since the early nineteenth century). This was made possible by a shift of the burden of support from the general taxpayer to the consumer. Protection was thus hidden, and the inevitably higher prices were justified as a fair reward for farmers and as a reflection of the realistic cost of food protection.

The overt cost of agricultural support to the Exchequer indeed fell. In real terms it peaked in 1961, and even at current prices the 1961 level was not reached again until 1973. (See figures 6.1 and 6.2.) The removal of the expenditure constraint which thus resulted also alleviated limitations on output, so that throughout the period from the mid-1960s to the 1980s British agriculture operated within an expansionist ideology. The first strategy for implementing this ideology was a policy of selective expansion coupled with the national plan of 1965.[2] Agriculture's contribution to this was to be two-fold – to release labour for other industries by a 5% per annum growth in productivity, and to hold down imports by meeting the estimated increase in consumer expenditure on food. Since 50 percent of this increased demand was expected to be in beef, production of this was given heavy priority.

A second strategy was to alter the structure of holdings in the agricultural industry. A White Paper in 1965 detailed how grants would be made available to persuade small farmers to leave the industry; small farms might then amalgamate into more competitive economic units, and greater coordination might be achieved through a new body, the Central Council for Agricultural and Horticultural Cooperation.[3] Other measures introduced included putting livestock headage payments on a long-term basis and at increased values (1965), the introduction of hill-ploughing grants (1967), and further structural measures (1969).

The selective expansion programmes continued into the 1970s, by which time they became redundant because of the wholly new political and economic context created by Britain's entry into the European Economic Community (EEC). By 1970, already, this had introduced a new argument for the ideology of maximum growth output: the reduction of Britain's bill for the Common Agricultural Policy (CAP) in the event of Britain's entry to the EEC. The largely political need to keep down this entry-bill via an expanding agricultural sector made maximum growth and output more desirable than ever, as was spelled out in the new policy document, *Food from Our Own Resources* (1975), which outlined a heavy expansion programme over five to ten years.[4] This document also gave another reason for the expansion of British agriculture – as a hedge against the price fluctuations and commodity shortages of the early 1970s, which had coincided with the massive OPEC-induced increases in the price of petroleum oil. Even the later document, *Farming and the Nation* (1979), produced by a Labour Government much more sympathetic to consumers than those of the '60s and the mid-'70s, endorsed agriculture's expansion and proposed another 'five-year plan'.[5] However, this document did express anxiety over the cost of agricultural support, the impact of the policy on the environment, and the problems that the CAP was causing for the Third World.

Indeed, the CAP now generates problems for its own First World, since the ideology of agricultural expansionism, which each of its members espouses in order to gain from the others, means that in the end all are worse off – besides creating the notorious 'food mountains'. Expansion, say, of Britain's agricultural output, by whatever means, improves Britain's CAP budgetary position at a high cost to the consumer; but given that the CAP operates under an increasingly nervous budget constraint, the net gain to Britain's budgetary position from expansion becomes far smaller than the gross gain.[6]

Britain's agricultural industry today, in the mid-1980s, has to reap the somewhat bitter fruits of the politicization of its original expansionist programme within the context of the CAP. The expansionist programme is now being checked and, some say, will have to be reversed. There is a clear need for a radically different CAP in order not only to render European agriculture more rational and more economically efficient but also to make the EEC more competitive against up-and-coming regions of economic strength, such as the Pacific Basin. Within a new CAP, British agriculture will experience different imperatives and constraints. And in so far as the YAS and other major agricultural societies, of late, have been showing more active concern for the national and wider contexts of farming, they could be in a position to influence the pattern of Britain's farming for the start of the new millenium.

Another comment in this introductory section is worth making. It would be useful here to give an overview of contemporary Yorkshire agriculture, as was done in Chapter 1. To do so, however, would introduce many features of a now more intricate industry with economic, institutional and political factors not strictly germane to the shape of our narrative. Readers who wish for information and discussion in this direction should refer to an excellent monograph by W. Harwood Long, *A Survey of the Agriculture of Yorkshire*, (published by the RASE, London, 1966).

In the previous chapter, it was intimated that in late 1963 a number of changes took place within the Society which were to introduce yet another period in its history. Those changes should be examined now, before we go on to analyse subsequent developments along the lines we have been following so far.

At the Council meeting of 13 May 1963, the President's Committee that had been set up to consider the future organization of the Society submitted a number of recommendations, the principal of which was to disband the important Finance and General Purposes Committee and to replace it by an Executive Committee. This newly created Executive Committee would consist of the President, the Deputy President, the Honorary Show Director, the Assistant Honorary Show Director and eight members of the Council. In the first instance, the eight ordinary members of the Council would be nominated by the Selection Committee, but subsequently two would retire by rotation each year and the vacancies would be filled by Council ballot. The recommendation further specified that 'The Committee will elect its own Chairman and will meet as frequently as required. It will be responsible for financial matters; have such powers as the Council may delegate, and will submit reports of its meetings to the Council'.[7]

At the same time, the President's Committee recommended the setting up of a Technical Committee 'to pay special attention to livestock development and extension of the Society's activities in technical fields'. This Technical Committee was also to consider whether the Society should appoint 'a Scientific Adviser as a member of the permanent staff' – a step which would have been comparable in its significance with the engagement of Joseph Spence as the Society's first 'Analysing Chemist' in 1844.

There was also to be a new, permanent Selection Committee. All the other committees, such as the Prizes and Judges Committee and the Showyard Committee, were to remain. At the same meeting, Major Seed was elected Honorary Show Director for three years in succession to Sir John. Various measures concerning future appointments to the Show Directorship were also decided, including the stipulation that 'the Honorary Show Director may not be elected Chairman of the Executive Committee', presumably to ensure that there would always be sufficient spread of executive power within the Society and to insure the Society's overall interests against encroachment by the ambitions of the show. A new Assistant Honorary Show Director (Colonel J.A.M. Phillips) was elected to succeed Major Seed. Finally, the Executive

Committee was charged with considering how the objects of the Society could be widened.

This new organization, inclusive of the Executive Committee and the new appointments, became effective on 1 August 1963. The new committee elected as its Chairman the Marquis of Normanby, and as its Vice-Chairman Mr Frank Abbey. Its first report to the Council was issued in October. Virtually at once, the Executive Committee became the policy-making nucleus of the Society, very much as the Finance and General Purposes Committee had been. Thus, the annual report of the Council for 1963 was essentially the third Executive Committee Report to Council, and the post of Chairman of Council seems naturally to have disappeared, although not officially, since his powers were now subsumed under the new committee.

Henceforth, all the fundamental policy determinations and financial decisions would be taken by the Executive Committee and the 'strongman' and lynch-pin of the Society's management would usually be this body's chairman. (See Table 7.1.)

Table 7.1: Chairmen of the Executive Committee

Marquis of Normanby	Aug. 1963–Dec. 1968
Lord Bolton	Jan. 1969–Oct. 1973
Mr James Holt	Oct. 1973–Mar. 1984
Mr Lance Gilling	Mar. 1984–Present

We may now examine in detail the development of the showground and the show and their consequences for the Society from late 1963.

The 1963 show was the usual qualitative success and brought in a slightly higher profit than in the previous year's event. There were, however, worrying indications that the cost of putting on the show, even with no further capital expenditure, would rise steadily with the general inflationary trend of the economy.[8] The question had therefore to be asked: how might future capital development of the showground be financed? The Executive Committee's answer, in August 1965, brought about its first conspicuous confrontation with Sir John, a confrontation which seems primarily to have centred on an ideological difference.

The Executive Committee envisaged financing the showground's further development by increasing show fees and public admission charges. Sir John, anxious that the show might overprice itself and thus not provide the sort of service he envisaged, suggested that alternatives should be considered, such as issuing unsecured debentures or loan stock at nominal interest rates. The Council instructed the Executive Committee, therefore, to consider his suggestion.[9] This they did, but still resolved to follow their original strategy and raise an extra £23,000 from the ensuing show by raising fees and charges.

However, there was some feeling that even in the short-term this might not work too well, for coupled with the problem of inflation and the sizeable task of showground maintenance there were anxieties over the popularity of the large agricultural show *per se*. At a meeting of the Executive Committee in February 1966, the Secretary General presented a report concerning the changing attitude of agricultural machinery exhibitors towards agricultural shows. His researches revealed that machinery exhibitors

> are unanimously and strongly of the opinion that there are far too many [county and regional shows], and that they are wrong in competing with each other for support, [and] that too many of them are aiming at Permanent Sites for which the exhibitors will be expected to pay, and that showing is now too expensive.[10]

He also asserted that the machinery exhibitors were willing to attend some five major regional shows, in addition to the Royal, which had established its own unique, export-oriented centre. These were: The Royal Highland, the Great Yorkshire, the Bath and West, the Peterborough, and the Shropshire and West Midlands. But they were willing to do so only if these five could work altogether within an overall policy and if they could be consulted collectively.

The Secretary General also claimed, on behalf of machinery manufacturers and exhibitors, that:

> It is considered of paramount importance that Societies should be deeply and seriously involved in projects for the improvement of agriculture quite apart from organizing an annual Show. Far too many Societies do nothing but run their shows and then wait for next year. The exhibitors (and many others, including NAAS) feel that other activities are of vital importance for the future of British Agriculture and therefore for their own future business.[11]

The Executive Committee gave serious consideration to this report, whose message was nothing less than 'a serious and urgent threat to the whole system of showing'. Invitations were sent out to the four regional societies mentioned in the report to meet with the YAS as soon as possible, in York, at which the YAS would be represented by the then President, Sir Kenneth Parkinson, along with Lord Normanby and Mr Baldwin.

A few months later, the Council resolved that the Society should take steps for the furtherance of agriculture more broadly by helping to set up a Northern Association for the Advancement of Research in Agriculture.[12] But consequent upon the meeting in York, which all but the Royal Highland attended, the Executive Committee over-ruled this resolution in favour of a proposal submitted in 1962, by Mr Harry T.E. Smith, to establish an Agricultural Development Association (ADA) in conjunction with the Bath and West, the Shropshire and West Midlands, and the Peterborough. Each society contributed £250 towards the initial expenses of the Association, whose objects were 'to encourage and sponsor agricultural development in its widest sense and to discuss matters of common interest'.[13] Sir Kenneth Parkinson and Mr Abbey were to represent the YAS.

Within a matter of months, Mr Smith had resigned from the National Agricultural Advisory Service to accept the appointment of Director of ADA, which began to function with excellent prospects, so much so for the YAS that in

March 1967 its own Technical Committee was disbanded since its brief was encompassed within that of the Association. The latter continued to exist, with its offices at Cliftonfield, until late 1972 when the number of societies involved in it was 14. By then, its functions had been taken over by developments within the agricultural industry.

The Association's significance for this *History* lies not so much in what it did but in what its establishment reveals of the YAS at this stage, and of Mr Baldwin's concerns. The YAS had certainly been promoting interests other than the show – 'Off the Grass', wild life, the recording of dairy beef and sheep, and in 1964 the tentative idea of setting up an Agricultural Communications Centre at the University of York.[14] It had also instituted an award for the farmer who submitted the most promising plan for the development of his farm – the Farmplan Award – which was awarded in 1965 and 1966, but then lapsed.

The Secretary General was personally committed to this expansionism and seems to have genuinely believed that agricultural societies should operate collaboratively and within a much wider vision than had become the custom. Hence, in addition to having given every support to Mr Smith's proposal for the ADA and having urged the Society to back it, in 1966 he convened and chaired a meeting of agricultural representatives from ten European nations to discuss the setting up of a European Federation of Agricultural Show and Show Societies. This meeting decided that the time was not yet ripe for such an organization, although there was an agreement to hold an annual conference in different countries to discuss technical matters related to agricultural shows.[15] This led to the creation of the European Agricultural Societies and Show Organizers Consultative Committee (EURASCO), of which Mr Baldwin was Secretary until 1977. EURASCO holds its 21st Anniversary Conference in 1987, fittingly in Harrogate.

To resume our analysis of the Great Yorkshire and its showground, the show itself was now entering a difficult period. As indicated, inflation was becoming a serious problem, noticeably reducing the show's profit from around £40,000 in the early 1960s to around £15,000 in the early 1970s. Making matters worse, as Mr Baldwin's report had suggested might happen, the revenue from trade stands began to drop alarmingly. Thus, the 21st Executive Committee report, in December 1969, was extremely pessimistic about the number of regular trade exhibitors who had said that they would not be attending the forthcoming show. Messrs J.C. Baker, Baldwin and R. Bushell undoubtedly identified the causes and their gravity when they suggested that

> not only was the situation affected by the present economic state but that little or no business was now done at Shows, and agricultural merchants could no longer afford to spend money on this sort of non-productive activity.[16]

A few months later, Lord Bolton (then Chairman of the Executive Committee) went so far as to suggest that the YAS's by then rather serious financial condition was attributable in large measure to the fall in trade stand receipts over the last few years. It was small comfort to know that this appeared to be a worldwide phenomenon at the time.[17]

With these difficulties to contend with, and with the Society's mounting debt curtailing capital expenditure, the Show Director in the late 1960s, Major General Dalton, had an uphill struggle on his hands. One public comment on the first show after he had taken over the post, in 1967, was that there was nothing new at the Great Yorkshire. But as he lamented, it was difficult to find suitable attractions 'and when found are expensive'. Nonetheless, new features were introduced, such as the 'Beef '68' demonstration at the 1968 show (which was held at the request of ADA and the Beef Recording Association), which also featured the 'Cock o' the North' horse jumping trophy and boasted an EEC stand (thanks to the initiative of Lord St Oswald). By 1970, there was more outside interest in the horse jumping competitions at the show, which were attracting sponsorship, and the Great Yorkshire was itself getting more extensive television coverage and sponsorship – both of which helped to lighten the gloom of the still-declining trade entries.[18] Another bright spot was the increasing use of the showground for events other than the show itself.

Nonetheless, the question about the future of the large agricultural shows, raised by Mr Baldwin, persisted. Indeed, it became a topic of considerable debate both within the YAS's Council and in the agricultural press in general.[19] In the Council it came to a head in December 1971 when Sir John, trenchantly criticizing the Executive Committee's financial strategy, expressed grave doubts over the large show's ability to generate revenue. He was not alone in his pessimism. At the AGM a few months later, a former Council member (Mr Ayres) raised the question of the viability of shows in general. Since, he felt, the purpose of a show was to improve agriculture and not to be an end in itself, a point with which Sir John was in passionate agreement, and since shows were losing money or just about breaking even, he felt that their entire future was in doubt. And as 7.8 acres of the showground had just been sold off (for reasons to be discussed later), he wondered whether it would be better to sell the whole showground. In reply, Lord Bolton said that 'the Show meant much to Yorkshire and could not lightly be abandoned so long as it provided a service to agriculture and pleasure to a large number of people'.[20]

The idea of selling the Great Yorkshire Showground did not remain as just that. An offer was made, of £950,000, which the Executive Committee had to consider seriously, especially since Sir John was strongly supporting it. An altercation between Sir John and Lord Bolton in the Council meeting of June 1972 brought to a head the differing ideologies upon which their positions *vis à vis* the show and the showground were based. Sir John began by pointing out that during the past three years the Society had been running deeper into debt. Now it had a golden opportunity to discharge all its liabilities and to have left over a fund of between £600,000 and £700,000, 'the income from which could be used in conformity with the objects of the Society'. He added:

> If we were to abandon our somewhat precarious existence, as a Show Society, with no reserves at all from which to supplement our income or provide cover for

weather-spoilt Shows and other contingencies, and if we were to change the character of the Society and convert it into a sort of Agricultural Trust, with a very large and increasing tax-free income, we should be in a position to give an infinitely greater service to agriculture than we shall ever be able to give under our present circumstances.[21]

It is ironical that Sir John, whose most conspicuous achievement was the foundation of a permanent Great Yorkshire Showground, was now arguing for its dissolution. The irony is doubled in that Mr Baldwin, who originated the idea of the permanent Showground and personally drew up the plan for the layout, seemed *not* to disagree with Sir John at this Council meeting. He advised Lord Bolton and others who were in favour of rejecting the £950,000 offer, that

> they, being responsible for the good management of the Society, and since there were two opposing views, take the precaution of seeking professional advice from Accountants, Solicitors and our Surveyors. [For] by doing so, they could protect themselves from being accused at some later date of acting unwisely. . . .[22]

The Executive Committee remained adamant that the Great Yorkshire Show should continue, and the substantial divide between its ideology (and its financial strategy) and the views of Sir John and Mr Baldwin culminated in the latter's early retirement immediately after the 1972 show and Sir John's withdrawal from Council meetings at about the end of that year. Whatever the relative merits of the two sides, however, it has to be recognized that Lord Bolton and his Executive Committee had a powerful sense of direction and the ability to steer the Society out of its crisis. The sale of 7.8 acres of the ground fetched £124,000, of which the Society actually used about 90 percent to set against its overdraft, and this, coupled with the implementation of a very helpful report by the YAS's new accountants, Peat, Marwick and Mitchell (appointed in late 1971), enabled the Society to recover financially and the show and showground to develop.

The 1972 show was, mercifully, a great success, partly because of the visit by HRH The Duchess of Kent who was that year's President, and partly because the downward trend in trade entries was reversing itself. Livestock entries were also up.[23] By the end of that year, the new Secretary General, Mr English, was generating new ideas for uses of the showground, such as one-day show jumping events, a 'Teaching Farm', family open days, and so on. Some suggestions eventually bore fruit. The squash courts were opened in 1974, and the ski slope in 1977. The 1973 show was also successful, its attendance of 109,000 being the highest since 1954, and its profit of £35,000 being almost at the same level that it was when Sir John had vacated the Show Directorship.

The show in 1974 was one of the most innovative so far, and it testified both to the Society's new buoyancy and to Major General Dalton's and Mr English's enthusiasm and imagination. There was an 'Adventure in Yorkshire' exhibition with a working steam engine, a model of the Humber Bridge, a display of 'Public Transport through the Ages', and helicopter rides. These were very popular with the children. There was also a Working Terrier Show and a Horse Shoeing Competition. For the first time, there was a demonstration of rare breeds of cattle, which included Longhorns and British Whites. Again, a sheep-shearing competition was held and a wood carving competition. All of these features drew in the crowds magnificently, with the second highest attendance on record, at 120,000. The cost of mounting this show was higher than usual, by about £10,000, but its enormous success seemed to indicate that future successes and showground development could come about only by making the show more entertaining for the general public (whilst striving, of course, to preserve its worth for the agricultural community).[24]

Such seems to have become the show and showground policy in the subsequent years, particularly under the present Honorary Show Director, Major General G. de E. Collin, who succeeded Major General Dalton after the 1976 show, and whose handling of the event has been highly entrepreneurial. The 1975 show continued in the innovative spirit of 1974, again with rather higher costs but also earning higher revenue. Indeed, the large increases in membership fees and trade stand fees in time for the show indicated how confidently expansive the handling of the event again was. For the '76 show, there were further optimistic developments: trade stand entries were up and there were record entries of horses and ponies.[25]

The Executive Committee was also intent on making up for the sale of land in 1971 by several new purchases. In 1974 a 2.5-acre field (behind The Traveller's Rest Inn) was bought for additional car parking, and in 1976 negotiations were started for the purchase of Bilton Court, a large house with some 25 acres of useable land adjacent to the showground. In May 1978 this latter deal was completed, as a result of which and thanks very largely to the astuteness of Mr James Holt, Chairman of the Executive Committee, the showground acquired an extra 22 acres for some £15,000 plus costs, a good deal indeed.

The show now went from strength to strength. That of 1977 was a special occasion, being in the year of the Queen's Jubilee and attended by Her Majesty The Queen and Prince Phillip. The new Show Director fully intended to sustain the show's momentum and was in the fortunate position of having the Society's rapidly increasing solvency to back his plans, which now included increased advertising for the show. The advertising allocation for the 1978 show was £7000; for 1979, £7800; and for 1987, about £20,000. Livestock entry records were broken at the '78, '79 and '80 shows, and by the time of the last of these events the new financial strategy for the show was so sound that it was able to boast substantial growth in revenue despite a substantial drop in attendance, due to poor weather.[26] It should also be noted that the 1979 Show chalked up an all-time record of attendance, at 131,075, with cash takings at the gate of over £$\frac{1}{4}$ million.[27]

Profit is not the only desirable outcome of the show, however, and since the warning sounded by Mr Baldwin in 1966 and the crisis of identity in the early seventies the managers of The Great Yorkshire have been conscious of the constant need to explore new ways of making the show more relevant to agriculture. On occasion, the spur to such experiment has come from outside the Society. For instance, in 1980 Mr Hurst, the Principal of Bishop Burton College of Agriculture (near Beverley, founded in 1954 as the East Riding Farm Institute), suggested that the show should cater more for arable farmers than it was doing. In an effort to meet some of his recommendations, the show in 1980 staged a display of farming equipment in No. 2 Ring. In the following year, Hurst submitted a paper to the Executive Committee proposing that the Society should establish a demonstration area for arable farming along with a technical advisory service.[28] This is now being implemented as a joint YAS–ADAS venture, in the form of an arable trials centre, to be called the Yorkshire Arable Centre, at New Forest Farm, Walshford, whose aim is also to maintain the advisory service now being withdrawn by ADAS itself.[29]

Returning to the show, we might try to summarize its character during the 1980s. The strategy for the show and the showground was neatly encapsulated in the annual report for 1980 which stated that although the YAS had spent more in 1980 than it had earned, 'spending on the showground must continue if the showground is to retain its reputation as the finest permanent site in the country.'[30] The present Show Director has implemented this policy enthusiastically and judiciously, reversing, for instance, a decision in 1978 to construct a new Member's Building since he felt more basic improvements should receive priority. Moreover, whilst pursuing an expressly 'aggressive' strategy for advertising, to create popular appeal, he nonetheless puts the quality of the show above mere figures of attendance and profit.

By the time of the 1982 show, the most vital aspects of the event in the Show Director's opinion, namely the trade stands and livestock entries, were uniformly excellent. Indeed, by June of that year all the trade stand space had been let and there was a waiting list of 145 firms wishing to exhibit, 52 of which were agricultural companies.[31] In that year, too, there was a sizeable number of overseas visitors, including a party of some 75 Australian farmers. Attendance and profit were lower than anticipated, despite the visit by HRH Princess Margaret, but this was not unduly worrying as the show again possessed a strong infrastructure thanks to the very substantial development programme that had begun in 1979, to the tune of almost £200,000.[32] The map opposite shows the form taken by the show recently.

One particular recent development on the showground deserves mention. As a memorial to Sir John, who died in the spring of 1979 at about the same time as did Major Seed, the Executive Committee decided to construct new stockmen's accommodation. In June 1980, an appeal to support this memorial was launched and the building was ready for use (at a cost of £321,178) at the 1983 show, being officially opened in June of the following year by Isobel, Lady Dunnington-Jefferson, Sir John's widow. This very handsome building, known as the 'Sir John Dunnington-Jefferson House', achieves three ends: it is a permanent tribute to the YAS's greatest Show Director, it provides an unrivalled standard of stockmen's accommodation at an agricultural show, and it enhances the out-of-show usage of the Showground. Indeed, the last of these points appears to have been very much in mind at its inception.[33]

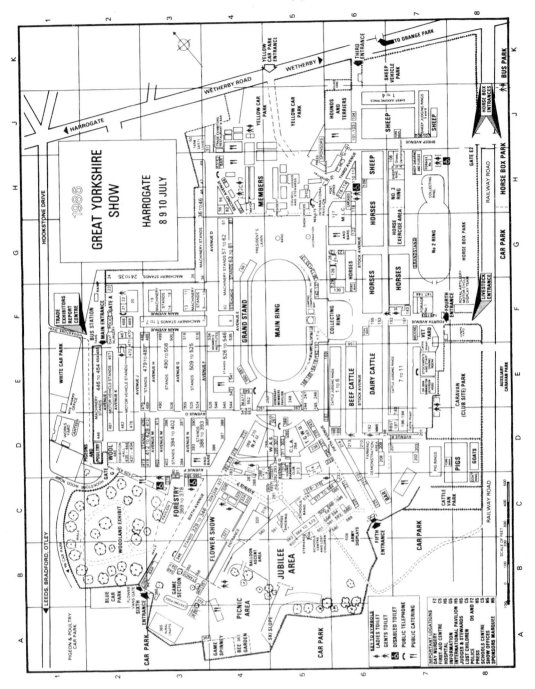

Other features, mostly innovative, of the Great Yorkshire Show in recent years include: a scheme to cater more systematically for overseas visitors and potential customers by incorporating the Overseas Pavilion with an Export Bureau, renamed the 'International Pavilion' in 1984; the steady increase in the popularity of rare breeds, the YAS becoming a corporate member of the Rare Breeds Survival Trust in 1984, believing the Trust's work to be of scientific importance; a new buoyancy in trade stands, and a general feeling amongst agricultural machinery dealers that the show is worth attending, particularly for the follow-up business it generates; the development of specialized areas of livestock management – such as fleeces, or limousins, introduced at the show in 1980, and other livestock breeds; and the award of prizes for the Schools Farm Project Competition which was started by the Honorary Show Director in 1985 'to stimulate interest by children in matters connected with agriculture, farming and the countryside, and in particular to encourage a link with a working farm.'[34] For this project in 1987, additional finance has been allocated to help poor and urban schools to send their children to farms. In this last concern, small as it might seem, for a close rapport between town and country the YAS comes full circle back to Earl Spencer's own ardent wish.

The magnitude of the task today, compared with that of the first Show in 1838, can be gauged from the fact that the Great Yorkshire Show now requires not only an almost full-time (although Honorary) Show Director but also some 30 sub-committees, each responsible for the smooth running of a particular component, as well as dedicated workers on the showground such as Mr Plimbley, Clerk of Works until 1983 and his successor Mr Mitchell, and Mr Shutt, Site Superintendant since 1979. In 1838 there was only one committee, and no Show Director. Yet, assuredly, the personal dedication of those who tried the first experiment was neither less nor greater.

On this note, we might go back to the start of this last period in the Society's history and trace the changes in its management. We shall at the same time examine developments in the Society's actual structure and legal character, for these have been fundamental.

The first Chairman of the Executive Committee, the Marquis of Normanby, gave his personal stamp of authority to the new post. Considerable authority, however, still lay with the President who again usually chaired the meetings of the Council. The President's authority was especially felt when someone such as Sir John occupied this position, as he did in the year March 1966–March 1967 (the Presidency now running from the AGM in March onwards). It is noteworthy that Sir John's nominations as Vice-President for 1965–6 and President for 1966–7 were 'approved with acclamation'.[35]

Other Presidents are also noteworthy, their appointments being indicative of various facets of the Society's endeavours and ideology during this period. Thus, one must mention Lord St Oswald (President 1968–9) for his interest in forging links between the Society and agriculture in the EEC; Messrs F.W. Furness (President 1970–1) and F.K. Abbey (President 1978–9) for their dedicated

22 First photograph of mechanical machinery in the *Transactions*: Fowler Gyrotiller, 1932

23 Aerial view of showground at Sheffield in 1935

24 Centenary Show, York, 1937

25 The 1938 show at Doncaster

26 Forestry section, with Hookstone Wood in background, 1952

27 Harrogate showground in the early 1950s

28 Cattle Parade in the Main Ring, 1954

29 Cattle Parade in the Main Ring, 1954

30   Vehicle trade stands in the late 1950s

31   Machinery on H. Bushell & Sons' stand in 1958, the company's centenary year

32 HRH The Princess Royal and Sir John Dunnington-Jefferson inspecting the Main Ring control tower under construction, accompanied by Mr F.M. Baldwin between Mr and Mrs C.I. Dickinson, 1957

33 The main entrance to the Harrogate showground in 1957. This building became the Society's permanent offices in 1974

34 Mr F.M. Baldwin, Secretary General; Lieutenant Colonel Sir John Dunnington-Jefferson, President; and Major J.H.A. Seed, Honorary Show Director, 1966

35 Opening of Sir John Dunnington-Jefferson House, 1984. Isobel, Lady Dunnington-Jefferson; Mr G.F. Lane Fox, Presdient; Lieutenant Colonel M.G.A. Young, Secretary General; Brigadier K. Hargreaves; Councillor A. McCarroll, Mayor of Harrogate; Mr F.W. Furness; The Marquis of Normanby; Mr T. Bolton, architect; Major General G. de E. Collin, Honorary Show Director; Colonel J.A.M. Phillips

36 The Society's oldest trophy, award in 1855, and the members' tokens flanked by the 1937 shows prize-winners' medallions

committee work, and their very popular standings in the North and West Ridings respectively; Mr L.C.G. Gilling (President 1981–2) for his role in Yorkshire agricultural education; and the three ex-Show Directors, Sir John, Major Seed (President 1969–70) and Major General Dalton (1977–8) who of course had been responsible for the Society's heaviest single task, namely the show.

On occasion, too, the President signified the Society's successful endeavour to be an integral part of the national agricultural scene, as was the case with the election of Mr Christopher York (President in 1975–6) who was also a central member of the RASE, becoming its President in 1979. Inevitably, far fewer of the recent Presidents have been representative of the landocracy and established county gentry than in the Society's early years, indicative of the profound distribution of influence and wealth since then. Nonetheless, a few family names do persist among the recent Presidents, such as Lord Bolton (President 1974–5), the Marquess of Zetland (1980–1) and G.F. Lane Fox (President 1984–5).

We must also, of course, examine other *loci* of authority within the Society. Sir John's successor as Director of the Show in 1963, Major Seed, retained the position for only two shows. Yet his sterling service as Sir John's assistant for the previous 15 years entitles him to recognition as one of the crucial figures in the development of the permanent showground.

The announcement of his resignation, in August 1965, introduces another question concerning the management of the YAS, namely that of the Executive Committee's authority *vis-à-vis* that of the Council. In October the Selection Committee made a recommendation for Major Seed's successor, but in the ballot, which was made compulsory under the new rules of 1963, the Council rejected the nomination. The Executive Committee was then asked to reconsider the matter. In March of the following year it apparently put forward its own nominee, but there was considerable doubt as to whether it possessed the authority to make an appointment independently of the Council. Lord Halifax, who had been President in 1963–4, argued that the Executive Committee did possess such authority, but in the end he was overruled and it was decided to amend Rule 7 in the constitution so that on this occasion, but more significantly on all future occasions, the Executive Committee could appoint the Honorary Show Director of its own accord.[36]

In one sense this decision was but a logical step in making the committee a more truly executive body, yet as Professor Bywater, then on the Technical Committee and later elected an Honorary Vice-President, objected, this was also a step backwards from another intention of the constitutional reform of 1963 – namely, that of making the Society more democratic. It appears that the Executive Committee now went ahead and made the appointment (of Major General Dalton) without officially informing the Council until several months later.

Of course, the Show Director is not the only crucial figure for the construction of the showground, and recognition must be given to the actual builders of the site, and in particular to Mr C.H. Dickinson, of Harrogate, who was the main show contractor from 1950 to 1968. On his retirement, the Council expressed the Society's indebtedness by conferring upon him its highest honour: the title of Honorary Vice-President. Sir John's personal tribute to him is worth recording:

> He had never let us down once and saved us tens of thousands of pounds, enabling us to develop in half the time it would otherwise have taken, and each year he presented the Society with an impeccable Showground.[37]

There were also many members of the Society who, as stewards or judges, served the show and thus helped justify the showground magnificently. They are really too many to mention by name, so (as we have done in previous chapters) just one might be mentioned as representative of them all: Mr C.W. Helm. At his death in 1969, the Council felt the Society and the Show had suffered a great loss, for he had been a member of the Society for 62 years, a member of Council for 46 and a Show Steward for over 40 years! Such dedication is still to be found on the showground today and is one of the most impressive features of the Society's character.

The show also depends upon the strategic vision of the Council and the Executive Committee, and in this sense the retirement of Lord Normanby as Executive Committee Chairman in December 1968 marked a decided change. Under his direction, the Executive Committee had allowed capital expenditure and maintenance on the showground to develop. But under his successor, due largely to the Society's precarious finances but also to a change in philosophy, the show would have to function within considerable constraints for several years. It was within these constraints and their accompanying tensions that Mr Baldwin's and Sir John's divergence from the Executive Committee and the Society's overall management has to be seen. Indeed, throughout the year 1971 Sir John was in conflict with the Executive Committee, not only over its handling of the Society's finances but also over other matters, such as the proposal to move the Society's offices from Cliftonfield to the showground.

We should now focus on the role of Mr Baldwin. Appointed the Society's Secretary in 1947, Mr Baldwin transformed his post during nearly 25 years in office, not only acquiring for it greater authority (by 1965 the job title was Secretary General) but also building up the professionalism of the Society's entire administration. As Mr Furness remarked in 1980, when Mr Baldwin was being offered Honorary Life Membership, 'the present quality of office staff owes much to Mr Baldwin's administration'.[38] His reputation was not only that of an administrator, however, for as we have seen, and as Sir John readily acknowledged, the *idea* of the Great Yorkshire permanent Showground was his. In the opinion of not a few of the Society's members, 'Mac' Baldwin was a key formulator of ideology, a creative thinker, 'the ideas man who foresaw public demand and suggested action to meet it' as the Yorkshire Gazette and Herald quoted a YAS member.[39]

Mr Baldwin seemed to be the right man for his job, given the post-war expansionism of the Society. Under him, the recruitment drive exceeded all sober expectations; his early perception of the structural changes needed if the

Society and the show were to develop, securing as it did Sir John's total support, enabled that development to take place; his planning of the showground as it is today testifies to his meticulous zeal and imagination, and the rapidity with which the first truly permanent show (that of 1952) was constructed indicates how hard he worked as part of a magnificent team.

On this last point, members of the Society might like to read Mr Baldwin's own words:

> We had always intended to develop the site and not merely to own a large field. But there were, probably fortunately, no precedents to go on and we had to fend for ourselves and start from scratch. When you recall . . . at that time nothing could be built without planning permission, and building licences were necessary for anything larger than a dog kennel. Steel was on licence, timber was on licence and cement unobtainable. Nevertheless, we set about it and made good. We had many good friends both inside and outside the Ministry and we are greatly indebted to them all . . . the restrictions put in our way spurred us on to achieve the impossible.
>
> The 1951 lay-out was a typical temporary one and the only permanent work undertaken was the making of a length of roadway, the laying-in of a high tension cable to a transformer house and the laying of a 4 inch water main right across the ground.
>
> But even before the 1951 Show was held, we were convinced that many improvements could be made. And from what we learned, I entirely re-designed the lay-out for the 1952 Show, and that lay-out remains basically unchanged. We employed no architect or surveyor but made models of the lay-out and of individual buildings.
>
> The principle of the new lay-out was to locate the Main Ring in the centre and from it have six principal avenues radiating to public entrances.
>
> This divided the ground into six sectors, into each of which we put the whole of one section of exhibits. Within each sector we grouped the exhibits according to type. This has had a marked effect on two things – it has simplified the task of finding one's way about, and it has reduced the walking-about necessary to see all the exhibits of any one kind. For instance, I measured the distance it was necessary to walk at one moveable show to see all the poultry appliances – $2\frac{1}{2}$ miles. At Harrogate, a similar tour covers only $\frac{3}{4}$ of a mile. No part of our 80 acre showground is more than 300 yards from the President's Box.
>
> Having settled the lay-out, we set to on our programme of major developments. The 1952 show was, quite definitely, a permanent show in spite of the most appalling restrictions. We were about to put up about £50,000 worth of buildings in September 1951 when the Chancellor of the Exchequer suddenly imposed a ban on all new buildings until March 1952. We had nine months work ahead of us and we couldn't have a licence until March. But we did get those buildings up in time for the show [of 1952] with the magnificent assistance of everyone who could help. We broke no laws but probably all records.[40]

These contributions by Mr Baldwin are well acknowledged and un-controversial. Indeed, his many contributions to the Society and to the agricultural community have generally been recognised, from his OBE in 1966, to being offered honorary life membership of the Society. But another of his contributions is a subject of some controversy, and since there are many members of the Society who recall this subject and hold differing interpretations of it, no responsible *History* should pass it by. The subject is Farm Records Limited.

It has been mentioned that in 1963 the Abbey Committee, which was set up to consider the Society's future interests, recommended that the YAS should establish an organization for the recording of beef cattle and sheep and that, on the President's instructions and with Council approval, Mr Baldwin presented a report on the matter. By 1965, this project got off the ground in the form of a commercial venture called Farm Records Ltd. Its foundation was certainly an aspect of the Society's expansionist ideology at that time, and it was also in keeping with government policy.

The government's 1965 Price Review announced a system of grants to be made available to farmers for employing persons to keep farm business records, the object of which was to encourage farmers to increase their productivity by better management. At that time, it was felt that the system would create an immediate demand for secretarial help on farms, and the Ministry of Agriculture was anxious that this work should be carried out by responsible organizations. The NAAS Director asked whether the YAS would consider taking on this task for the north.

This was indeed done, first by purchasing the York branch of the Farmers' Secretarial Service, on the recommendation of the Executive Committee and with Council's sanction, and then by re-constituting the Service as a separate company to be called Farm Secretarial Services Ltd, and actually named Farm Records Ltd. It was set up with a capital of 3000 × £1 shares (10s paid up), with a Board consisting of central figures in the YAS's management: Sir Richard Graham as Chairman, Lord Bolton, and Messrs Abbey (then Vice-Chairman of the Executive Committee), Baldwin and Watmough. The YAS was thus putting £1500 into establishing the venture.[41]

The work of the company was done by a staff who went all over the region offering its record-keeping services to the agricultural community on a fee basis. From the start it proved to be useful, so much so that by the middle of 1966 it had clients from as far away as South Lincolnshire. At that stage, it was thought politic to invite the Peterborough Agricultural Society to become a partner (the Peterborough already being a member, with the YAS, of the Agricultural Development Association). That would have been straight-forward had there not been a general credit squeeze, which made it more economic to create a separate company, Farm Records (Eastern) Ltd. The Board of this company comprised Sir Richard Graham as Chairman, Mr Baldwin, two members of the Peterborough and two members of the Shropshire and West Midlands Agricultural Society.

By mid-1966, Sir Richard Graham reported to the YAS that Farm Records Ltd was making good progress and requested that the Society should guarantee a bank loan of £10,000 by its own bankers, the Westminster. This was done. In November, following upon the announcement that Farm Records Ltd had incurred a loss of £6600 on its first year in operation, the bank loan was raised to £14,000. The Executive Committee believed that it was entirely appropriate to supply or guarantee funds to the company in its infancy in this way since its business was developing and a profit was being forecast for its second year.[42] Besides, it had no capital on which to draw.

Shortly afterwards, a demand for the service developed in the West Midlands, and in 1967 the Shropshire and West Midlands Agricultural Society became a partner. There were now three area-managers: one for York, where the office of Farm Records Ltd was situated, one for Peterborough, and one for the West Midlands. In September 1967 the Executive Committee resolved to make a loan to Farm Records Ltd, to enable the company to discharge its liabilities to the Westminster Bank up to £20,000, and in November of the same year this further financial commitment seemed again to be justified by the announcement of a small gross profit on the second year, although there was still a net loss of £8961. There was, however, good reason to expect the company to break even by spring 1968. Meanwhile, Farm Records (Eastern) Ltd had been operating for just over a year and had incurred a sizeable net loss, at which the Peterborough and Shropshire directors were becoming worried.

There might well have been a considerable financial improvement for both companies in 1968 had it not been for a foot-and-mouth epidemic, during which farmers were naturally worried that the disease might be spread by the peripatetic Farm Records workers. This created an immediate cash-flow difficulty, and at Sir Richard's request the Executive Committee guaranteed a further £5000 loan. Already, by December of the previous year, the YAS had guaranteed £25,000 to Farm Records Ltd, and that company had guaranteed a £5000 overdraft to Farm Records (Eastern) Ltd. The Westminster Bank at Peterborough now insisted that the YAS should take over the latter guarantee too. Additionally, the YAS guaranteed £4900 towards the current funding of Farm Records (Eastern) Ltd. Thus by February 1968 the total of the YAS's liability towards these two companies was £34,900, of which £25,000 went exclusively to Farm Records Ltd. The total overdraft of the latter company, £24,800, was guaranteed as follows:

	£
By the YAS	9900
By the Peterborough	9900
By the Shropshire and West Midlands	5000

At Sir Richard's suggestion, an independent report on the affairs of the two companies was made by the Leeds firm of accountants, Messrs Peat, Marwick, Mitchell and Co. Their report was received by the Executive Committee in February 1968 and it spelled out three possible courses of action: (i) to continue financing the companies and incur higher liabilities in the short term future; (ii) immediate liquidation; (iii) to sell the companies to a commercial competitor.

The Executive Committee (and the Council) agonized over what best to do. In April, Farm Records Ltd showed strong signs of trading improvement and it was agreed not to liquidate or sell for the time being. By July, Farm Records Ltd was making a monthly profit and by the end of that year Farm Records (Eastern) Ltd seemed set too for profitability on its own account. It was now decided that the YAS should acquire both companies in order to oversee their management more closely and to give them the benefit of charity status.[43] This was effected, with the agreement of the other two agricultural societies who left their guarantees and loans in support of Farm Records (Eastern) Ltd. It was also agreed that when the overdrafts and loans had been repaid, any surpluses would be made available to the three societies to support their charitable objectives in proportion to the risk they each had taken and agreed to *continue* taking: the YAS approximately 70 percent, the Peterborough 23 percent, and the Shropshire 7 percent.

In December 1968, Farm Records Ltd (as the product of the merger was called) became a charitable trust. Its Managing Director was the same as that of the pre-merger Farm Records Ltd: Mr Baldwin. Throughout 1969 and into 1970 the new Farm Records Ltd made excellent progress, and the YAS Council seemed entirely satisfied with Mr Baldwin's direction. Thus, at the AGM in March 1969 when he was presented with a gold watch and a scroll in appreciation of his 21 years of service with the Society, there was no hint of discontent. But in 1970 the finances of Farm Records Ltd became seriously disarrayed, and in October the Executive Committee was negotiating their sale.[44] Several commercial firms were approached, but without success. The National Farmers' Union seemed interested as they operated a similar scheme, but they then decided to run down their own service. An offer was also made by the General Manager of Farm Records Ltd itself, and after lengthy deliberation it was resolved to sell him the business for a nominal sum of £100.[45] By March 1971 the transaction was completed.

The matter actually lingered on, however, for several years as the Society sought to recover at least its own direct loans. These were finally repaid by the end of 1976, although there remained interest repayments and other matters which persisted until 1980 and caused the already strained relationship between the Executive Committee and most of Council on the one hand and Mr Baldwin on the other to persist. It was only in 1980 that financial matters between the Society and Mr Baldwin (including the issue of a partial loss of pension due to his slightly early retirement) were sufficiently, although by no means totally, settled for the Executive and Council to feel it appropriate to offer him honorary life membership.[46] In fact, Mr Baldwin declined, believing that the issue of his pension had not fully been settled.

The affair of Farm Records Ltd has been discussed here in sufficient detail to illustrate several features of the Society's history, and perhaps to serve as a lesson for agricultural show societies in general. It illustrates at least four points:

1 The danger of a non-commercial, charitable institution undertaking directly commercial ventures.

2   The difficulty for such an institution of trying to manage two, or more, capital-demanding ventures of very different natures and with different calls on its sense of priorities at one and the same time. For at the very time that Farm Records Ltd needed financial support, so did the showground.

3   The extreme risk for an institution which depends upon a highly sensitive and variable source of income (such as an agricultural show) undertaking a venture which, any seasoned businessman could predict, would require a period of consistent (or even increasing) investment in anticipation of eventual profitability.

4   The vulnerability of profit-oriented concerns (as Farm Records Ltd had to be before it was taken over by the YAS) to changes in ideology. Thus, whilst Farm Records Ltd was a highly appropriate venture, and Mr Baldwin a most comfortable figure for the YAS's expansionist ideology of the mid-1960s, the fit was much less acceptable when the Society drew in its horns in the late '60s and early '70s.

The most important single cause of that retrenchment and change in ideology related not to Farm Records Ltd but to the difficulty of managing the showground. This brings us to consider the whole area of the YAS's finances in this period.

At the end of 1963, several months after Sir John's retirement as Show Director, the Society had an overdraft of £213,000 as a result of showground development. The profits from subsequent shows, particularly those of 1964 and 1967, and the revenue being generated by buoyant membership enabled the overdraft to be reduced steadily, but not very rapidly. Indeed, as the Financial Report in March 1967 stated, the steadily rising cost of construction and maintenance combined with the high bank rate to slow down the repayment. By the end of 1967 the Society's total loans amounted to £196,000, of which some 85 percent was due to the showground. At this juncture, the Executive Committee appointed a small committee to investigate how best to expedite the repayment. It is worth noting that there was no mention of Farm Records Ltd in this committee's brief.

A President's appeal for interest-free loans from members of the Society was now launched, but the response was slow and it became clear that the urgency of the problem required another measure. Indeed, the Society's finances by 1969 were being assailed from several directions: the general inflation in the national economy, the inevitably increasing cost simply of maintaining and repairing the showground, the uncertainty over Farm Records Ltd, and even a deficit in the Society's administrative account. Yet, and this was one of the most noticeable features of the Society's records in this period, at the AGM in March of that year there was scant intimation of the Council's and the Executive Committee's anxiety!

Another step was taken in June 1969 to raise more cash: the creation of a new class of membership – Honorary Membership. Although this did bring in some useful revenue, it was too little and too slow in coming. By the following AGM, the Executive Committee realised that there were only two workable alternatives: either to reshape the show and sell off some land, or to launch a professionally-run appeal for funds. Lord Bolton's report to this effect at the AGM was the first clear indication to members that the YAS's finances were in a critical condition. It is also worth noting the principal causes to which Lord Bolton, now Chairman of the Executive Committee, attributed this condition: the decline in attendance by trade exhibitors, a very high bank rate, and inflation.

By spring of the following year it was becoming apparent to one or two members of the Council that even the public appeal might not be sufficient, and that recourse would have to be made to the other alternative, of selling off a part of the showground.

The Society's overdraft was now costing £50 a day in interest payments. The Executive Committee was nonetheless understandably and rightly reluctant to sell, Lord Bolton in particular wishing to work on the assumption that the appeal would succeed. Yet, by the autumn of 1970, by which time Farm Records was causing considerable anxiety, the Executive Committee was seeking planning permission for a portion of the showground in case it had to sell.[47] By January 1971, that option became imperative; the appeal had raised only £45,000 in pledges, Farm Records was on the point of being disposed of at a nominal sum, and the prospects for trade stand fees at the show were bleaker than ever. The Executive Committee now proposed selling off about six acres of the showground.[48]

Yet again, at the AGM in March, there was no indication of the gravity of the Council's and the Executive Committee's deliberations. The annual report for 1970 was, if anything, buoyant. It announced that the appeal was 'making very good progress and confidently expected to achieve the target of over £100,000'. It announced the disposal of Farm Records 'on what might be considered generous terms' with the possibility of the Society recouping its investment. It made no mention, however, of the plan to sell off some of the showground. This decision was made known to the meeting, but only via the Show Director's progress report on the 1971 show.[49] The bitter pill of the Society's financial condition was apparently being sweetened for the ordinary members' consumption.

To the taste of one prominent member of Council, Sir John, this was too much. At a special meeting of Council in September that year, held in response to several requests 'to discuss matters of general interest for which time was not generally available at the regular meetings', daggers were drawn. Sir John criticized the handling of the appeal, which by then had raised only £50,000, only £5000 more than in January. He deplored the proposed 'mutilation' of the showground and felt that, rather than tinker, an entirely new strategy was required, such as selling the entire showground and setting up a wealthy trust, 'the income from which could be used to support the work of others who were doing a good job.'

A number of Council members, whilst disagreeing with Sir John's suggestion to sell the whole site, nonetheless aligned themselves with him in their anxieties over the Society's management. Mr Furness thought that the Society's finances had been grossly mismanaged ever since Sir John had retired from the Honorary Directorship although, unlike Sir John, he blamed Farm Records principally. Mr York agreed with Mr Furness that 'no one knew where we were since Sir John had retired.' Moreover, he did not trust the audited accounts, and he felt that the appeal was a flop. Mr Furness alleged that the appeal had lost a chance of a £25,000 donation 'because of a marked lack of cooperation and friendship between administration and exhibitors' at the show. Many minor criticisms were also made.

The Executive Committee held its ground, with Lord Bolton firmly resisting Sir John's onslaught. He declared himself firmly convinced 'that the Appeal, coupled with the sale of land, would put the Society in such a position that it could once again be a viable concern'.[50] Within a mere three years, Lord Bolton's stand was to be vindicated. The sale of 7.8 acres of the north-western corner of the showground in late 1971 fetched £124,000, of which about 90 percent went towards reducing the Society's bank loan. Thanks also to the appeal, by the end of the following year the overdraft was down to £88,000; by the end of 1973 it was further reduced to £44,000; and by late 1974, due largely to the sale of Cliftonfield, the YAS at last had a credit balance (with the exception of a loan account which was scheduled to be paid off after two and a half more years and which the Executive Committee decided to allow to run off as scheduled). At this stage, some £20,000 was still owing from Farm Records, so far as the Society was concerned.[51] The management of Farm Records thought otherwise.

By mid-1976, the repayment of the loan account was complete and once again the Society was purchasing property to augment the showground, having just bought Bilton Court. The period of grave anxiety over finance and of enforced retrenchment of showground development was over. Furthermore, a new investment strategy began to unfold. By autumn 1977, the Society's balance stood at about £230,000, mostly on short-term investment. By the end of that year, it seemed eminently sensible to consider a strategy of medium-term investments, and by the autumn of the following year (1978) the Executive Committee, feeling that the Society really was growing more secure week by week, recommended that the bulk of its balance be placed on long-term investment, with £50,000 to be kept on short call.[52]

By early 1980, the Society's balance was up further at about £370,000, and by the middle of 1981 its investment strategy was set for the rest of the decade. Now, its investments were spread widely, among government stock, bank deposits and a loan to Harrogate Council, with longer term investment being considered from time to time and a hefty sum held permanently in reserve (at October 1981, at least £150,000). In 1982, '83 and '84 the cash reserves were of course depleted by the cost of the Sir John Dunnington-Jefferson House, but by March 1985 even these had recovered and, moreover, in June the Executive Committee was insisting that an annexe should be built onto the stockmen's accomodation without delay.[53] This annexe was not in fact begun, but the idea that it should be illustrates the Society's new financial strength which seems now to be growing at an unprecedented rate.

Between the Financial Statement in April '85 and that in April '86, the Society's funds grew by over £220,000, to £749,000. By the time of the sesquicentenary, they are projected to be c.£1.1 million. In that period, too, negotiations were well in hand for the lease of a few acres of the showground for the erection of a 'superstore' which, if completed, will enormously enhance the Society's wealth. By the time of its sesquicentenary in October '87, the Society might well feel it has left its past well behind.

In one sense, of course, it has. Today, the YAS is not the same body – either legally or structurally – as it has been for most of its past, for at the end of 1982 it became incorporated as a limited, private company. The idea of its incorporation was proposed to the Council in June 1981, and its members promptly agreed, apparently needing little persuasion for so long as the Society retained its original status the officers and members of the Executive Committee and Council would remain *personally* responsible for all of its affairs. The Articles of Association were issued in September 1982, and at the Council meeting on 2 December the assets and liabilities of 'The Old Society' (as the original YAS was now technically termed) were transferred to the private company, No. 1666751 (under the Companies Act 1948), the new Yorkshire Agricultural Society.[55] By March of the following year all the necessary procedures had also been taken to register this new YAS as a charitable institution. (See Appendix E for the Society's present executive and administrative structure.)

If the YAS of today is technically only five years old, its founding ideology remains and has been reinvigorated. We recall that the pursuit of science was an integral component of the vision of agricultural progress championed by the founding figures, Earl Spencer, H.S. Thompson, George Legard and their like. Since 1976, with the setting up of an 'Aid to Agriculture' committee to advise the Council on how more fully to 'advance the cause of agriculture in Yorkshire', the YAS has devoted a considerable sum of money to promoting education and science.[56] Indeed, in the previous few years and even during the financial crisis of the late '60s and early '70s support had been given to this end; but it was only in 1976–7 that such aid became a central component of its ideology once again, with key figures in the Society engaged with it.[57] Between 1976 and 1986, the total expenditure in this direction, under the supervision of the Aid to Agriculture sub-committee, has been just over £90,000 which has gone towards a variety of research and educational recipients: Nuffield Scholarships, science and technology researches, agricultural workers awards, agricultural conferences and demonstrations, publications, a woodman training scheme, and the two agricultural institutes at Askham Bryan and Bishop Burton with which the Society today maintains a close relationship. (See Appendix F for a detailed list, 1976–87.)

In all of this, the new Secretary General, Lt Col Martin Young (who succeeded Mr English in 1978) takes a keen interest. Indeed, the great variety within his job today, coupled with his own approachable and outgoing style, means that the web of communications and interests being spun by the YAS is as wide as ever. For not only is Martin Young the Society's official representative on such bodies as the Nuffield Farming Scholarships Trust and the Yorkshire Federation of Young Farmers, but his own enthusiasm and sound judgement have contributed to the success of some major activities of recent years, such as the 'Barley '84' and 'Northern Beef '85' demonstrations, both held in conjunction with the RASE and ADAS, which were valuable agricultural exercises and also financially rewarding. It is Martin Young's task to coordinate such activities as the distribution of the Society's own magazine, the *Great Yorkshire Farmer* (which began in March 1984, ceased publication in July 1986, and, it is hoped, will be succeeded by another publication), the coordination of the Society's sesquicentennial celebrations, of which this *History* is a part, and the recruitment of new members, for whom there is no longer a waiting list. In such tasks, of course, he requires much behind-the-scenes support, and in this respect the experience and loyalty of Mr Alan Martindale as Deputy Secretary, of Mr Barry Jackson as Assistant Secretary, and of his right-hand man, Mr David Ward, are utterly invaluable. Messrs Jackson and Ward are chiefly responsible for the running of the 'Show Office' and their full-time commitment is to the Great Yorkshire Show.

At this point, it is appropriate to recall that much of the groundwork for the present excellence of this administration was laid not only by Mr Baldwin but also by Mr Stanley Holgate, who had joined the Society earlier in 1929, had returned after the Second World War as Chief Clerk, had been promoted to Assistant Secretary in 1950 and Deputy Secretary in 1962. His death in 1973 shortly before he was due to retire was a sad loss to the Society and must have added to the low psychological ebb that the Society then was at.

The losses of key figures during 1972–3, however, illustrates a truism in history that few appreciate: that individuals *can be indispensable*, not in their actual persons but in the continuance of what they have created. And what had been created within the YAS by figures like Sir John, Mr Baldwin and Mr Holgate was an infrastructure of sufficient durability that once the financial storm of the late '60s and early '70s had been weathered the Society could once again cultivate an ideology of broadly serving the community.

The degree of support nowadays given by the YAS to agriculture at large deserves notice. In the wake of the Society's difficulties in the 1960s and early '70s when it became so directly involved in outside ventures, the management have determined that the Society should not again become the sole agent of anything apart from the Great Yorkshire Show. Tellingly, the title of the sub-committee is *Aid to* Agriculture.

Whereas in 1965 the Executive Committee had recommended that the Society should become more involved in outside agricultural concerns, since 1976 the intention has been to give support to others in their agricultural concerns. Ironically, in this current policy, the Society is acting very much as Sir John advocated when he argued for the sale of the showground: as a charitable trust with a very substantial income. Out of the anguish of that time, the best of both sides' visions has been preserved: the show, which many visitors today acknowledge to be held on the finest showground in Britain, and the functions of a trust.

Indeed, through both of these means the YAS today promotes agricultural progress. Its Show features state-of-the-art agricultural techniques and technology, has room for representations by educational institutions and research groups, and generally provides a valuable forum not only for purchasing things but also for exchanging ideas. The conviviality and colourfulness of the show are apt to give the casual visitor the impression that the scientific progress of agriculture is far from mind. Yet that is not the case. It is simply that, as in the founding days, the steering of agriculture's 'Progress with Science' is still in most English and most affable hands.

Indeed, the sensitive historian, perceiving the Society as it is today in its social and historical context cannot fail to be struck by its Englishness. For instance, one notes the Society's Harvest Thanksgiving Service which began in 1949 at York Minster and which, since 1977, has gone in rotation between York Minster, Beverley Minster and Ripon Cathedral; one remarks the fact that the Society now has an Honorary Chaplain, the first appointee being Canon Paul Burbridge, and the current appointee being the Reverend Roger Noyes who is also on the Society's Poultry Committee; one watches the gentlemanly manner with which the Honorary Show Director cultivates the Press in order to ensure that the general public understand the nature of a large agricultural show; one is impressed by the military approach to the show's logistics and running; one recalls the metaphors in which the present managers and members talk about the show, often with restrained but deep pride. And one concludes that Earl Spencer, 'Honest Jack', would undoubtedly be thoroughly at home in the spirit of the Society and its show today.

EPILOGUE

Having offered a detailed analysis of the Society's history covering 150 years of tremendous development, the historian might be allowed to offer his own speculation as to its future. One thing can be predicted with certainty: that the Society will undergo radical changes as society itself changes. Of course, the time-scale of change cannot be forecast with any precision, yet even on this question something useful might be said.

The history of the Society has seen so many developments occurring so rapidly and unexpectedly that one may anticipate similar degrees of surprise and change in the future. A former British Prime Minister once commented that in politics one week is a very long time, meaning that one cannot predict how political issues will develop from week's start to week's end. In agricultural affairs, the time-span for 'a long time' must be somewhat longer. The YAS's own past suggests that three years is about a maximum period of predictability, and that anything longer than that enters into the realm of risk and fiction. Thus, in this the Society's 150th year we might be able to imagine with reasonable accuracy what it will be like in 1990: rather prosperous, supportive of progress in agriculture at large both nationally and in the European context, concerned over other rural and environmental matters, and the owner (literally so, since the YAS has had its own identity since its incorporation) of one of the most prestigious and charming agricultural shows in the country. Whether any of this will hold at the end of this century is anyone's guess. To suppose so is simple hope.

The Society's survival, however, will surely depend critically upon the continuing dedication of Yorkshire's agricultural community. And as that dedication is as visible as ever, especially in the meetings of the Council and Executive Committee and on the showground in working for the show, one has good reason to be optimistic. In fact, one of the most pleasant rewards of writing this *History* has been to appreciate how critically the Good of History derives from the goodness of individual men and women. Even with its new corporate character, the Yorkshire Agricultural Society is testimony to the vision of human affairs quoted from Karl Marx at the opening of this book: 'History is not like some individual person, which uses men to achieve its ends. History is but the actions of men in pursuit of their ends.'

It is in this spirit that this *History* has been written. It is in this spirit that the Society might continue to flourish through the new and perhaps critical challenges of the future.

Appendix A

Presidents of the Yorkshire Agricultural Society and venues of the show

Year	President	Show venue
1837	Earl Spencer	
1838	,,	York
1839	,,	Leeds
1840	,,	Northallerton
1841	Lord Wharncliffe	Hull
1842	,,	York
1843	,,	Doncaster
1844	Earl of Zetland	Richmond
1845	Earl of Feversham	Beverley
1846	Lord Wenlock	Wakefield
1847	Earl of Harewood	Scarborough
1848	Sir John Johnstone, Bart	York: with RASE
1849	Earl of Carlisle	Leeds
1850	Duke of Leeds	Thirsk
1851	Lord Londesborough	Bridlington
1852	Earl Fitzwilliam	Sheffield
1853	Lord Hotham	York
1854	Earl de Grey	Ripon
1855	Earl of Carlisle	Malton
1856	Lord Wharncliffe (Aug.–Oct. '55) Earl of Effingham (Oct. '55–Jul. '56)	Rotherham
1857	Lord Greenock	York
1858	Lord Bolton	Northallerton
1859	Lord Herries	Hull
1860	Earl of Harewood	Pontefract
1861	Earl of Cathcart	RASE at Leeds
1862	H.S. Thompson	York
1863	Earl of Zetland	Stockton
1864	Lord Wenlock	Howden
1865	Duke of Devonshire	Doncaster
1866	Rt Hon. A. Duncombe	York
1867	Sir George Wombwell, Bart	Thirsk
1868	George Lane Fox	Wetherby

1869	George Legard	Beverley
1870	Sir Lionel Pilkington	Wakefield
1871	Lord Wenlock	York
1872	Earl of Feversham	Malton
1873	John Dent Dent	Harrogate
1874	Lord Auckland	Sheffield
1875	W.H. Harrison Broadley	Driffield
1876	Lord Cavendish	Skipton
1877	Earl of Zetland	York
1878	Rt Hon. George Lascelles	Northallerton
1879	Col. Gunter	Leeds
1880	W.T.W.S. Stanhope	Barnsley
1881	Christopher Sykes	Hull
1882	Sir Henry Edwards, Bart	Halifax
1883	Earl of Feversham	RASE at York
1884	Basil T. Woodd	Ripon
1885	Lord Londesborough	Selby
1886	Duke of Norfolk	Sheffield
1887	Lord Wenlock	York
1888	Sir John Ramsden Bart	Huddersfield
1889	Arthur Wilson	Hull
1890	Earl of Harewood	Harrogate
1891	Lord Masham	Bradford
1892	Rt Hon. James Lowther	Middlesborough
1893	Lord Savile	Dewsbury
1894	Lord Herries	Beverley
1895	Sir Savile Crossley, Bart	Halifax
1896	HRH The Duke of York	York
1897	Earl of Harewood	Harrogate
1898	Ernest Beckett	Leeds
1899	Lord Middleton	Hull
1900	F. Bacon Frank	Doncaster
1901	Viscount Mountgarret	Bradford
1902	Earl of Feversham	Leeds
1903	Earl Fitzwilliam	Sheffield
1904	Sir John Ramsden, Bart	Huddersfield
1905	Lord Herries	Hull
1906	Marquess of Zetland	Middlesborough
1907	Viscount Halifax	Barnsley
1908	Lord Savile	Halifax
1909	Arthur Wilson	Beverley
1910	Rt Hon. R.E. Beckett	Leeds
1911	Earl Fitzwilliam	Rotherham
1912	Lord Wenlock (until Feb 1912)	RASE Show at York
	Rt Hon. H.W. Fitzwilliam	

1913	Rt Hon. H.W. Fitzwilliam	York
1914	Walter Morrison	Bradford
1915	[No President]	[No Show]
1916	Earl of Harewood	,,
1917	,,	,,
1918	,,	,,
1919	,,	,,
1920	Lord Middleton	RASE-YAS Show at Darlington
1921	Maj. John Dent	Leeds
1922	Col. Sir George Duncombe Bart	Hull
1923	Lt. Col. E.W. Stanyforth	Sheffield
1924	Lord Deramore	York
1925	Capt. C.S. Greenwood	Bradford
1926	Viscount Lascelles	Harrogate
1927	Col. W.H.A. Wharton	Darlington
1928	Sir Harold Mackintosh	Halifax
1929	,,	RASE at Harrogate
1930	Capt. J.L. Wickham-Boynton	Hull
1931	Maj. L.B. Holliday	Huddersfield
1932	Lord Irwin	Leeds
1933	Marquess of Zetland	Middlesborough
1934	Sir James Hill, Bart	Bradford
1935	Earl Fitzwilliam	Sheffield
1936	Lord Middleton	Beverley
1937	HRH The Princess Royal	York
1938	Col. W. St Andrew Warde-Aldam	Doncaster
1939	Brig. Gen. Sir Edward Whitley	Halifax
1940	,,	[No Show]
1941	,,	,,
1942	,,	,,
1943	,,	,,
1944	,,	,,
1945	,,	,,
1946	,,	,,
1947	,,	,,
1948	,,	RASE Show at York
1949	Earl of Scarborough	Wakefield
1950	,,	Malton
1951	HRH The Princess Royal	Harrogate
1952	Earl of Feversham	Harrogate
1953	Lt. Col. Sir John Dunnington-Jefferson	,,
1954	Sir Alfred Ayckroyd, Bart	,,
1955	Lord Bolton	,,
1956	Sir William Prince-Smith, Bart	,,

1957	HRH The Princess Royal	,,
1958	Maj. Le G.G.W. Horton-Fawkes	,,
1959	Sir William Worsley, Bart	,,
1960	Lord Hotham	,,
1961	Col. F. Lane Fox	,,
1962	Marquis of Normanby	,,
1963	Earl of Halifax	,,
1964	G.R.H. Smith	,,
1965	Sir Kenneth Parkinson	,,
1966	Lt. Col. Sir John Dunnington-Jefferson, Bart	,,
1967	Lord Crathorne	,,
1968	Lord St Oswald	,,
1969	Maj. J.H.A. Seed	,,
1970	F.W. Furness	,,
1971	Brig. K. Hargreaves	,,
1972	HRH The Duchess of Kent	,,
1973	R.A. Bethell	,,
1974	Lord Bolton	,,
1975	Christopher York	,,
1976	Lord Middleton	,,
1977	Maj. Gen. J.C.D'A. Dalton	,,
1978	F.K. Abbey Esq.	,,
1979	Col. J.A.M. Phillips	,,
1980	Marquess of Zetland	,,
1981	L.C.G. Gilling	,,
1982	A.J. Preston	,,
1983	Brig. R. Heathcoat-Amory	,,
1984	G.F. Lane Fox	,,
1985	P.S. Atkinson	,,
1986	Lord Martin Fitzalan Howard	,,
1987	Marquis of Normanby	

Appendix B

The Liebig-Muspratt Venture, 1845–6

Since 1840, Liebig had wished to eliminate the general practice of crop-rotation, for he believed that the system – often with a period of fallow – as commonly practised in England yielded crops well below the theoretical productivity of most soils. If only the correct mineral manure could be devised for each type of crop on each type of soil, then just one crop might be grown continuously on the same land. By means of his ash-analyses of crops, he believed that he had discovered the way to conduct such monoculture.

Accordingly, he entered into a business venture with the Muspratts (who were chemical manufacturers in Liverpool). The Muspratts agreed to manufacture six types of mineral manure following his patent specifications. Each manure was designed to restore to the soil exactly those minerals taken out of it by a particular crop.[1] Liebig also thought it necessary to reduce the solubilities of the manures so that none would be washed out of the soil by rain before being absorbed by the plants. The Muspratts were therefore instructed to make the manures much less soluble than normal. This, it was discovered in the next few years, was a mistake, for even very soluble salts are not totally washed away by heavy rain. By a complex series of double-decomposition reactions with soil-components (mainly silicates and aluminates), almost all salts are absorbed by the soil and are held there until extracted by roots. The experimental basis for this realization was laid in 1845 by Joseph Spence and H.S. Thompson.[2] It was developed and publicized by the professional agricultural chemist, John Thomas Way (1821–84) in the late 1840s and '50s.[3] At that time, Way held the influential post of consulting chemist to the RASE.

Liebig's Muspratt manures were therefore too insoluble to be useful and the Muspratts had to alter their recipes. The fiasco incurred heavy losses for the Muspratts and made a considerable number of farmers wary of chemistry. Thus, in 1849 Thomas Anderson (1819–74), consulting chemist to the HASS, wrote in its *Transactions* that recently tenant-farmers in the North had been

> misled by the far too laudatory terms in which the application of chemistry to agriculture were talked of some years ago. Hopes were then excited which, to those intimately acquainted with chemistry, it was very evident could not be sustained, but which the enthusiastic embraced at once; only, however, when they were disappointed to abandon as worthless the whole science itself. . . .[4]

And as late as 1896 there was a paper in the *JRASE* by a farmer recalling that:

Anyone who may have read what was known as 'scientific agriculture' half a century ago must have been struck with the number of theories then promulgated which have since been disposed of. When a farmer adopted them in practice, he as a rule lost money. Liebig, while doing great good in some directions, prepared the way for the ruin of not a few capable farmers by his mineral theory: among them, a personal friend of my father's.[5]

References

1. See Justus Liebig, *An Address to the Agriculturists of Great Britain, explaining the principles and use of his artificial manures*, Liverpool, Thomas Barnes, 1845, p. 5.
2. H.S. Thompson, 'On the Absorbent Power of Soils' *JRASE* 1850, *11*: 68–74.
3. J.T. Way, *JRASE*, 1850, *11*: 313–79; and 1852, *13*: 123–43.
4. T. Anderson, 'On the relations of Science to Practice in Agriculture', *Trans. High. Agr. Soc.*, 1849, p. 17.
5. J.W. Malden, 'Recent Changes in Farm Practices', *JRASE*, 1896, 7 (3rd ser.): 22–39(22).

Appendix C

Summary of contents and comparative sizes of the Transactions of the Yorkshire Agricultural Society, *1873–1964*

Year and Volume	Summary description
1837–43 (*1–7*)	Quite substantial, containing articles and reports by members of the Society and possessing a clear scientific orientation.
1844–6 (*8–10*)	Very substantial, containing original articles and reports with an increasingly confident scientific orientation.
1847–53 (*11–16*)	Very substantial and science-orientated, but the preponderance of material now comes from the *JRASE*.
1854–7 (*17–20*)	Diminishes to 60 percent of its previous size, and now contains hardly any of its own members' material, and scant science.
1858 (*21*)	Quite substantial volume in 1858 (*21*) of about 100 pages.
1859–86 (*22–49*)	Much diminished, about 40–50 pages on average, containing only list of premiums, the annual report, and list of members.
1887–91 (*50–54*)	More substantial volumes, containing detailed reports on a range of agricultural issues mainly arising out of the Show Reports. One broad national survey, 'British Agriculture in 1890', but no articles specifically by its own members and no science-orientation.
1892–9 (*55–62*)	As substantial as for 1887–91, now with some excellent reports on British agriculture generally in successive volumes. Especially notable is 'The Agricultural Show of the Future', 1899 (62). Still no science.

1900–11

(*63–74*) Reasonably substantial, with articles on issues concerning farming in Yorkshire and national agriculture and discussing legislative and institutional questions in some depth. Still no science.

1912–20

(*75–7*) Brief, and actually no publication during the war.

1921–4

(*79–82*) Reasonably substantial again, with some useful articles on Yorkshire agriculture. Now evinces a scientific orientation.

1925–39

(*83–97*) Very substantial (almost at the size of the 1840s) with a clear concern for science: see for instance 'Science and the improvement of British livestock' and 'Colloids and Agriculture' in volume 88. Also concerned with government policy.

1940–5 No issues.

1946–55

(*98–106*) Slim issues (40–55 pages each), each containing a couple of short articles, agricultural statistics and a summary of YAS affairs. But volume 100 more substantial (75 pages of articles).

1956–64

(*107–115*) Reasonably substantial again (80–90 pages on average) with some scientific orientation, some detailed reports on the Askham Bryan Conferences, and useful articles on small farming and farm management.

Appendix D

Correspondence between Lawes and Gilbert and H.S. Thompson, and between Pusey and Thompson, showing the editorial strategy that Thompson was directing within the *JRASE* in the polemic with Liebig.

I

In 1855, Lawes and Gilbert sent a very long paper to the Journal Committee of the RASE. It was a massive critique of Liebig. Thompson, as chairman of the Journal Committee and as its most chemically oriented member, edited it, but apparently the depth of his editing caused Lawes to wonder whether the paper would be better off in another publication. Thompson, however, was determined that the *JRASE* (and himself) should have the honour of championing the Rothamsted researches, and he ends his letter defending his editorial amendments as follows:

> I trust, however, that when it appears and you have a little more time to look at the case in all its bearings (I mean with reference to the Journal) that you will still feel it is *better in* the Journal and that that publication may still render good service in extending and consolidating the high and well merited reputation of the Rothamsted laboratory.

(Folios 74 and 75, Gilbert Letters, vol. 1, Rothamsted Archives.)

But Thompson was not only editing down Lawes's and Gilbert's overlong paper. He also added a long, highly partisan editorial postscript to reinforce the consequences for Liebig. The whole paper was printed as 'On some points connected with Agricultural Chemistry' in the *JRASE*, 1856, *17*: 411–98, with Thompson's postscript on pages 498–502.

II

Probably in connection with a later paper by Lawes and Gilbert, another letter by Thompson reveals his personal war with Liebig. It also reinforces the impression that he was fully up to date on the researches of the agricultural chemical community in England. The letter is more likely to be to Gilbert than to Lawes.

Kirby Hall,
Dec. 29. [n.d.]

Dear Sir,

I beg to thank you for your letter and return you Professor Voelcker's. The paper is certainly much too long for an agricultural periodical but under the peculiar circumstances, I am doing everything in my power to make room for as much of it as possible. I have devoted a great deal of time to making myself thoroughly master of it before attempting to retrench a sentence, and I trust that the scissors have left all the pith and marrow. The paper will I fear not be a very acceptable New Year's Gift to Baron Liebig but he deserves it all.

I am
Yours truly
H.S. Thompson.

(Folios 91 and 92, Gilbert Letters, vol. 1, Rothamsted Archives.)

III

The following two letters show how zealously Thompson was promoting *English* agricultural chemistry (to use Acland's telling phrase) and how free was Lawes' and Gilbert's access to the *JRASE* after Thompson took charge from Pusey.

Thomas's Hotel
Dec. 3. [Probably 1855 or '56]

My Dear Lawes,

I was in hopes of seeing you at the Council today – Do have pity on poor Editors & put all the steam on. Neither your nor Way's paper is received & I am almost in despair – Do not go through the form of sending it to me but put it at once into the printer's hands, merely giving me a line to say that you have done so.

I am
Yours truly
H.S. Thompson.

(Folio 89, Gilbert Letters, vol. 1, Rothamsted Archives.)

Scarbro
Nov. 10 [probably 1856, or 1860*]

---

* Thompson's reference to tables suggests that he was referring to Lawes's and Gilbert's paper 'On the growth of wheat by the Lois Weedon system, on the Rothamsted soil' which was printed in *JRASE*, 1856, *17*: 582–617. That paper contains a lot of tabular data and is critical of Liebig. But there is a later paper to which Thompson could be referring, their 'Report of experiments on the growth of red clover by different manures', *JRASE*, 1860, *21*: 178–200.

My dear Lawes,

I too was in hopes of seeing you in Hanover Sqe. We are, I am sorry to say dreadfully behind-hand. Almost every post brings reasons why this or that paper is not forthcoming by the time promised. Your paper will take a great deal of printing and correcting in consequence of the tables. Could you let me have a portion of it? Please to send it direct to the printer which will save time. How many pages do you want? if you will let me know this I will let you know how much space we can allot you in this number of the Journal. I am very anxious to see your reply and hope it will be as effective as one of our new 39 inch shells.

Believe me

Yours very truly

H.S. Thompson.

(Folio 78, Gilbert Letters, vol. 1, Rothamsted Archives.)

IV

The following letter from Pusey to Thompson is particularly interesting for historians of nineteenth-century agriculture and chemistry. It is currently believed that Pusey was the principal champion of Lawes and Gilbert against Liebig within the English agricultural community in the 1840s and '50s. (See for instance W.H. Brook (Herausgegeber), *Justus von Liebig and August Wilhelm Hofmann in ihren Briefen, 1841–1873*, Weinheim, Verlag Chemie, 1984, pp. 21 and 22 and letters 65, 69, 70, 72 and 75.) But the following letter suggests that it was Thompson (a touring companion of Lawes in the late '30s) who was impressing the virtue of Lawes's work upon Pusey and thus upon the *JRASE*.

Pusey. Aug. 15. 1849.

Dear Thompson,

I am most anxious to give Lawes the utmost facility and I value his experiments highly but to give twice the space of the last article is simply impossible. It took 64 pages. The whole number of pages allowed by the Post Office is only 360 of which 125 would form a full third. Hundred page articles are very rare in periodicals. I remember one by Macauley on Lord Bacon fourteen years ago which came from India, but everything from India is long. Generally speaking from 20 to 40 pages are the limits of an article.

. . . . . .

The sketch of what Lawes means to write is interesting. Condensation must be tried: and as he will probably not even so find it possible to bring his matter within compass I should advise his stating as he goes along the points of inquiry at which he is aiming, and bringing his experiments to bear upon these points at once. This will carry the reader along and allow of suspending the discussion for six months as the reader sees his way, which he does not, where the inferences are reserved to be summed up at the end.

Yrs. truly ever

Ph. Pusey.

(Folios 288–9, Gilbert Letters, vol. 2, Rothamsted Archives.)

Appendix E

The executive and adminstrative structures of the YAS (1987)

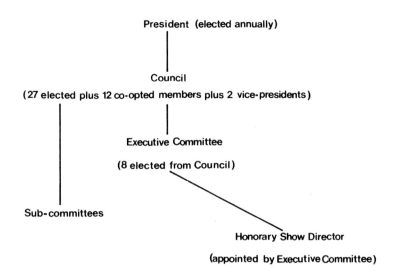

Offices and Council of the Yorkshire Agricultural Society, 1987

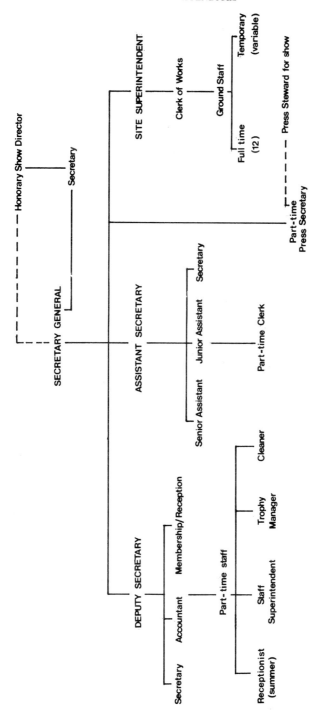

Staff of the Yorkshire Agricultural Society, 1987

Appendix F

'Aid to Agriculture' grants, 1976–87.

Year	Income to fund	Aid paid	Balance in fund
1976	10,000	3,090	
1977	10,000	1,970	
1978	10,000	5,120	
1979	5,000	18,750	
1980	10,000	11,487	
1981	11,160	9,827	
1982	6,000	8,287	
1983	6,000	9,482	
1984	12,000	6,234	
1985	7,250	10,528	
1986	7,000	6,272	
	94,410	91,047	3,363
Less money allocated but not spent			6,100
Money available for allocation			−2,737

Year	Aid beneficiary	Sum allocated	Aid paid	Balance
1976	Annual donations	800	800	
	Bishop Burton Town and Country Day	100	100	
	Arable Fair	2,000	2,000	
	Annual subscriptions	190	190	
1977	Annual donations	800	800	
	Mayor of Harrogate Jubilee Appeal	1,000	1,000	
	Annual subscriptions	170	170	
1978	Annual donations	800	800	
	Nuffield Scholarships YAS Award 1978 (T.J. Pick)	1,100	1,100	
	P.K. Willmott	1,500	1,500	
	Bishop Burton Town and Country Day 1978	200	200	

Overseas Brochure for 1978 show	1,300	1,300	
Annual subscriptions	220	220	
1979 Bishop Burton Town and Country Day 1979	200	200	
MLC Refrigerated Trailer	1,500	1,500	
Overseas Brochure 1979	1,500	1,500	
Nuffield Scholarships YAS Award 1979 (M.G. Holmes)	2,000	2,000	
Bishop Burton Sheep Event	500	500	
Hovercraft development	2,000	2,000	
Liverpool University research	2,000	2,000	
Bishop Burton Student Exchange	100	100	
Annual donations	800	800	
Rare Breeds Survival Trust	400	400	
NFU/Radio Humberside Broadcasting	3,000	3,000	
Annual subscriptions	250	250	
Overseas Brochure for 1980 show	750	750	
FWAG Conference	100	60	40*
Federation of Young Farmers' Clubs projector	150	150	
Nuffield Scholarship YAS Award 1980 (J. Lucas)	2,750	2,795	45†
Agricultural Workers Awards 1980 (P. Jarvis)	600	395	205*
Bishop Burton Town and Country Open Day 1980	250	250	
Northern Horticultural Society	100	100	
1980 Woodman Training Scheme	500	500	
Energy on the Farm display at show	2,000	770	1,230*
Standing donations	1,300	1,300	
Association of Agriculture subscription	50	50	
Liverpool University Research	1,000	1,000	
British Trust for Conservation Volunteers	50	50	
Annual subscriptions	210	210	
D. Hodgson trip to New Zealand	100	100	
Askham Bryan Computer	6,000	5,327	673*
Overseas brochure for 1981 show	1,500	1,500	
ADAS/YAS Computers on the Farm event	1,000	650	350*
FWAG posters	30	30	

1981	Dr P.S. Ward – Splayleg Syndrome	200	200	
	Standing donations	1,300	1,300	
	Nuffield Farming Scholarships 1981	2,750	2,034	716*
	(E.W. Tuer)			
	Agricultural Workers Awards 1981	800	715	85*
	(W.C. Hardwick and H.M. Moore)			
	BBC Radio Humberside	3,000	3,000	
	Arthur Rank Centre Food and Farm Facts Unit	100	100	
	North Humberside FWAG	100	100	
	Annual subscriptions	198	198	
	Royal College of Veterinary Surgeons	100	100	
	Overseas brochure for 1982 show	1,500	1,500	
	North Yorkshire FWAG conference	75	80	5†
	S.G. Ward study tour	500	500	
	Break Crops '82	1,500		1,500*
	(1,160 profit to 'Income to Fund')			
1982	Standing donations	1,550	1,550	
	Nuffield Farming Scholarship 1982	2,588	2,588	
	(F. Tyler)			
	Agricultural Workers' Award 1982	1,200	1,090	110*
	(D. Chandler, R. Hounsfield and A. Pinder)			
	Institute of Agricultural Secretaries	100	100	
	FWAG Askham Bryan Conference	200	152	48*
	City Farms	100	100	
	Food and Farm Facts Unit northern rep.	500	500	
	National Tractor and Farm Museum projector	309	309	
	Annual subscriptions	198	198	
	Overseas brochure for 1983 show	1,500	1,500	
	Bishop Burton Machinery Event	200	200	
1983	Bishop Burton College Sheep Event	200	200	
	ADAS Cereal Conference	500	500	
	HIS Exhibit at Essen Equitana	500	500	
	Yorkshire Federation of Young Farmers Clubs Field Officers	2,000	2,000	
	Humberside Federation of Young Farmers' Clubs Field Officers	1,000	1,000	
	Lincolnshire NFU leaflet	200	200	
	Agricultural Workers' Award 1983	1,000	580	420*
	(A. Metcalf and F.C. Allinson)			
	Nuffield Scholarship Award 1983	2,500	2,500	
	(D. Holmes)			

	Farmers Clubs Walks	500		500
	Annual Subscriptions	299	299	
	ADAS Milk Conference	500	253	247*
	Farriery Film	250	250	
	Overseas brochure for 1984 Show	1,000	1,000	
	Bishop Burton Machinery Event	200	200	
	Barley '84	1,000		1,000*
	Northern Beef '85	1,000		1,000*
1984	Standing donations	1,620	1,620	
	FWAG meeting	20	45	25†
	Barley Follow up conference	600		600*
	Cambridge Veterinary School	50	50	
	Nuffield Scholarship YAS Award 1984 (T.S. Knox)	2,419	2,419	
	Agricultural Workers' Award 1984 (P. Anderson, M.D. Chester and J. Powell)	1,200	1,200	
	Lincolnshire NFU leaflet reprint	200	200	
	Humberside Federation of Young Farmers' Clubs Field Officers	1,000	700	300
	Yorkshire Federation of Young Farmers' Clubs Field Officers	2,000		2,000
1985	Standing donations	1,500	1,500	
	RURAL	50	50	
	Schools Competition Shield	300	300	
	Nuffield Scholarships YAS Award 1985 (P.R. Swindells)	4,000	4,000	
	Agricultural Workers' Award 1985 (B.S. Burrows, J.G. Green) A. Barker and R.I. Turner)	1,500	250	1,250
	Whirlow Hall Farm Trust trailer	1,350	1,190	160*
	Great Yorkshire Grain Trail	88	88	
	RURAL Farm Woods Project	200	200	
	River Derwent Appeal	250	250	
	Voluntary Service Overseas	400		400
	South Yorkshire FWAG leaflet	200	200	
	Royal Forestry Society Bursary (over 4 years)	600		600
	Dennis Hurst Memorial Trust Fund	500	500	
	Northern Beef '85 Follow up conference	1,000		1,000*
	North Yorkshire FWAG adviser	100	100	
	North Humberside FWAG adviser	100	100	
	ADAS cattle weight crush	1,643	1,500	143*

	Yorkshire Grassland Society (over 2 years)	600	300	300
1986	Woodman Training Scheme	973	473	500
	Standing donations 1986	1,500	1,500	
	Marcus Woods Yukon travel	50	50	
	Nuffield Farming Scholarship YAS Award 1986 (P.W. Hayward)	4,249	4,249	
	Conservation Year – Hay-a-Park, Knaresborough	200		200
	East Yorks Horticultural Training Group	50		50

* Indicates money allocated but not required.
+ Indicates overspending on allocations.

Notes and References

Introduction pp. 19–22

1. K. Hudson, *The Bath and West. A Bicentenary History*, Bradford on Avon, Moonraker Press, 1976.

Chapter 1 pp.23–39

1. K. Hudson, *Patriotism with Profit: British Agricultural Societies in the Eighteenth and Nineteenth Centuries*, London, Hugh Evelyn, 1972.
2. H.S. Thompson, 'Agricultural Progress and the Royal Agricultural Society', *J. Roy. Agr. Soc.*, 1864, *25*: 1–51 (1).
3. Earl Cathcart, 'Sir Harry Stephen Meysey Thompson, Bart', *J. Roy. Agr. Soc.*, 1874, *10* (2nd series): 519–40(525).
4. For an important new assessment of this well-worked area of agricultural history, see A.R. Wilkes, 'Adjustments in Arable Farming after the Napoleonic Wars', *Agr. Hist. Rev.*, 1980, *28*: 90–103.
5. W.W. Rostow, *The British Economy of the Nineteenth Century*, OUP, 1948; J. Burnett, *A History of the Cost of Living*, 1969; B. Murphy, *A History of the British Economy, 1740–1970*, Longman, 1973.
6. J.D. Chambers and G.E. Mingay, *The Agricultural Revolution, 1750–1880*, London, Batsford, 1966; E.L. Jones, *The Development of English Agriculture*, 1968; C.S. Orwin and E.H. Whetham, *History of British Agriculture, 1846–1914*, Newton Abbot, David and Charles, 1973.
7. 'Address of the Committee', *Trans. Yorks. Agr. Soc.*, 1837–8, *1*: 5–6.
8. *J. Roy. Agr. Soc.*, 1840, *1*: clxx–clxxi.
9. H. Handley, *A letter to Earl Spencer on the formation of a National Agricultural Institution*, London, James Ridgway and Sons, 1838, p. 33.
10. J. McCulloch, *The British Empire*, 1846, pp. 463–4.
11. For a concise discussion, see P.J. Perry, 'High Farming in Victorian Britain: Prospect and Retrospect', *Agr. Hist.*, 1981, *55*: 156–66 (esp. p. 160).
12. Rostow, *op. cit.* 5, pp. 109 ff.
13. Yet curiously, this area has received scant attention. Perry, *op. cit.* 11, p. 162.
14. See D. Cannandine, 'The landowner as millionaire: The finances of the Dukes of Devonshire, c.1800–c.1926', *Agr. Hist. Rev.*, 1976, *24*: 77–97.
15. A perception neatly encapsulated in the title of Hudson, *op. cit.* Note 1 above.
16. Earl Cathcart, *op. cit.* 3, pp. 519–20, 536–7.
17. For a discussion, see Hudson, *op. cit.* 1, chap. 4. For the British Association, see J. Morrell and A. Thackray, *Gentlemen of Science: Early years of the British Association for the Advancement of Science*, Oxford, Clarendon, 1981.
18. See P.J. Perry, 'High Farming in Victorian Britain: The Financial Foundations', *Agr. Hist.*, 1978, *52*: 364–79(370).

19. For the start of this investment, see the *TYAS*, 1839, *2*: 97.

20. See Murphy, *op. cit.* 5, pp. 514–18.

21. There is evidence, too, that the average size of English farms had not varied from the time of Arthur Young's Tour through the Northern Counties, in 1769, when he had put this figure at 287 acres. See J.R. McCulloch, *The British Empire*, 1846. It should, however, be added that for the finer details of this overview conditions in Scottish farming were rather different.

22. See G.E. Fussell, *Crop Nutrition: Science and Practice before Liebig*, Kansas, Coronado Press, 1971, and *The Classical Tradition in West European Farming*, Newton Abbot, David and Charles, 1972.

23. See Orwin & Whetham, *op. cit.* 6, pp. 3–7.

24. The main uses of lime and chalk at this time could be seen in the practice on the East Riding Wolds, where it was found to correct the 'sourness' of much of the soil and to check the turnip-disease of Fingers-and-Toes. See G. Legard, 'Farming of the East Riding of Yorkshire', *Trans. Yorks. Agr. Soc.*, 1848, *11*: 105.

25. Most conspicuous in this regard was the work of Humphry Davy for the many agriculturist-members of The Royal Institution in London. See M. Berman, *Social Change and Scientific Organization: The Royal Institution, 1799–1844*, New York, Cornell Univ. Press, 1978.

26. F.M.L. Thompson, 'The Second Agricultural Revolution 1815–1880', *Econ. Hist. Rev.*, 1968, *21* (2nd series): 62–77(63).

27. J. Caird, *English Agriculture in 1850–1851*, London, Longman and Co., 1851. All extracts in this book are from the 1968 reprint by Cass and Co., London.

28. Thorp, 'Report of the Committee on Agricultural Geology', *TYAS*, 1841, *4*: 105, quoting the returns made by the Driffield Navigation Company for freightage of corn along their canal.

29. Perry, *op. cit.* 11, p. 164.

30. Caird, *op. cit.* 27, p. 287.

31. J.H. Charnock, 'On the farming of the West Riding of Yorkshire', *TYAS*, 1848, *11*: 157.

32. *Ibid.*, pp. 159, 161.

33. *Ibid.*, p. 159.

34. *Ibid.*, pp. 171–2.

35. *Ibid.*, p. 174.

36. Caird, *op. cit.* 27, p. 298.

37. The earliest systematic discussion of its use in British agriculture was by J.F.W. Johnston, 'On Guano', *J. Roy. Agr. Soc.*, 1841, *2*: 301–21. Johnston also discussed its introduction to continental Europe in the 1810s by Alexander von Humboldt, but its first trial in England was c.1839.

38. For an indication of the new perspective on Liebig's contributions to English agriculture which the author of this *YAS History* is engaged in, see W.H. Brock, 'Liebigiana: Old and New Perspectives', *Hist. Sci.*, 1981, *19*: 201–18, and his *Justus von Liebig und August Wilhelm Hofmann in ihren Briefen (1841–1873)*, Weinheim, Verlag Chemie, 1984.

39. G. Legard, 'Farming of the East Riding of Yorkshire', *TYAS*, 1848, *11*: 69–121.

40. R. Denison, in a private communication to H.S. Thompson, appended to Thompson's paper. 'On subsoil ploughing', *TYAS*, 1841, *2*: 44–60.

41. Legard, *op. cit.* 39, p. 76.

42. Caird, *op. cit.* 27, pp. 304–5.

43. P.J. Perry, 'The Shorthorn comes of age (1822–1843)', *Agric. Hist.*, 1982, *56*: 562.

44. M.M. Milburn, 'On the Farming of the North Riding of Yorkshire', *TYAS*, 1848, *11*: 204.

45. Caird, *op. cit.* 27, p. 321.

46. 'Holiday Rambles', *Yorks. Gazette*, 1878.

47. Milburn, *op. cit.* 44, p. 185.
48. *Ibid.*, p. 186. See too, Thompson's own accounts of his farming, in Chapter 2.
49. T. Walkden, 'On the advantages of ploughing up Down-land', *J. Roy. Agr. Soc.*, 1843, *4*: 85.
50. For a general discussion and source of these comments, see S. Macdonald, 'The lease in agricultural improvement', *J. Roy. Agr. Soc.*, 1976, *137*: 19–25. See too, Perry, *op. cit.* 18, pp. 372–3.
51. Legard, *op. cit.* 39, p. 88.
52. Caird, *op. cit.* 27, p. 329.
53. For a critical discussion, see Perry, *op. cit.* 11 (pp. 158–9) and 18. Also Fussell, *op. cit.* 22.
54. F.M.L. Thompson, *op. cit.* 26.
55. Thompson, *op. cit.* 26. Also Orwin and Whetham, *op. cit.* 6, Chapter 1.
56. Perry, *op. cit.* 18, p. 371.
57. See E.L. Jones, 'The Changing Basis of Agricultural prosperity', *Agric. Hist. Rev.*, 1962, *10*: 102–19; and D.C. Moore, 'The Corn Laws and High Farming', *Econ. Hist. Rev.*, 1965, *18* (2nd series): 544–61.

Chapter 2 pp. 41–88

1. *TYAS*, 1837–8, *1*: 1.
2. For a fuller discussion, see E.A. Wasson, 'The Third Earl Spencer and Agriculture, 1818–1845', *Agr. Hist. Rev.*, 1978, *26*: 89–99.
3. *Ibid.*, p. 93.
4. Earl Cathcart, 'Sir Harry Stephen Meysey Thompson', *J. Roy. Agr. Soc.*, 1874, *10* (2nd series): 527.
5. These details of the 28 and 29 Aug. gatherings are taken from Cathcart, *ibid.*, p. 526, supplemented by the report, 'Yorkshire Agricultural Society', in the *Yorkshire Gazette*, 2 Sep. 1837.
6. *Yorks. Gazette*, 29 Jul. 1837, p. 3.
7. But Mr Brian Horner has conducted some research for the Yorkshire Museum of Farming. I am grateful to him for allowing me to see his research-notes (as yet unpublished). The details of the Wharfedale Agricultural Society I owe to him. The activities of the larger of these local societies can be gleaned from the local newspapers, and I have found the *Yorkshire Gazette* most useful in this respect.
8. *Yorks. Gazette*, *op. cit.* 5.
9. *Ibid.*
10. Minutes of 10 October 1837, YAS Minute Book No. 1. This version differs slightly from that in the *Yorks. Gazette*, which mentions Denison proposing only four resolutions.
11. *Yorks. Gazette*, op. cit. 5.
12. This whole list of resolutions occupies pp. 1–5 of YAS Minute Book No. 1.
13. Minutes of Gen. Comm., 10 Oct. 1837, Minute Book No. 1.
14. Gen. Comm. meeting, 13 Nov. 1837, Minute Book No. 1.
15. For a discussion of its report on bones in 1829, see Sir E.J. Russell, *A History of Agricultural Science in Great Britain*, London, Allen and Unwin, 1966, p. 91.
16. *TYAS*, 1837–8, *1*: 6.
17. Gen. Committee, 19 Dec. 1837, Minute Book No. 1.
18. 'Address', *TYAS*, 1838, *1*: 5.
19. J.G. Ruddock, *The Lincolnshire Agricultural Society*, Published by the Society at Lincoln, 1983, p. 15.
20. See too K. Hudson, *op. cit.*, Chapter 1, ref. 1, pp. 73–82.
21. Gen. Committee, 2 May 1838, Minute Book No. 1.

22. See too *TYAS*, 1838, *1*:
23. Gen. Com., 26 Aug. 1839, Minute Book No. 1.
24. Gen. Comm., 24 Jun. 1840, Minute Book No. 1.
25. Council, 4 Aug. 1842, Minute Book No. 1.
26. Council, 21 Dec. 1842, Minute Book No. 1.
27. All details and comments on the York Show are taken from the *Yorkshire Gazette*, 1 Sept. 1838, p. 2.
28. *TYAS*, 1838, *1*: 79.
29. Gen. Comm., 27 Aug. 1839, Minute Book No. 1.
30. Gen. Comm., 27 Aug. 1839, Minute Book No. 1.
31. J. Phillips, *Illustrations of the Geology of Yorkshire. Part 1: The Yorkshire Coast*, York, 1829.
32. J. Phillips, *Illustrations of the Geology of Yorkshire. Part 2: The Mountain Limestone District*, York, 1836.
33. For a fuller discussion of Phillips' career, see Morrell & Thackray, *op. cit.*, Chapter 1, ref. 17, pp. 439–44.
34. H. Davy, *On the analysis of soils as connected with their improvement*, London, 1805, and *Elements of Agricultural Chemistry*, London, Longman Hurst, 1813. Davy's work and its social context is superbly discussed in M. Berman, *op. cit.*, Chapter 1, ref. 25.
35. *Parliamentary Papers*, vol. 5, Session 1833.
36. Dundonald, *A treatise, shewing the intimate connection that subsists between agriculture and chemistry*, London, 1795. W. Grisenthwaite, *A new theory of agriculture*, Wells, H. Neville, 1819, 2nd ed. 1830.
    D. Low, *Elements of practical agriculture*, London, Longman Brown Green and Longman, 1838.
37. As indicated in his Preface. For a discussion of his work and its likely influence among English agriculturists, see Fussell, *op. cit.*, Chapter 1, note 22.
38. See H.S. Thompson, *TYAS*, 1844–5, *8*: 43. And Cathcart, *op. cit.* 4, p. 530.
39. H.S. Thompson, 'The subsoil plough', *TYAS*, 1839–40, *3*: 44–60, with Spence's list on p. 60.
40. On his British following, see J. Morrell, 'The Chemist Breeders', *Ambix*, 1972, *19*: 1–46. Also Morrell and Thackray, *op. cit.*, Chapter 1, ref. 17.
41. Sir J.A. Scott-Watson, *A history of the Royal Agricultural Society of England, 1839–1939*, London, RASE., 1939.
42. See Hudson, *op. cit.*, Chapter 1, ref. 1, pp. 46–8. Also L.J. Peel, 'Practice with Science: The first twenty years', *JRASE*, 1976, *137*: 9–18, which however neglects the YAS's role.
43. Orwin & Whetham, *op. cit.*, Chapter 1, ref. 6, pp. 30–1.
44. For Holden joining Spence in serving the YAS, see the 'List of Offices for the year August 1852–August 1853', *TYAS*, 1851–2, *15*.
45. Gen. Comm., 11 Mar. 1840, Minute Book No. 1.
46. *TYAS*, 1839–40, *3*: 8.
47. *Ibid.*, pp. 37–43.
48. *Ibid.*, pp. 49–50.
49. *Ibid.*, p. 46.
50. *JRASE*, 1841, *2*: 26–7.
51. The Royal Charter, incorporating the English Agricultural Society as the RASE, 26 Mar. 1840, *JRASE*, 1840, *1*: clxx.
52. Address, *TYAS*, 1839, *2*: 95.
53. For this point with respect to national needs and the premiums offered by the BWES, see Hudson, *op. cit.*, Chapter 1, ref. 1, pp. 80–2.
54. 'List of the Premiums', *TYAS*, 1839, *2*: 9–23.
55. *Ibid.*, p. 97.
56. Gen. Comm., 18 Dec. 1839, Minute Book No. 1.

57. Gen. Comm., 11 Mar. 1840, Minute Book No. 1.

58. As indicated by Earl Cathcart, *op. cit.* 4, pp. 527–8.

59. Gen. Comm., 6 Aug. 1840, Minute Book No. 1. His essay was printed in *TYAS*, 1838–9, *2*: 27–40.

58. 'Exhibition of Implements', *TYAS*, 1840, *3*: 26.

59. 'Address', *TYAS*, 1840, *3*: 7.

60. Gen. Comm., 29 Sept. 1840, Minute Book No. 1.

61. *Op. cit.* 59, p. 8.

62. *TYAS*, 1840, *3*:

63. Comparing the list of Officers and Council in *TYAS*, 1840, *3* with *JRASE*, 1840, *1*.

64. *TYAS*, 1841, *4*: 37–139 (37–8).

65. *Ibid.*, p. 38.

66. *Ibid.*, p. 59.

67. Mulder's investigations began in 1839, with his theory being elaborated in his *Proeve eener algemeene Physiologische Scheikunde*, 2 vols, Rotterdam, 1845–9, and in his main agricultural treatise, *De Scheikunde der Bouwbare Aarde*, 4 vols, Rotterdam, 1860. His researches were also published in Continental science journals, including at first Liebig's own *Annalen*.

68. See Chambers & Mingay, *op. cit.*, Chapter 1, ref. 6.

69. J. Madden, *Quart. J. Agr.*, June 1841.

70. 'Report of the Committee on Agricultural Geology', *TYAS*, 1841, *4*: 61–8.

71. H.S. Thompson, *JRASE*, 1855, *16*: 499.

72. The locus classicus of which was the paper by Pusey, 'On the progress of agricultural knowledge during the last eight years'. *JRASE*, 1850, *10*: 381–438.

73. See 'Liebig', *Dictionary of Scientific Biography*, 1973, vol. 8, pp. 329–50.

74. See W.H. Brock (ed.), *Justus von Liebig und August Wilhelm Hofmann in ihren Briefen (1841–1873)*, Weinheim, Verlag Chemie GMBH 1984, esp. letters 69, 70, 71 and 75.

75. Council, 2 Aug. 1841, Minute Book No. 1.

76. *Ibid.*

77. Council, 3 Aug. 1841, Minute Book No. 1.

78. Council, 5 Aug. 1841, Minute Book No. 1.

79. Printed in *TYAS*, 1842, *5*: 31–52.

80. *Ibid.*, pp. 58–9.

81. See J. Liebig, *An Address to the Agriculturists of Great Britain . . .*, Liverpool, Thomas Barnes, 1845; and his later *The relations of chemistry to agriculture and the agricultural experiments of Mr. J.B. Lawes*, Albany N.Y., Luther Tucker, 1855.

82. *Op. cit.* 79, pp. 49–50.

83. The phrase was virtually coined by T.D. Acland in *Meat, Milk and Wheat: An elementary introduction to the chemistry of farming . . .*, London, J. Ridgway, 1857, pp. 39–40. See too K. Hudson, *The Bath and West*, Bradford on Avon, Moonraker Press, 1976, Chapter 5.

84. *TYAS*, 1845, *8*: 85.

85. See F.W.J. McCosh, *Boussingault*, Dordrecht, Reidel, 1984. For an excellent scientific and historiographic discussion of the nitrogen question, see G.P.H. Chorley, 'The Agricultural Revolution in Northern Europe, 1750–1880: Nitrogen, legumes and corn productivity', *Econ. Hist. Rev.*, 1981, *34*: 71–93.

86. 'Address' of Council, *TYAS*, 1841, *4*: 9–14. See too *Yorks. Gazette*, 5 Aug. 1843, p. 2.

87. *TYAS*, 1842, *5*: 15.

88. *Yorks. Gazette*, 5 Aug. 1843, p. 2.

89. Council, 1 Aug. 1842, Minute Book No. 1.

90. *Yorks. Gazette*, 5 Aug. 1843, p. 2.

91. *Ibid.*, Fitzwilliam's speech after the lecture.

92. Figures calculated from membership lists in successive issues of the *TYAS*.

93. Council, 29 Sept. 1840, Minute Book No. 1.
94. His terms set at Council, 13 Mar. 1844, Minute Book No. 1.
95. I have not found any decision by Council to name it the 'Great Yorkshire Show'. The earliest I have found it so named is in the *Yorks. Gazette*, 2 Sept. 1843, p. 7, by the reporter at the Meeting of the Northallerton Agricultural Association.
96. Council, 21 Dec. 1842, Minute Book No. 1.
97. Council, 13 Mar. 1844, Minute Book No. 1.
98. Council, 31 Oct. 1844, Minute Book No. 1.
99. Council, 30 Oct. 1845, Minute Book No. 1.
100. Council, 13 Mar. 1846, Minute Book No. 1.
101. Council Address, *TYAS*, 1846, *9*: 157–8.
102. Cathcart, *op. cit.* 4, p. 539. On Spencer's genuine concern for his own tenants, see Wasson, *op. cit.* 2, and 'Agricultural Worthies', *JRASE* 1890, *51*, p. 141.
103. From Thompson, 'Agricultural Progress and the Royal Agricultural Society', *JRASE*, 1864, *25*: 22.
104. 'Trial of Implements', *TYAS*, 1844, *7*: 24.
105. 'Trial of Implements', *TYAS*, 1845, *8*: 23.
106. Council, 6 Aug. 1844, Minute Book No. 1.
107. Council, 15 Oct. 1846, Minute Book No. 1.
108. Council, 10 Mar. 1847, Minute Book No. 1.
109. Council, 26 Jan. 1848, Minute Book No. 1.
110. *Ibid.*, Resolution No. 5.
111. See *Yorks. Gazette Supplement*, 14 Jul. 1848.
112. H.S. Thompson, 'Report on the Exhibition of Implements at the York Meeting', *TYAS*, 1848, *11*: 28.
113. *Yorks. Gazette Supplement*, 14 Jul. 1848, p. 2. The whole lecture was later printed as 'The present state of agriculture in its relations to chemistry and geology', in *JRASE*, 1848, *9*: 200–236, and as such it was a very influential piece of agricultural science.
114. *TYAS*, 1847, *10*: 72.
115. J. Liebig, *Organic chemistry in its applications to agriculture and physiology*, London, Taylor & Walton, 1840, p. 85.
116. *Ibid.*, 1843 edition, p. 54.
117. J.B. Lawes, 'On Agricultural Chemistry', *JRASE*, 1848, *8*: 226–60.
118. *Op. cit.* 114, p. 77.
119. *TYAS*, 1848, *10*: 166.
120. See E.J. Russell, *op. cit.* 15.
121. Earl Cathcart, *op. cit.* 4, p. 528.
122. Letter from Thompson to Lawes, dated 3 Dec. [probably 1855/56], Rothamsted Archives, 'Gilbert Letters', vol. 1, f. 89. See Appendix D.
123. Hudson, *op. cit.* Introduction, ref. 1.
124. 'Annual Address', *TYAS*, 1847–8, *10*: 179.
125. *Ibid.*, p. 181.
126. 'Report of experiments with coprolites, peat charcoal, and other kinds of hand tillage, as manure for turnips', *TYAS*, 1849–50, *13*: 213–26.
127. Quoted in K. Hudson, *op. cit.*, Chapter 1, ref. 1, p. 60.
128. K. Hudson, *op. cit.* 123, 'The Acland Revival'.
129. 'Address', *TYAS*, 1849, *12*: 185–9.
130. Pusey, *JRASE*, 1850, *11*: 430. Reprinted in *TYAS*, 1850, *13*: 115–75.
131. *Ibid.*, p. 438.

Chapter 3 pp. 89–108

1. J.G. Cornish, *Reminiscences of Country Life*, London, Country Life, 1939, p. 83.
2. For recent critical analysis of this area, see P.J. Perry, 'High Farming in Victorian Britain: The Financial Foundations', *Agr. Hist.*, 1978, *52*: 364–79; and his 'High Farming in Victorian Britain: Prospect and Retrospect', *Agr. Hist.*, 1981, *55*: 156–66.
3. Perry, *ibid.* 1981, pp. 162–3.
4. Pusey P., 'On the progress of agricultural knowledge during the last four years', *JRASE*, 1842, *3*: 204–5.
5. Caird J., 'A general view of British agriculture', *JRASE*, 1878, *XIV* (2nd series): 290.
6. Clapham J.H., *An economic history of modern Britain*, Cambridge, CUP, 1932, vol. 2, p. 278.
7. Fletcher T.W., and Ojala *Econ. Hist. Rev.*, 1961, *XIII* (2nd series): 432.
8. Several Reports and papers in *JRASE* throughout the 1860s.
9. Quoted in Jones E.L., 'The changing basis of agricultural prosperity, 1853–73', *Agric. Hist. Rev.* 1962, *10*: 102–19(115). Much of what I write here relies on this excellent paper.
10. *Ibid.*, and his *The Development of English Agriculture, 1815–1873*, Studies in Economic History Series, London, Macmillan, 1968.
11. Continental contributors were already in its first volume (1840).
12. Cathcart, *op. cit.* 4, chapter 1, p. 526.
13. *TYAS*, 1849, *12*: 9; 1850, *13*: 9; and Council, 5 Oct. 1876, Minute Book No. 3.
14. Council, 10 Oct. 1850, Minute Book No. 1.
15. Council, 29 Dec. 1853, Minute Book No. 1.
16. For the decision on 2 days, see Council, 22 Oct. 1852, Minute Book No. 1. and for three days see Council, 28 Nov. 1861.
17. Council, 4 Aug. 1852, Minute Book No. 1.
18. Council, 8 Jan. 1858, *ibid.*
19. Council, 10 Dec. 1861, *ibid.*
20. Council, 15 Oct. 1863, *ibid.*
21. Council, 18 Dec. 1852, *ibid.*
22. Council, 18 Jan. 1872, Minute Book No. 2.
23. Council, 14 Jan. 1875, *ibid.*
24. Council, 8 Apr. 1863, Minute Book No. 2.
25. Hannam J., 'The Economy of Waste Manores', *YAS*, 1842–3, 6:43–108.
26. Thus, the topic for the Council Dinner at the 1854 Show was 'The best way to obtain General Servants in Agriculture, and to obviate the evils arising from the present system of hiring without Character'. Council, 29 Jun. 1854, Minute Book No. 1.
27. 'Report of Finance Committee', Council, 20 Oct. 1864, Minute Book No. 2.
28. Council, 12 Jan. 1865, *ibid.*
29. Council, 13 Jul. 1865, *ibid.*
30. Council, 14 Dec. 1865, *ibid.*
31. Council, 14 Dec. 1865, *ibid.*
32. Minutes of a Special General Meeting of Members, 20 Dec. 1866, *ibid.*
33. Council, 7 Jan. 1869, *ibid.*
34. Council, 4 Oct. 1866, *ibid.* A new warehouse was acquired in 1871, from the York Blue Coat School: Council, 6 Jul. 1871, *ibid.*
35. See Hudson, *op. cit.*, Chapter 1, ref. 1.
36. Council, 18 Apr. 1867, Minute Book No. 2.
37. Council, 30 Apr. 1868, *ibid.*
38. Council, 20 Dec. 1870, *ibid.*

39. Council, 6 Aug. 1868, *ibid.*
40. Council, 14 Oct. 1869, *ibid.*
41. Council, 6 Jul. 1871, *ibid.*
42. Council, 18 Jan. 1872, *ibid.*
43. Council, 6 Jan. 1870, *ibid.*
44. Council, 19 Jan. 1871, *ibid.*
45. 'Yorkshire Agricultural Society. The Meeting of 1870', *Yorks. Gazette*, 6 Aug. 1870, p. 5.
46. Council, 12 Oct. 1871, *ibid.*
47. Council, 9 Jan. 1868, *ibid.*
48. Council, 9 Oct. 1873, *ibid.*
49. Council, 8 Oct. 1874, *ibid.*
50. Council, 7 Oct. 1875, *ibid.*
51. Council, 16 Feb. 1865, *ibid.*
52. Council, 27 Apr. 1871, *ibid.*
53. Council, 19 Dec. 1871, *ibid.*
54. Council, 18 Jan. 1872, *ibid.*
55. Council, 9 Oct. 1873, *ibid.*
56. 'Chemical Report', Council, 17 Jul. 1873, *ibid.*
57. Council, 29 Jan. 1885, *ibid.*
58. 'Yorkshire Agricultural Society. Meeting at Pontefract', *Yorks. Gazette*, 4 Aug. 1860, p. 4.
59. 'Yorkshire Agricultural Society. Great Show at York', *Yorks. Gazette*, 5 Aug. 1871, p. 4.
60. These names appear as one glances at the very numerous reports on agricultural activities in the county's newspapers, especially in the *Yorks. Gazette*.
61. Council, 7 Dec. 1853, Minute Book No. 1.
62. Council, 18 Dec. 1856, *ibid.*
63. Council, 3 Aug. 1859, *ibid.*
64. Council, 5 Dec. 1867, Minute Book No. 2.
65. Special Meeting of Council, 21 Jun. 1866, *ibid.*
66. Alexander Ramsay, *History of the Highland and Agricultural Society of Scotland*, Edinb. and London, 1879, pp. 302–3.

Chapter 4 pp. 109–135

1. C.S. Orwin & E.H. Whetham, *History of British Agriculture, 1846–1914*, David and Charles, Newton Abbot, 1971, Ch. 9.
2. *Ibid.*, and P.J Perry, 'Where was the 'Great Agricultural Depression?', *Agr. Hist. Rev.*, 1972, *20*: 30–45.
3. Orwin and Whetham, pp. 242–5.
4. Perry, *op. cit.* 2.
5. Council, 18 May. 1876, Minute Book No. 3.
6. Council, 25 Jan. 1877, *ibid.*
7. Council, 4 Oct. 1877, *ibid.*
8. Council, 24 Jan. 1878, *ibid.*
9. Council, 7 Feb. 1878, *ibid.*
10. Council, 7 Feb. 1878, decided to appoint four stewards in total. But Council, 21 Mar. 1878, raised this to eight.
11. Council, 3 Oct. 1878, *ibid.*
12. Council, 31 Oct. 1878, *ibid.*
13. Council, 2 Oct. 1879, *ibid.*
14. See the report of the Council Meeting at the 1880 Barnsley Show in 'Yorkshire

Agricultural Society', *Yorks. Gazette*, 7 Aug. 1880, p. 9.

15. 'Yorkshire Agricultural Show at Middlesborough', *Yorks. Gazette*, 6 Aug. 1892, p. 6.
16. Council, 7 Oct. 1886, Minute Book No. 4.
17. Council, 6 Oct. 1887, *ibid.*
18. Council, 17 Dec. 1889, *ibid.*
19. Council, 2 Oct. 1890, *ibid.*
20. Council, 11 Oct. 1894, *ibid.*
21. Council, 13 Feb. 1896, *ibid.*
22. Council, 15 Dec. 1896, *ibid.*
23. Council, 14 Feb. 1895, *ibid.*
24. Council, 13 Feb. 1896, *ibid.*
25. Council, 15 Dec. 1896, *ibid.*
26. Council, 20 Dec. 1898, Minute Book No. 5.
27. Council, 6 Apr. 1899, *ibid.*
28. Council, 9 Feb. 1899, *ibid.*
29. Council, 21 Sep. 1899, *ibid.*
30. Council, 5 Aug. 1899, *ibid.*
31. Council, 20 Sep. 1900, *ibid.*
32. Council, 18 Dec. 1900, *ibid.*
33. Council, 31 Jan. 1901, *ibid.*
34. 'The Agricultural Show of the Future. A plea for permanent Showyards', *TYAS*, 1899, *62*: xxix.
35. *Ibid.*, p. xxxiv.
36. Curiously, this is not mentioned in Sir E.J. Russell, *A History of Agricultural Science in Great Britain* (1966).
37. Council, 14 Jan. 1875, Minute Book No. 3.
38. Council, 5 Oct. 1876, *ibid.*
39. Council, 9 Jul. 1885, Minute Book No. 4. The quotation is from the report of the Council, in *York Herald*, 10 Jul. 1885.
40. Council, 28 Jan. 1886, *ibid.*
41. Council, 14 Feb. 1889, *ibid.*
42. Russell, *op. cit.* 36, Chapters 6 and 7.
43. Council, Dec. 1888, Minute Book No. 4.
44. Council, Dec. 1888, as reported in *York Herald*, Dec. 1888.
45. Council, *op. cit.* 41.
46. Council, 6 Aug. & 16 Dec. 1890, *ibid.*
47. Council, 7 Aug. 1895, *ibid.*
48. As reproduced, significantly, in *TYAS*, 1890, *53*: 21–2.
49. H.E. Dale, *Daniel Hall, Pioneer in Scientific Agriculture*, London, John Murray, 1956.
50. *Op. cit.* 48, p. 23.
51. On the Dairy Schools set up by the BWES in the late '80s, Hudson, *op. cit.* Introduction, ref. 1, pp. 141–6.
52. Council, 15 Dec. 1891, Minute Book No. 4.
53. Council, 3 Oct. 1901, Minute Book No. 5.
54. Council, 2 Oct. 1902, *ibid.*
55. Council, 13 Oct. 1904, *ibid.*
56. Council, 1 Dec. 1908, *ibid.*
57. Council, 6 Oct. 1910, *ibid.*
58. Council, 3 Oct. 1912, *ibid.*
59. Council, 18 Dec. 1906, *ibid.*
60. Council, 3 Dec. 1907, *ibid.*
61. Council, 1 Feb. 1906, *ibid.*, thus rescinding a resolution for non-affiliation, 4 Feb. 1904.
62. Council, 10 Dec. 1912, *ibid.*

63. Council, 6 Apr. 1911, Minute Book No. 6.
64. Council, 9 Dec. 1913, Minute Book No. 6.
65. Council, 5 Feb. 1914, *ibid.*
66. Council, 13 Apr. 1905 and 1 Feb. 1906, Minute Book No. 5.
67. Council, 11 Oct. 1906, *ibid.*
68. Council, 20 Jul. 1905, *ibid.*
69. Council, 13 Apr. 1905, *ibid.*
70. Council, 12 Oct. and 19 Dec. 1905, *ibid.*
71. Council, 22 Jul. 1914, Minute Book No. 6.

Chapter 5 pp.137–160

1. E.H. Whetham, *The Agrarian History of England and Wales, VIII, 1914–39*, Cambridge, CUP, 1978.
2. E.H. Whetham, 'The Agriculture Act, 1920 and its Repeal – the "Great Betrayal"', *Agr. Hist. Rev.*, 1974, *22*: 36–49.
3. Whetham, *op. cit.* 1, p. 315.
4. T. Rooth, 'Trade Agreements and the Evolution of British Agricultural Policy in the 1930s', *Agr. Hist. Rev.*, 1985, *33*(2): 190.
5. *Ibid.*, p. 189.
6. Council, 4 Feb. 1915, Minute Book No. 6.
7. Council, 14 Dec. 1915, *ibid.*
8. *Ibid.*
9. Council, 16 Jan. 1919, *ibid.*
10. Council, 4 Feb. 1915, *ibid.*
11. Council, 22 Feb. 1919, *ibid.*
12. AGM, 16 Dec. 1919, *ibid.*
13. Report of Special Committee, 26 Jun. 1920, *ibid.*
14. *Ibid.*
15. Council, 8 Jan. 1921, *ibid.*
16. Council, 2 Dec. 1920, *ibid.*
17. Council, 24 Nov. 1921, *ibid.*
18. Council, 29 Sep. 1921, *ibid.*
19. Council, 24 Nov. 1921, *ibid.*
20. Council, 19 Apr. 1923, *ibid.*
21. Quoted in Council, 14 Jan. 1926, Minute Book No. 7.
22. Council, 21 Oct. 1926, *ibid.*
23. AGM, 11 Jan. 1927, *ibid.*
24. 'Report of Council', AGM, 19 Jan. 1928, *ibid.*
25. Council, 14 Apr. 1934, Minute Book No. 9.
26. 'Annual Report of Council', AGM, 16 Jan. 1937, Minute Book No. 9.
27. Council, 3 Apr. 1937, *ibid.*
28. General Meeting, 13 Jul. 1937, *ibid.*
29. 'Yorkshire Show', *Yorkshire Gazette*, 16 Jul. 1937, p. 14.
30. Council, 9 Oct. 1937, Minute Book No. 9.
31. Council, 29 Nov. 1923, Minute Book No. 6.
32. General Purposes Committee meeting, 15 Jan. 1925, Council Minute Book No. 7.
33. Council, 19 Jan. 1935, Minute Book No. 9.
34. Finance Committee Meeting, 20 Jan. 1934, Council Minute Book No. 9.
35. Council, 23 Jan. 1947, Minute Book No. 9.
36. Council, 2 Dec. 1920, Minute Book No. 6.
37. 7 Apr. 1921, *ibid.*
38. Council, 8 Jan. 1921, Minute Book No. 6.

39. Council, 19 Jan. 1922, *ibid.*
40. Council, 17 Jan. 1929, Minute Book No. 8.
41. On this Act see Sir E.J. Russell, *op. cit.* 36 previous chapter. On Lea's Report, see Council, 18 Jan. 1936, Minute Book No. 9.
42. Council, 22 Jan. 1938, *ibid.*
43. Most of the data in this section are taken from N.M. Comber, 'The Development of Agricultural Education in Yorkshire', *JRASE*, 1935, *96*: 109–23.
44. Council, 19 Apr. 1923, Minute Book No. 6.
45. Council, 17 Apr. 1924, Minute Book No. 7.
46. Council, 12 Apr. 1927, *ibid.*
47. Council, 23 Oct. 1924, *ibid.*
48. Council, 2 Apr. 1938, Minute Book No. 9.

Chapter 6 pp. 161–179

1. J.K. Bowers, 'British Agricultural Policy since the Second World War', *Agr. Hist. Rev.*, 1985, *33*(1): 66. Section 1 of this chapter relies almost wholly on this paper.
2. Agricultural Act (1947), Section 1, quoted in *ibid.*
3. Cmnd 8556, para 12h, quoted in *ibid.*
4. *Agriculture*, Cmnd 1249 (1960).
5. Council, 4 Feb. 1943, Minute Book No. 9.
6. See the tribute to him by Major Seed, Council, 13 May 1963, Minute Book No. 10.
7. Council, 4 Feb. 1943, Minute Book No. 9.
8. General Meeting, 20 Jan. 1944, *ibid.*
9. Council, 24 Jan. 1946, *ibid.*
10. Council, 25 Oct. 1945, *ibid.*
11. Council, 17 Oct. 1946 and 23 Jan. 1947, *ibid.*
12. Council, 24 Jul. 1947, *ibid.*
13. Council, 13 Nov. 1947, Minute Book No. 10.
14. *Ibid.*
15. Council, 30 Sep. 1948, *ibid.*
16. Council, 22 Jan. 1948, *ibid.*
17. Council, 6 May 1948, *ibid.*
18. Council, 30 Sep. 1948, *ibid.*
19. Private communication to the author by Mr Baldwin, 3 Oct. 1986.
20. *Op. cit.* 14.
21. Council EGM., 19 Feb. 1949, Minute Book No. 10.
22. *Ibid.*
23. *Ibid.*
24. Council, 2 Jun. 1949, *ibid.*
25. All these details of negotiations are from Council, 2 Jun. 1949, *ibid.*
26. Council EGM, 21 Jun. 1949, *ibid.*
27. Council, 12 Oct. 1950, *ibid.*
28. Council, 2 Mar. 1950, *ibid.*
29. *Ibid.*
30. Council, 12 Oct. 1950, *ibid.*
31. Council, 2 Mar. 1950 and 12 Jul. 1950, *ibid.*
32. Council, 2 Mar. 1950, *ibid.*
33. Council, 1 Mar. 1951, *ibid.*
34. Council, 10 Jul. 1951, *ibid.*
35. Council, 1 Mar. 1951, *ibid.*
36. Council, 1 Oct. 1959, *ibid.*
37. Council, 1 Mar. 1951, *ibid.*

38. Council, 11 Dec. 1951, *ibid.*
39. *Ibid.*
40. Council, 7 Jun. 1951, *ibid.*
41. *Ibid.*
42. Council, 5 Jun. 1952, *ibid.*
43. Council, 3 Jun. 1954, *ibid.*
44. Council, 29 Oct. 1954, *ibid.*
45. Council, 27 Oct. 1954, *ibid.*
46. Council, 4 Oct. 1951, *ibid.*
47. Council, 3 Oct. 1957, *ibid.*
48. Council, 3 Mar. 1960, *ibid.*
49. Council, 1 Jun. 1961, *ibid.*
50. Council, 7 Mar. 1963, *ibid.*
51. Council, 2 Mar. 1961, *ibid.*
52. Council, 28 Mar. 1961, *ibid.*
53. Council, 4 Oct. 1962, *ibid.*
54. Council, 7 Mar. 1963, *ibid.*
55. 'Great Yorkshire Show, Harrogate, 1951', *TYAS*, 1952, *103*: 63.
56. Council, 2 Jun. 1955, Minute Book No. 10.
57. Council, 4 Mar. 1954, *ibid.*
58. Council, 22 Jan. 1948, *ibid.*
59. Council, 4 Oct. 1951, *ibid.*
60. Council, 7 Dec. 1961 and 1 Mar. 1962, *ibid.*
61. Council, 1 Jun. 1961, *ibid.*
62. Council, 7 Mar. 1963, *ibid.*

Chapter 7 pp. 181–204

1. J.K. Bowers, 'British Agricultural Policy since the Second World War', *Agr. Hist. Rev.*, 1985, *33*(1): 71. Again, for the first section of this chapter, I am heavily reliant on Bowers' paper.
2. Cmnd 2764 (1965).
3. *The Development of Agriculture*, Cmnd 2738, 1965.
4. *Food from Our Own Resources*, Cmnd 6020, 1975.
5. *Farming and the Nation*, Cmnd 7458, 1979.
6. J.K. Bowers, 'Who pays the cost of UK agricultural expansion?', Univ. of Leeds School of Economic Studies, Discussion Paper 110, 1982.
7. Council, 13 May 1963, Minute Book No. 10.
8. Council, 5 Mar. 1964, Minute Book No. 11.
9. Council, 26 Aug. 1965, *ibid.*
10. 'Report from Secretary General concerning the changing attitude of exhibitors towards Shows', 23rd. Meeting of Executive Committee, 18 Feb. 1966, Minute Book No. 11.
11. *Ibid.*
12. Council, 9 Jun. 1966, *ibid.*
13. Executive Committee, 2 Sep. 1966, *ibid.*
14. 5th Executive Committee Report, 1 Oct. 1964, *ibid.*
15. Executive Committee, 3 Oct. 1967, *ibid.*
16. Council, 4 Dec. 1969, *ibid.*
17. Council, 31 Mar. 1970, *ibid.*
18. AGM, 29 Mar. 1971, *ibid.*
19. See *Yorks. Gazette and Herald*, 9 Jul. 1971, pp. 5, 8 and 9.
20. AGM, 29 Mar. 1972, *ibid.*

21. Council, 1 Jun. 1972, *ibid.*
22. *Ibid.*
23. Council, *ibid.*
24. Council, 27 Mar. and 18 Jan. 1974, Minute Book No. 12.
25. Council, 9 Jun. 1976, *ibid.*
26. Council, 3 Oct. 1980, Minute Book No. 13.
27. Council, 4 Oct. 1979, Minute Book No. 12.
28. Council, 4 Dec. 1981, *ibid.*
29. Council, 26 Mar. and 3 Jun. 1986, Minute Book No. 14.
30. Annual Report, in Council, 24 Mar. 1981, Minute Book No. 13.
31. Council, 11 Jun. 1982, Minute Book No. 13.
32. Council, 9 Jun. 1979, *ibid.*
33. Council, 7 Oct. 1982, *ibid.*
34. 'The Great Yorkshire Show. Farm Project for Schools. 1986', a pamphlet printed for the YAS by G. Prudhoe and Co. Ltd, Darlington.
35. Council, 3 Dec. 1964 and 2 Dec. 1965, Minute Book No. 11.
36. Council, 3 Mar. and 9 Jun. 1966, *ibid.*
37. Council, 21 Feb. 1968, *ibid.*
38. Council, 28 Mar. 1980, Minute Book No. 13.
39. *Yorks. Gazette and Herald*, 9 Jul. 1971, p. 5.
40. Draft of a lecture by Mr Baldwin, kindly made available to the author.
41. Most of these, and the following, details on Farm Records Ltd. are taken from the Report thereon, in Council, 21 Feb. 1968, Minute Book No. 11.
42. Council, 15 Sep. 1966, *ibid.*
43. Council, 18 Oct. 1968, *ibid.*
44. Council, 1 Oct. 1970, *ibid.*
45. Council, 5 Jan. 1971, *ibid.*
46. 60th Executive Committee Report, 28 Mar. 1980, Minute Book No. 12.
47. Council, 1 Oct. 1970, Minute Book No. 11.
48. Council, 5 Jan. 1971, *ibid.*
49. AGM, 29 Mar. 1971, *ibid.*
50. Council, 16 Sep. 1971, *ibid.*
51. Council, 2 Oct. 1974, Minute Book No. 12.
52. Council, 5 Oct. 1978, *ibid.*
53. Council, 6 Jun. 1985, Minute Book No. 13.
54. 85th Report by the Executive Committee, 3 Jun. 1986, Minute Book No. 14.
55. Council, 2 Dec. 1982, Minute Book No. 12.
56. Council, 9 Jun. 1976, *ibid.*
57. Council, 9 Jun. 1977, *ibid.*

INDEX

prizes in class

The contents of this certificate are true, to the best of my belief and knowledge.

Dated_____(Signed)_____

For Classes 4, 5, 6, 7, 8.

I,   of   near   o

hereby request you to enter my (cow or heifer, state colour),   named

bred by   calved on the   sire

dam by   for the prizes in class

I also hereby certify, that the above-named   is in (calf or milk).

The contents of this certificate are true, to the best of my belief and knowledge.

Dated_____(Signed)_____

For Classes 9, 10, 11.

I,   of   near   d

hereby request you to enter my (state colour)   bred by   calved on the

for the prizes in class   I also hereby certify, that the animal has been in my possession since the 1st of May

last, and has been fed on

The contents of this certificate are true, to the best of my belief and knowledge.

Dated_____(Signed)_____

For Classes 12, 13, 15, 16.

I,   of   near   d

hereby request you to enter my   aged   bred from the flock of

for the prizes in class

I also hereby certify, that the above-named   was shorn bare on or since the 20th of May last.

The contents of this certificate are true, to the best of my belief and knowledge.

Dated_____(Signed)_____

For Class 14.

I,   of   near   do

hereby request you to enter my Five Ewes, aged   bred from the flock of   for the

prizes in class 14.

I also hereby certify, that the said Ewes have had and suckled Lambs up to the 6th of July last, and were shorn bare on

or since the 20th of May last.

The contents of this certificate are true, to the best of my belief and knowledge.

Dated_____(Signed)_____

Any person who shall give a false Certificate, shall forfeit every unpaid
future year.   Sweepstakes from one to two sov

GENERAL

No Stock can be admitted for Exhibition, unless a Certificate of entry, in writing, in the above-mentioned
Members intending to exhibit Extra Stock, must give notice to the Secretary, on or before Wednesday, J
Tickets of admission into the Show-Yard, for Stock and Implements, may be obtained from the Secretary
to the Show.   These Tickets will be delivered to Members gratis.

Non-Subscribers to pay ten shillings for every head or lot of Live Stock, and also ten shillings for every lo
All Stock intended for Exhibition for Prizes, or Sweepstakes, or as extra Stock, must be in the Show-Yar
Stallions, which will be admitted up to TEN o'Clock.   And no Stock whatever will be allowed to leave the Yard b
Persons intending to exhibit Implements, &c., must give notice of their intention to the Secretary, and fur
Show-Yard on the day before the Show.

All Subscriptions to Sweepstakes must be paid to the Secretary on or before Tuesday, August 1st.

The TRANSACTIONS of the Society for the Year 1842—price 1s., are now published, and may be obtained GRATIS by M
Spurriergate, York; RAY, Barnsley; KEMP, Beverley; FURBY, Burlington; KNOWLES, Bedale; WHITE, Doncaster,
boro'; BAINES, Leeds; SMITHSON, Malton; LANGDALE, Northallerton; WALKER, Otley; BELL, Richmond; PROCT
field; HORNE & Co., Whitby.

Thorpfield, Thirsk, Jan. 2, 1843.

By

J. Coultas, Printer, C